FRONTIERS OF FITNESS

A Monograph Published Under the Auspices of the Canadian Association of Sports Sciences

Publications Committee

Donald M. Aitken
Juri V. Daniel
Thomas Fried
Roy J. Shephard (Chairman)
Bryce M. Taylor

FRONTIERS OF FITNESS

Compiled and Edited by

ROY J. SHEPHARD, M.D., Ph.D., F.A.C.S.M.

Professor of Applied Physiology
Department of Physiological Hygiene, School of Hygiene
University of Toronto
Toronto, Ontario, Canada

CHARLES C THOMAS • PUBLISHER
Springfield • Illinois • U.S.A.

Published and Distributed Throughout the World by
CHARLES C THOMAS • PUBLISHER
BANNERSTONE HOUSE
301-327 East Lawrence Avenue, Springfield, Illinois, U.S.A.
NATCHEZ PLANTATION HOUSE
735 North Atlantic Boulevard, Fort Lauderdale, Florida, U.S.A.

With THOMAS BOOKS *careful attention is given to all details of manufacturing and design. It is the Publisher's desire to present books that are satisfactory as to their physical qualities and artistic possibilities and appropriate for their particular use.* THOMAS BOOKS *will be true to those laws of quality that assure a good name and good will.*

Printed in the United States of America
EE-11

CONTRIBUTORS

E. W. Banister, *Exercise Biology Laboratory, Simon Fraser University, British Columbia, Canada.*

G. Borg, *Institute of Applied Psychology, Solna, Sweden.*

A. de Coster, *Department of Respiratory Diseases, St. Peter's Hospital, Brussels, Belgium.*

G. R. Cumming, *The Children's Hospital of Winnipeg and University of Manitoba, Winnipeg, Manitoba, Canada.*

John A. Faulkner, *Department of Physiology, University of Michigan, Ann Arbor, Michigan.*

M. H. Frick, *Cardiovascular Laboratory, First Department of Medicine, University Central Hospital, Helsinki, Finland.*

H. Friedrich, *Department of Physiology and Biophysics, Dalhousie University, Halifax, Nova Scotia, Canada.*

Phillip D. Gollnick, *Exercise Physiology Laboratory, Washington State University, Pullman, Washington.*

Eric Hultman, *Department of Clinical Chemistry, St. Erik's Hospital, Stockholm, Sweden.*

P. Jenik, *Institut für Arbeitswissenschaft der Technischen Hochschule, Darmstadt, West Germany.*

P. F. Iampietro, *Physiology Laboratory, Aeromedical Research Branch, Department of Transportation, F.A.A., Aeronautical Center, Oklahoma City, Oklahoma.*

Rodolfo Margaria, *Institute of Human Physiology, University of Milan, Milan, Italy.*

R. F. Mottram, *Physiology Department, University College, Cardiff, England*

P. E. Di Prampero, *Department of Physiology, University of Milan, Milan, Italy.*

Phillip J. Rasch, *Physiology Division, Naval Medical Field Research Laboratory, Camp Lejeune, North Carolina.*

P. M. Rautaharju, *Department of Physiology and Biophysics, Dalhousie University, Halifax, Nova Scotia, Canada.*

W. Rohmert, *Institut für Arbeitswissenschaft der Technishen Hochschule, Darmstadt, West Germany.*

Loring B. Rowell, *Division of Cardiology, University of Washington School of Medicine, Seattle, Washington.*

Roy J. Shephard, *Department of Physiological Hygiene, School of Hygiene, University of Toronto, Toronto, Ontario, Canada.*

H. Wolf, *Department of Physiology and Biophysics, Dalhousie University, Halifax, Nova Scotia, Canada.*

INTRODUCTION

THERE ARE few frontiers that remain to be explored and charted in our present world. One of the objectives of the International Biological Programme has been to study the adaptation of the human organism to its environment, basing its research on primitive peoples who have as yet escaped the ravages of civilization. But in a sense, the programme has come too late. Progress has already reached the frontier. In Canada we set our sights on the wilderness of the Arctic North, planning a careful interdisciplinary study of nutrition, growth, working capacity, and ecology on a small population of Eskimo hunters living in tents and igloos and existing on the harvest of the sea and ice. But when the first scientists reached the settlement, they found most of the Eskimos busy assembling three-bedroom bungalows recently shipped by a benevolent Department of Indian Affairs and Northern Development. And the rest of the community, instead of fishing, were busy building an airstrip that would accommodate quite large passenger and transport aircraft. Today the village is but six hours journey from the bright lights of Montreal, two thousand miles to the south.

The same problem of a disappearing frontier haunts the physiologist in a more general sense. A hundred years ago, physiology was a relatively new science. There was much to discover, and the few journals of physiology were in their infancy. At this time it seemed as if almost every paper that was published carried news of an important discovery and indeed stood a good chance of becoming a classic in its particular field. But the time of the giants has long since passed. Today the average issue of a physiological journal is scarcely a cause for excitement. There are those who would attribute this situation to the poor quality of present-day students and their mentors. However, at the risk of seeming partisan, I would challenge such a view. If there has been a change in the basic intelligence of students and staff, it has been in an upward rather than a downward direction, as a larger proportion of a growing world population have gained access to institutions of higher learning. True, the average investigator has less time to think than his predecessors, but the resources available for use during periods of thought and of laboratory activity have increased enormously over the past century. There are other problems peculiar to our era—the philosophy of "publish or perish," the "quick" piece of research to satisfy a government agency. But the main problem of our day is surely that the frontiers of physiology are already charted. The earnest research worker may confirm a phenomenon, using a more elegant technique. He may measure a constant on a larger population, defining the mean value and its limits with wondrous precision. He may explore a topic in relentless detail. But the new discovery is a rarity. Surprisingly the lack of adequate topics for research is not reflected in either the number of physiologists or their output of papers and communications. The International Union of Physiological Societies and the various national organizations have all grown rapidly over the past two decades. The hallowed journals of physiology are yearly forced to increase either the number of issues per annum or the size of their pages. Each month brings tidings of a less-hallowed journal that a hopeful publisher is devoting to some specialized area of physiology. Similar problems afflict meetings of the physiology societies. The American Physiological Society has even considered the possibility of prerecording communications and replaying them to members at an accelerated speed.

The student new to the discipline has a real problem with this plethora of (largely) insignificant information. Even the more experienced research worker is often perplexed. How can he distinguish the findings with real promise, the areas worthy of further exploration? Each investigator develops his own technique for reviewing the literature. However, most of us find it helpful to discuss our questions with an acknowledged expert— not so long acknowledged that he is no longer fully conversant with the problem, but an eager enthusiast, young in spirit at least, active in research, and with a wide knowledge of that part of the world's literature that relates to our particular interest. Unfortunately, specialization is now so intense that there are few people in any one city who can offer an intelligent overview of a given topic. Personal counsel must be sought on a national and even an international basis. So it seems appropriate to invite a panel of experts from many parts of the world to share a rather intimate discussion of the *Frontiers of Fitness* in the form of a short monograph.

By confining reviews to the areas of fitness and exercise physiology, I have in a sense eased the task of the contributors. Systematic study of the human response to graded intensities of exercise is a relatively recent development. Many of the giants—Christensen, Dill, Hill, Larson, Margaria, Mueller, Robinson—are either still active among us or of recent memory. The jungle of repetitive work has had little time to grow. There are even uncharted territories that await discovery. But already we see warning signs of the problem that confronts the student in other areas of physiology—an increasing population of exercise physiologists, a proliferation of specialist journals, an earnest determination to conduct more and more research on smaller and smaller problems. *Frontiers of Fitness* is addressed to this situation. Hopefully, it will focus our attention on significant developments of the recent past and growing points of future knowledge. Hopefully, also it will help many of us to deploy our research efforts with greater profit, and perchance some farsighted spirit may catch a glimpse of an uncharted continent.

This monograph is the first of a series to be published under the auspices of the Canadian Association of Sports Sciences, and as a young but vigorous association, we are indeed honored that so many distinguished authors have agreed to contribute to this first volume. The interests of the association are much broader than exercise physiology, and subsequent monographs will doubtless reflect a concern with such topics as the sociology and psychology of sports, athletic medicine, the treatment of injuries, and the relation of physical activity to community health. Not all of the present panel would admit to being physiologists, but many find in physiology their prime allegiance. All write so competently that I have found it necessary to impose few editorial restraints; however, my general aim has been to hold the discussion to a level that should be comprehensible to graduates with a commitment to fitness, while providing an adequate bibliography of some one thousand recent references for those who would read further.

The titles of individual contributions are self-explanatory. At the risk of ignoring several of the more interesting reviews, it is tempting to note certain patterns in our growing understanding of fitness. Certainly, the scientist who can marry his knowledge of exericse physiology to expertise in some other discipline is at a premium.

Much is being learned from excursions into biochemistry, using samples of blood (Denolin, di Prampero), tissue biopsies (Hultman) and investigations of the arm as a functional unit (Mottram). Cellular physiology and electron microscopy (Gollnick) are teaching the intimate nature of muscle contraction and hitherto unsuspected responses to training. Computers, both digital and analogue (Rautaharju), are adding a new dimension to interpretations of the exercise electrocardiogram. Physical principles are being applied increasingly to such problems as the thermal events accompanying muscular contraction (Banister) and body motion, terrestrial and extraterrestrial (Margaria). The psychologist is learning to measure the sensations of effort and in turn to apply this knowledge to predictions of working capacity (Borg).

Procedures long accepted are also being critically reviewed and submitted for international standardization. Can one reasonably compare measures of aerobic power from different laboratories? Are the goals of standardization realistic (Shephard)?

Finally, we may trace a concern with man's changing environment, the problem with which I began this introduction. What is the interaction between physical activity and environment? How far can man adapt to a world that is presently hostile and threatens to become more so? Is the working capacity of the schoolchild deteriorating in the inactive environment of the conurbation (Shephard)? What is the influence of overnutrition?

How well can man adapt to exercise in the heat (Iampietro)? In making such adaptations, are new physiological mechanisms such as a redistribution of circulation brought into play and if so, is the health of vital organs compromised (Rowell)? What is the influence of moderate altitude on performance? Were physiologists able to predict the outcome of the Mexico Olympics (Faulkner)? Is fitness further modified by the onset of disease (Frick)?

These are all fascinating problems, and I must admit that I personally have learned a great deal from my modest contribution to the assembly of this monograph. I trust that other readers will share this happy experience.

R. J. Shephard

CONTENTS

SECTION THREE

TECHNIQUES OF MEASURING HUMAN PERFORMANCE

SECTION FOUR

THE INFLUENCE OF AGE, HEALTH, AND ENVIRONMENT ON WORKING CAPACITY

FRONTIERS OF FITNESS

SECTION ONE
PHYSIOLOGY AND BIOCHEMISTRY OF MUSCLE

Chapter 1

ENERGETICS OF MUSCULAR CONTRACTION

E. W. BANISTER

Introduction

ALTHOUGH MUSCLE has been studied intensively for several decades, it is only recently that a degree of fruition has been reached in relating the thermal and mechanical events of contraction to their biochemical and ultrastructural analogues.

Even so, there is much that remains controversial, and enthusiasm for comprehension recently gained must be tempered by the facts that no definite ultrastructural locations exist for some of the proposed theoretical constructs of muscle (specifically the series elastic and parallel elements). The precise chemical roles played by certain elements and compounds responsible for the spread of contraction and relaxation are not apparent. The comparative physiology of different types of muscle also awaits clear definition (25), and some previously accepted aspects of the mechanisms for regulation of the immediate and continued substrate supply for muscular energy, especially during elevated metabolism, are now questionable.

It is not the purpose of this chapter to provide comprehensive description of all that relates to muscle. Rather, generally held current concepts of muscle structure and function will be described with reference only to striated muscle (skeletal and cardiac). Contraction mechanisms, muscle models, thermodynamics, efficiency, energy substrate supply, and the effect of training on muscle function will also be discussed.

Skeletal Muscle

Current concepts of skeletal muscle include acceptance of the proteins myosin and actin, linked by crossbridges (themselves

5

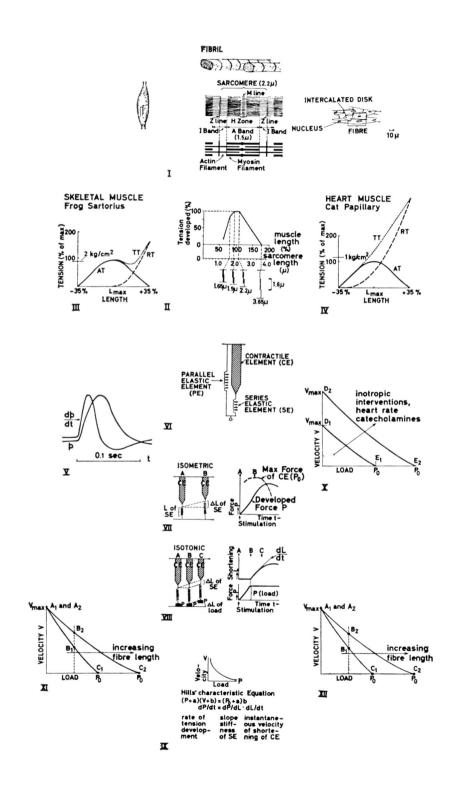

FIGURE 1-1. *I:* A diagrammatic representation of fibril arrangement; many
fibrils are contained by a sheath or sarcolemma and surrounded by
cytoplasm to form the muscle fiber. The cell unit is determined at the
level of the cross striation (Z lines) and termed a sarcomere. Thick
(myosin) and thin (actin) myofilaments and contractile proteins com-
pose the sarcomere. They interreact and interdigitate when stimulated
by an action potential to produce the force of contraction (9).

II: An arrangement of myofilaments showing the extent of overlap, according to the sliding filament theory, appropriate to the active tension developed during stimulation in frog skeletal muscle (41).

III: Length-tension relations in skeletal muscle, showing the relative contributions of resting (RT) and active tension (AT) to total tension
(TT) development (9).

IV: Length-tension relations in heart muscle (9).

V: dp/dt, the rate of change of tension development in an isometric
contraction. dp/dt both in terms of the timing and amplitude of its
peak has been regarded as indicative of the onset, magnitude, and
maintenance of the active state of the muscle. The latter itself is a
factor which determines the course of a contraction. A twitch, for
example, which allows insufficient time for full development of the
active state, records less force development than a sustained tetanus
(95).

VI: The three-component Hill model of muscle, showing the contractile
(CE) series and elastic (SE) and parallel elastic (PE) components
(49).

VII: Isometric contraction in terms of the Hill three-component model
without PE. The dashed line represents the maximum force potential
of CE, the active state, and the full line, the recorded developed
force. The differences in skeletal and heart muscle are evident from
the more slowly developing active state characteristic of heart muscle
(100).

VIII: After loaded isotonic contraction and the instantaneous shortening
velocity of CE dL/dt used in characterization of the state of myocardial muscle (98, 99, 100, 103).

IX: The displaced rectangular hyperbola force-velocity relation of muscle.
The characteristic theoretical-experimental equation independently
developed by Hill from thermal studies may be also fitted to this curve
of the purely mechanical aspects of shortening. The constant "a" of
each derivation, however, has been shown recently to have different
values (49, 51).

X: Force velocity relations in heart muscle as they are modified by
inotropic influences (9).

XI: Force velocity relations in skeletal muscle as they are modified by
increasing initial muscle length (9).

XII: Force velocity relations in cardiac muscle as they are modified by increasing initial muscle length (Frank-Starling principle) (9).

The diagrams in this composite figure are due to the individual authors noted in the legend references. They are reproduced here with
permission of the publishers.

myosin molecules), as the basic elements of the contractile system
(53, 88, 113). These proteins undergo interdigitation according
to the sliding filament theory (Fig. 1-1,I and 1-1,II) during
contraction (54). The elements are actuated by ionic currents in
a transverse tubular system (T system) (Fig. 1-2,II) carrying
the action potential (AP) and nourishing fluids from the surface
of the fiber (sarcolemma) to the innermost myofibril, a distance
of something of the order of 50μ (85). The coupling between
this excitation and contraction (e-c coupling) is triggered from
calcium ions released by the ionic currents into another tubular
system, pervading the myofibrils within the cytoplasmic flund of
the cell and called the sarcoplasmic reticulum (SR) (Fig. 1-2,I)
(85, 92, 96). Calcium ions are essential to the action of an
enzyme, ATPase, which is associated with the protein myosin.
In the presence of magnesium ions, ATPase catalyzes the breakdown of high energy phosphate ATP to ADP and orthophosphate
with the immediate energy release of 11,000 cal per mole to
sponsor the contraction or twitch. Following contraction the SR
recaptures calcium ions and induces relaxation (88). During this
time ATP is regenerated by the dephosphorylation of another
high energy compound, phosphoryl creatine (PC), which, in
turn, is finally replenished by the catabolism of food.

Cardiac Muscle

Concepts originally applied to skeletal muscle are now considered relevant to cardiac muscle with certain modifications (2,
7, 8, 38, 103). The unique features of cardiac muscle are that
a) it cannot be tetanized; b) it has a significant resting tension
at those muscle lengths where contractile tension is normally
developed and where the resting tension is subject to self-
regulatory control mechanisms (Fig. 1-1,IV); and c) the active
state, a measure of the potential force of contraction, is slow to
develop, prolonged in length, and variable in intensity, the latter
resulting from various inotropic mechanisms able to act on it.
The course of both contraction and relaxation in skeletal and
cardiac muscle is similar (86, 87).

Morphology of Striated Muscle

The morphology of functionally different striated muscles is similar. Points of divergence seem logical modifications adapted to special function. Thus, heart muscle, requiring synchronous regular contraction, has calcium storage depots immediately below the cell surface sarcolemma as well as along the T tubules (Fig. 1-2,III) (85). It also has an abundance of mitochondria, which are the major store of high energy phosphate, ATP, and a less extensive SR system. In some vertebrates the SR system apparently breaches the sarcomere boundaries, making the muscle longitudinally continuous (88). Rapid acting, intermittently active skeletal muscle has fewer mitochondria and an extensive SR system reportedly able to supply the immediate ATP needed for contraction. Rapid, continuously acting skeletal muscle such as the flight muscle of insects or the cricothyroid muscle of the bat, concerned with high pitch noise production, contain both an extensive SR system and well-developed mitochondria.

Models of Muscle

Several models have been constructed to interpret the mechanical and thermal aspects of contraction (93, 111). The most widely accepted is still the A.V. Hill three-component structure of the contractile (CE), series elastic (SE), and parallel elastic (PE) elements (Fig. 1-1,VI) (49). In this model, isometric and isotonic contractions are explained by the interaction of the CE and SE—the PE being largely associated with control of muscle tension at extreme lengths.

Energy Changes in Contraction

The energy changes involved in both isometric and isotonic contractions are essentially a result of activation of the muscle, maintenance of the active state, and interaction of the CE and SE elements (Fig. 1-1,V) (37, 49, 95). After stimulation and the breakdown of ATP to energize the contraction, the CE shortens and stretches the SE, developing tension in the latter (Fig. 1-1,III). In the isometric contraction (Fig. 1-1,VII) tension

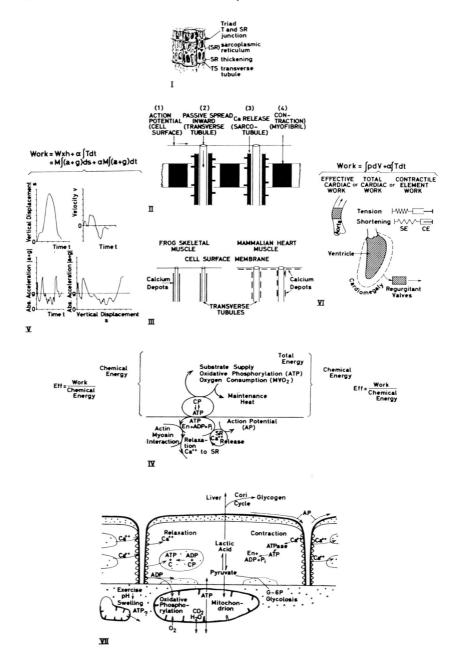

FIGURE 1-2. *I:* A diagrammatic representation showing the apposition of the sarcoplasmic reticulum and transverse tubules at the level of the Z lines in a system termed the triads (92).

II: Typical steps in the excitation-coupling sequence of frog twitch-type skeletal muscle (85).

III: Schematic diagram of critical differences in the form and distribution of calcium storage depots in frog twitch-type skeletal muscle and mammalian heart muscle (85).

IV: A typical sequence of steps in the conversion of food into the energy for contraction of muscle. The harnessing of all the energy available from food for energy in the metabolic process is determined at two points in the sequence, the efficiency of storage of energy as high energy phosphate (Ep) and the efficiency of the process of conversion of effective energy into external work (E_c) (see text).

V: Determination of the efficiency E_c depends on sufficient evaluation of external work. This is most effectively done by consideration of the accelerations of the body (directly dependent on muscular effort) in all phases of its movement. Shown are acceleration-time and acceleration-distance curves of movement in a vertical plane for accelerations above 1 g for a stepping action in man. The area between the curves and the -g (or absolute 0) base line gives the work done per unit mass. Direct evaluation of the metabolic cost of well-defined phases in the movement enables average metabolic costs per unit of work to be calculated. By this means equivalent work may be represented either in dyne-cm or dyne-sec units and a transform function α between the two calculated.

VI: Work of the heart evaluated according to a) the amount of external work done in the systemic circulation (pressure elevation × volume of blood ejected), b) the tension developed in the myocardium, c) the contractile element work done in stretching SE and developing tension in the myocardium. Energy expended in developing external work is a small fraction of the energy expended in developing and maintaining tension in heart muscle (9).

VII: A schematic representation of the energetic transformations at cellular level during contraction by the muscle. Shown bottom left is a deformed mitochondrion typically seen after exhaustive work. Speculation on this type of modification seen in the transition from rest to work might suggest that it, in itself, is a regulatory mechanism in the provision of high energy phosphate for the increased metabolic process.

The diagrams in this composite diagram are due to the individual authors noted in the legend reference. They are reproduced here with permission of the publishers.

development continues, and no external shortening occurs. In the isotonic contraction (Fig. 1-1,VIII) the CE will shorten and lift the load after developing sufficient tension to do so. The characteristics of shortening in skeletal muscle depend on the initial length of the muscle (Fig. 1-1,XI). The force is transmitted through the stretched SE component. This latter type of contraction results in a greater amount of energy being mobilized than in a pure isometric contraction, a result first observed by Fenn from thermal measurements and now termed the Fenn effect (36). This has been confirmed both by Carlson *et al.* (16), Fales (35), and Ernst (34). Hill demonstrated that the extra energy of shortening was due to a) the work done by the muscle and b) an extra heat of shortening. The heat resulting both from shortening and the external work done occupied a central position in the development of the Hill equation characteristic of skeletal muscle (Fig. 1-1,IX),

$$(P+a)(V+b) = P_o+a)b \qquad (1)$$

since the heat of shortening was considered to be dependent only on the extent of shortening. In an isotonic shortening over a distance X with an applied load P, the energy expended in shortening would be $Px + ax$ or $(P+a)x$, a being a constant of heat energy per unit length change of the muscle. The rate of energy expenditure would then be $(P+a)dx/dt$ or $(P+a)V$, where V is the velocity of shortening. Hill showed experimentally that $(P+a)V$ decreased proportionately to the load, so that

$$(P+a) \propto (P_o-P) \qquad (2)$$
$$\text{or } (P+a)V = b(P_o-P) \qquad (3)$$

where P_o is the isometric tension apparent at zero velocity of shortening and b is a constant relating $(P+a)V$ to the load. Equation (3) transforms easily to equation (1). Hill has recently proposed that the constant a of equations (1) and (2) are not the same and that the heat of shortening is also dependent on the work done (51, 52).

It is unfortunate that no biochemical evidence of ATP breakdown can be associated with shortening heat, and other events have been proposed to explain it (28).

Biochemical studies have also failed to account for activation heat in muscle by ATP breakdown, and again other sources of this heat production have been suggested (88).

Within the last decade the Hill model of muscle and the characteristic equation (1) have also been applied increasingly to the characterization of myocardial contractility (100), using the equation

$$(P+a)(V+b) = P_o+a)b \qquad (1)$$

in conjunction with the relationship

$$\underset{\substack{\text{rate of} \\ \text{tension} \\ \text{development}}}{dp/dt} \quad = \quad \underset{\substack{\text{slope} \\ \text{stiffness} \\ \text{of SE}}}{dp/dL} \quad \cdot \quad \underset{\substack{\text{velocity} \\ \text{of} \\ \text{shortening} \\ \text{of CE}}}{dL/dt} \qquad (4)$$

together with the corresponding rate of ventricular outflow and midwall circumferential fiber shortening. This allows the separate effects upon the myocardium of increasing fiber length, increasing heart rate, and inotropic agents to be quantified in terms of the force velocity equation of the contractile element (Figs. 1-1, X and XII). Such studies, made initially on animal preparations, have now been extended to quantification of the contractility of the human myocardium *in vivo* in health, exercise, and diseased states (9, 10, 91, 98, 99, 101).

However, the energetic interactions between cardiac muscle and blood flow in the systemic circulation are probably more complex than indicated simply from the Hill model analysis. The recent concepts of myocardial ventricular impulse and inertial blood flow suggest that ventricular fiber shortening follows ventricular emptying rather than actively implementing it and is effective only in the generation of the initial ventricular impulse at the onset of ventricular contraction (78, 79, 80, 94, 102).

Muscle as a Machine

The analogy between muscle primed with a fuel and delivering power for various tasks and inanimate machinery has led naturally to attempts at expressing the efficiency of the process (44, 52). Such attempts have always been hampered by the fact that external work performed by the muscle is inadequately expressed in a conventional physical manner; energy is always transformed, whether effective physical work is performed or not.

This has led to the use of units involving force and and time, the dyne-second or the so-called tension-time integral, thereby allowing expression of the energy involved in developing and maintaining tension without delivery of external work (98). As has been seen previously, tension is developed by contractile element work against stretching of the SE. This is denoted by the integral $\alpha \int Tdt$ where the constant α, relating to maintenance heat, is rather better known for skeletal muscle than cardiac muscle (13).

In the case of myocardial muscle the oxygen consumption required for this type of CE tension development is much greater than the extra CE shortening and metabolism that accompanies the performance of external work. The extra oxygen consumption that accompanies the overall shortening of the muscle and ejection of blood into the systemic circulation has been called the cardiac correlate of the Fenn effect in skeletal muscle (10). This extra metabolism has been related totally to the increased external work of the heart and not to any concomitant shortening heat. For heart muscle, as for skeletal muscle, ATP breakdown has been shown to be linearly related to the sum of the CE work performed in developing tension and initiating shortening. A greater proportion of cardiac metabolism serves the needs of tension development than the performance of external work. The economy in the overall energetics of cardiac muscle effected by reducing the oxygen cost of tension development is important in alleviating anginal pain. This is illustrated in Figure 1-2,VI. The energy required to perform external work is the sum of the integrals $M \int (a+g)ds + \alpha M \int (a+g)dt$ and $\int Pdv + \alpha \int Tdt$ for skeletal and heart muscle, respectively (13), where M is body mass, a is the acceleration above 1 g, g is the acceleration because of gravity, P is the pressure, V is the volume, T is the myocardial muscle tension, and t is time. The constants α are not the same in skeletal and heart muscle, but both have the dimensions of velocity (LT^{-1}).

A potentially profitable method of assessing the external work and power (26, 112) performed both in skeletal and heart muscle is to represent all movement as absolute acceleration against either distance or time in the manner proposed by Starr (104). A further extension of this concept would consider the metabolic cost of movements which could be represented by either a force-distance integral or a tension-time integral; a transfer function, α, would then be calculated, permitting the estimation of tension-time integral work in physically interpretable terms. The acceleration may be calculated for any movement where both displacement (s) and time (t) have been recorded. It is then possible to derive the integrals $\int M\alpha(a+g)ds$ and $\int M\alpha(a+g)dt$, where a is the increased acceleration of the body mass M above 1 g (61). It would seem more logical to interpret the dynamics of skeletal and cardiac muscle in terms of the actual accelerations and decelerations which they develop during contraction, relaxation, and forced stretch rather than to interpret the work they perform merely from the loads they lift. No direct comparison between evaluations of the work done based on the acceleration-distance curve of shortening and those based on the simple multiple of tension developed and distance shortened appears to have been made. Theoretically they should be identical. Figure 1-2,V shows typical absolute acceleration-distance and absolute acceleration-time integrals of the center of mass of a body during stepping which could be used in the type of analysis discussed above. The above reasoning is pertinent to the suggestion that cardiac muscle does not experience any afterload once it has imparted the initial ventricular impulse to the blood. If in the subsequent contraction the myocardial fibers shorten secondary to and merely following ventricular outflow, it would seem better to characterize their performance in terms of the initial acceleration of contraction rather than its velocity.

One unfortunate aspect of the classical development of the Hill equation was perhaps its expression in velocity units, power output, or rate of doing work rather than acceleration units, since from that time muscle physiologists have concerned themselves mainly with the velocities of muscle movement and not with its antecedent, acceleration.

In the case of skeletal muscle the interaction of the CE and SE during any phase of cyclic activity modifies the energetics of the subsequent phases. Thus, if a muscle undergoes forced stretch followed by shortening, the stored energy of the SE augments the work relative to that achieved by a similar shortening without preliminary stretching or complete isometric tetanus. Not only is any subsequent isotonic contraction enhanced by the energy stored in the SE, but the contractile properties of the CE are apparently increased (18, 19, 20). The energetics of negative work originally proposed as a reversal of chemical processes (1, 50) has been revised in the light of recent thermal and bio-chemical evidence showing a reduced rate of energy production (3, 43, 55, 72).

Thermodynamics of Muscle and Efficiency

The chemical reactions involved in muscle contraction are governed by the normal laws of thermodynamics and energy transformation. Physiological systems differ from the usual physical machine in that the reactions involved take place at constant temperature and pressure; the usual concept of a heat engine is that it works between a higher and a lower temperature, delivering an amount of work proportional to the difference in absolute temperature and the heat absorbed.

The concepts involved in energy transformations in a physio-chemical system are heat absorbed (Q), external work done (W), internal energy (E), enthalpy or heat content (H), entropy (S), and free energy (G) (62,111). These concepts will be briefly reviewed.

The absolute levels of some of these parameters are usually indeterminable, but this is not important since we are interested primarily in the difference of energy between two systems.

The first law of thermodynamics states that energy is conserved or that the change in internal energy of a system is equal to the difference between the heat absorbed and the external work done:

$$\Delta E = Q - W \qquad (5)$$

One would expect, therefore, that where the internal energy of a system decreases work would be done and heat evolved

$$-\Delta E = -Q + W \qquad (6)$$

where the negative signs indicate energy decrement and heat evolution.

Irrespective of external work, work is involved in changing the dimensions of a system. This depends on the accompanying pressure and volume change ($P\Delta V$). The true change in heat content (enthalpy) of a system therefore depends on both the change in internal energy (ΔE) and the accompanying dimensional component ($P\Delta V$), so that

$$H = \Delta E + P\Delta V \qquad (7)$$

The second law of thermodynamics implies that the direction of a reversible chemical reaction is controlled not only by the heat content of the system but also by its entropy or degree of randomness. A well-ordered system always has a smaller level of entropy than a less well ordered system, and the tendency of energy-flow in the universe is towards random distribution or maximum entropy. In a situation of maximum entropy there is energy equilibrium with no possibility of energy transformation or life. Entropy may therefore be viewed as an overriding influence, inducing change towards random order. Wherever energy is degraded to heat, entropy is increased. The difference between total heat content change and the entropy change is termed the free energy. This free energy may do work or be degraded as heat.

$$\text{from (7):} \quad \Delta G = \Delta H - T\Delta S \qquad (8)$$
$$\text{if } P\Delta V = 0 \quad \Delta G = \Delta E + P\Delta V - T\Delta S \qquad (9)$$
$$\text{from (6):} \quad \Delta E = \Delta G + T\Delta S \qquad (10)$$
$$\text{and} \quad -Q + W = \Delta G + T\Delta S \qquad (11)$$
$$-Q = \text{Heat evolved} = \Delta G + T\Delta S - W \qquad (12)$$

T = the absolute temperature

If no energy is degraded to heat, then

$$T\Delta S = 0$$
$$Q = 0$$
$$\Delta G = W \qquad (13)$$

and all the free energy is available as work. However, this situation rarely obtains in practice.

The free energy of a reaction is deduced from its equilibrium constant according to the relation

$$\Delta G^\circ = -RT \ln K_e \qquad (14)$$

R = Gas constant
(1.987 cal mole^{-1}deg^{-1})
T = Absolute temperature
K_e = Equilibrium constant

However, in ATP splitting the reaction lies so far to the right that a direct determination of ΔG° is technically impossible. Resort is then made to a coupled reaction (the amination of glutamic acid to glutamine, powered by ATP hydrolysis). ΔG°, the standard free energy at pH 7, 37 C, and unimolar concentration or unit activity of the reactants is calculated to be −7900 cal mole^{-1}. At physiological concentrations (several orders of magnitude less than 1 mole), ΔG is certainly much larger than this and is calculated from ΔG° by the relation

$$\Delta G^{\text{physiological}}_{\text{concentration}} = \Delta G^\circ + RT \ln C_{ADP} \cdot C_{HPO4}{}^{2-}/C_{ATP} \qquad (15)$$

C = physiological concentration

Recently the thermodynamics of irreversible processes has been successfully applied to predict the shape of the force velocity curve, and the theory has been discussed with regard to other known physiological properties of muscle (14, 15, 114). In the controversy surrounding shortening heat the biochemically equivalent ATP splitting was sought in 2,4 dinitrofluorobenzene (DFNB) poisoned muscle, where ATP hydrolyzed cannot be resynthesised from CP (28, 64). In these experiments on amphibian muscle a linear relation was observed between the total ATP split and the external work performed, with an overall thermodynamic efficiency (external work/free energy change) of 55 percent, assuming approximately 10 kcal per mole of ATP free energy = enthalpy = CP enthalpy. There was no evidence of free energy degradation to account for the heat of shortening, and evidence was adduced from a previous molecular model to suggest that a reversible negative entropy change yielded the experimentally observed heat (27).

Since the energy changes during contraction and relaxation of muscle are complex, involving both enthalpy and entropy (or configurational) changes, simplifying assumptions used in calculations of muscular efficiency limit application of the results (16, 115).

Even so, the attempt has been made. It has been proposed that in the steady state of muscle activity, ATP hydrolysis is quantitatively related to oxygen consumption in the amount of 6 ATP moles per mole of oxygen used, assuming a P:O ratio of 3. The production of 3 ATP molecules is coupled to the passage of 2 electrons down the cytochrome chain of the mitochondrion and to the use of one atom of oxygen (109). A value of thermodynamic efficiency (E_c) similar to the average value described for amphibian muscle in the velocity range 0 to 6 cm per sec (28) has been reported for humans performing bicycle ergometer work. However, when correction is made for ATP usage in pumping calcium ions into the sarcoplasmic reticulum, the value obtained (49%) is considerably different from the 70 to 95 percent value reported for amphibian muscle at speeds of 2 cm per sec. The product of thermodynamic efficiency and phosphate coupling efficiency (E_p) gives the overall efficiency with which food is transformed into work. Uncertainty exists in the value to assign to the free energy of ATP, since it is only recently that firm values for the *in vivo* enthalpy of CP hydrolysis have been obtained (16, 32, 115). If ATP is immediately resynthesised from CP, its free energy must be similar to its enthalpy (10-11 kcal/mole^{-1}). On this assumption E_p is 60 percent (69). Assuming that 38 molecules of ATP at 11 kcal mole^{-1} are conserved per mole of glucose (686 kcal mole^{-1}), metabolized,

$$E_{muscle} = E_p \times E_e$$
$$= 60\% \times 49\%$$
$$= 29\%$$

In practice the allocation of the total free energy change to muscular work is an approximation, since considerable metabolic activity continues in other organs. As has been argued by Ernst (34), this latter activity has no bearing on the efficiency of the skeletal muscle considered as a machine. Account should also be taken of the external work involved in acceleration and deceleration, which in practice is often neglected. In a bicycle ergometry study (46) where accelerations of the center of mass are small, there were discrepancies of from 1 to 17 percent between the ergometer load setting and the measured power output through the cranks in the range 100 to 400 w. The peak forces exerted in a complete pedal revolution were twice the ergometer load setting, and the question may be posed as to how efficiently ATP splitting is coupled to transient peak and trough loads in cyclic activity. Some investigations on this point have recently been presented (105).

It appears that the blood flow to a working muscle can considerably influence the efficiency for dynamic work. Within certain limits the ability to do work is unimpaired by less blood flow, whereas the oxygen uptake may be considerably less (31).

Other thermodynamic constants describing the power and capacity of muscle have been proposed by Margaria and his coworkers (29, 30, 72) in terms of alactacid, oxidative, and lactacid mechanisms. Respective values of 48, 13, and 25 kcal per kilogram hour have been assigned to the power of the three mechanisms in humans. The corresponding capacities were reported as 100, infinitely large, and 220 kcal per kilogram; the last estimate has recently been revised to 270 kcal per kilogram in dogs (21).

Substrate Supply and Regulation of Muscular Work

The ability of muscle to perform work depends on the adequacy of the blood, oxygen, and food supply. The rate of oxygen supply, as has been seen previously, is tied to the utilization of ATP; this in turn is maintained at an adequate level by substrate metabolism of glucose (involving glycolysis and oxidative phosphorylation); of free fatty acid (directly into the citric acid cycle via acetyl-CoA); and amino acid metabolism involving transaminations, deamination, and oxidation (17, 33, 69, 73).

The energy produced by substrate metabolism is coupled to its storage as high energy phosphate at several well-defined points in the metabolic pathways. It takes place whether an adequate oxygen supply is present or not, although in the latter case the capacity for work is severely limited. The process may be illustrated by glucose metabolism in the extramitochondrial and intramitochondrial compartments of the muscle cell. Glycolysis takes place in the extramitochondrial portion of the cell; in the presence of oxygen it is termed aerobic glycolysis, and in the total absence of oxygen it is termed anaerobic glycolysis. Glucose uptake from the blood and the rate of glycolysis is increased by oxygen lack. The distinction between this precise terminology and the imprecise descriptions of anaerobic metabolism in much of the current literature has been discussed by Olson (83). Extramitochondrial NADH may reduce the end product of glycolysis, pyruvate, to lactate. Two moles of ATP are produced in this sequence for each mole of glucose that is metabolized. In the presence of oxygen, pyruvate may also enter the citric acid cycle and undergo complete degradation to carbon dioxide and water. In this sequence the oxidation of substrate is coupled to a further 36 moles of ATP, and a correspondingly larger portion of the free energy of the glucose molecule is available for the production of work. The intramitochondrial and extramitochondrial NADH involved in these reactions can be distinguished in terms of the intensity of their fluorescence (56). The major site of ATP production is within the mitochondrion (Figure 1-2, VII). Several of the mechanisms regulating carbohydrate utilization have been discussed by Lowenstein, (Fig. 1-3) (71); principal among these is control of the rate of glycolysis by inhibition of the enzyme phosphofructokinase, which catalyses phosphorylation of fructose 1 phosphate by ATP. Inhibition is overcome in the presence of ADP, AMP, P_i, and fructose 1:6 diphosphate, so that the natural accumulation of ADP with hydrolysis of ATP actuates the phosphofructokinase reaction.

The extramitochondrial production of lactate occurs whenever extramitochondrial NADH levels are high or there is little demand for ATP splitting. This may well account for the substantial levels of lactate in resting muscle, where NADH levels are high and metabolism is low. Similarly, the initial rate of glycolysis may be greater than that of oxidative phosphorylation, so that pyruvate accumulates and is temporarily transformed to lactate. Evidence of this has been presented by Keul and his co-workers (59) and by Jöbsis and Stainsby (58). The former investigators

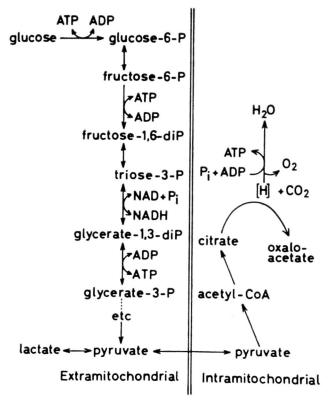

FIGURE 1-3. A schematic diagram of glucose metabolism in the intra-mitochondrial and extramitochondrial compartments, from the original by Lowenstein (71). (Reproduced by permission of the publisher.)

showed that during rest and light work the muscle extracts lactate and pyruvate from the circulation, while at higher work loads it produces increasing amounts of lactate; however, in their view the venous oxygen tension never approaches critical levels (see Chapter 15). The inability of oxidative phosphorylation to keep pace with glycolysis in skeletal muscle is related to the relatively low mitochondrial count. Heart muscle, which has an abundance of mitochondria, does not discharge lactate even at high working rates. The increasing role played by free fatty acid metabolism at higher work rates (33, 42) may identify pyruvate decarboxylation as one site where glucose metabolism is restricted when, despite an adequate ability of the mitochondria for oxidative phosphorylation, pyruvate may not enter the citric acid cycle (48, 59). It also seems apparent that the pH of the cellular environment inhibits the ability of skeletal muscle to make full use of glycolysis. In this case the hexose monophosphate shunt is preferentially activated with production of NADPH (65).

DiPrampero and his co-workers have suggested the important contribution of muscle lipid stores as a source of substrate to account for metabolite balance in exercise (33). It is probable that during the performance of heavy work not more than 2 percent of the total energy production is accounted for by glycolysis, since this reaction proceeds only as far as lactate, which is then discharged from the muscle cell. Jöbsis and Stainsby (58) have obtained similar evidence from *in vivo* studies of oxidative phosphorylation in the gastrocnemius muscle of the exercising dog, using the elegant fluorimetric methods developed by Chance and his co-workers (22, 23). At no time during stimulation and contraction of this preparation was the muscle measurably hypoxic, yet lactate was produced. These workers concluded that lactate production resulted from a transient imbalance between pyruvate production by aerobic glycolysis and its removal by respiration and oxidative phosphorylation. Such results have important implications for the concepts of alactacid and lactacid oxygen debts. It is significant that the basis of the alactacid debt has already been reappraised in biochemical-energetic terms of high energy phosphate breakdown, particularly CP splitting (30, 32, 90). The concept of phosphagen (GP) denoting the coupled reactions between CP and ATP ($GP = ATP + CP$) has been used in this latter work. The total concentration of GP has been shown to diminish linearly with increasing work load (4).

Effects of Disease and Exercise Training on the Ultrastructure of Muscle

The most obvious effect of exercise on muscle is that eventually fatigue occurs, and it must be rested. Some of the mechanisms of fatigue may be understood in the light of the foregoing discussion, but the basis of the adaptations which muscle makes to repeated exercise (107) (improved performance and/or hypertrophy) is not so obvious. Changes in the muscle constituents differ, depending on whether low force or high force exercise is used in training. In the former type of activity, myofibrillar protein concentrations tend to decrease while sarcoplasmic protein concentration increases (40). The reverse situation is observed in forceful types of activity. Collagen increases in proportion to total muscle protein (108). In heart muscle, increases in the amount of connective tissue and synthesis of myofibrillar protein both contribute to hypertrophy (11).

Increased concentrations of mitochondrial proteins develop concomitantly with increased endurance, and the fine structure of both skeletal and cardiac muscle shows evidence of mitochondrial adaptation to repeated and exhaustive exercise (39, 47, 63).

Cardiac hypertrophy has been attributed to myocardial ischemia resulting from functional overload or general hypoxia (6, 12, 106), but a recent report (89) has suggested that myocardial ischemia is not the prerequisite to hypertrophy—a simple systolic overload is the prime requirement.

One mechanism proposed to account for hypertrophy is that an increased intensity of function of structures (IFS) stimulates synthesis of cellular structural proteins (75, 76). Those structures having an energy production function are augmented prior to those immediately regulating the function of the cell.

Well-defined destruction of the mitochondria from the skeletal and myocardial muscle has been shown during exercise stress and experimentally induced pathological conditions (45, 97, 110). The changes observed under pathological conditions include detachment of cristae from the inner mitochondrial membrane, fragmentation of cristae, development of cystlike swellings, and rupture of the mitochondrial membrane. Similar though less well-defined changes occur in the myocardial mitochondria of animals subjected to exercise by continuous swimming for varying periods; abnormalities are usually confined to mitochondrial swelling (without the appearance of a less electron dense matrix except after the longest [8 hour] periods of swimming) and the development of invaginations (66, 67).

However, a basis for effective comparison of the pathological and exercise models does not exist at present. Similar stages of myocardial hypertrophy have yet to be shown in both models. No evidence of cystlike formations or total disruption of the mitochondrial membrane have been demonstrated following exercise. The most probable reason is that swimming, the exercise method usually used, is not particularly suited to the development of hypertrophy, at least in skeletal muscle. Even untrained rats have the capacity to swim continuously for six hours if the water temperature is suitably adjusted (47).

Biochemical studies (23, 81) suggest that even where ADP and Pi levels are sufficiently high to maintain a large capillary wall-cell membrane oxygen gradient, cytochrome oxidase and pyridine nucleotide remain in a highly oxidized state and function in oxidative phosphorylation. Only where NAD is 90 percent reduced, at intracellular PO_2 levels of 0.1 mm Hg, is oxidative phosphorylation too slow to maintain necessary ATP levels, and some critical physiological function such as EEG or respiration ceases. Cellular changes might thus be anticipated before overt changes in physiological function and could occur at lesser degrees of cellular hypoxia consistent with the changes shown in the above micrograph (Fig. 1-4). Packer (84) has noted that mitochondria shrink under conditions of oxidative phosphorylation and that the mitochondrial membrane appears to regulate escape of ATP. Thus, under conditions where there is obvious swelling and total disruption of some cell mitochondrial membranes, there might be no measurable decline in the ATP levels of biopsy specimens or whole heart homogenates (70), as has been noted (91). Despite this, it is conceivable that ATP needed for the essential function of maintaining individual membrane integrity has been reduced. Enhanced escape of intramitochondrial ATP in response to acidosis of the cellular environment may be considered another regulatory and reversible response to tissue need for high energy phosphate.

Recent reports (4) on the possible autonomicity of mitochon-

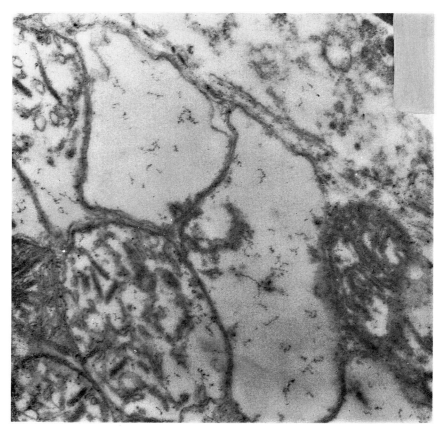

FIGURE 1-4. An electron micrograph of right ventricular tissue from the myocardium of a rat immediately after exhaustive treadmill running. The mitochondria show absence of the inner matrix (cristae) on which the processes of energy transformation are carried out. Magnification ×33,500. (Banister, E.W., Tomanek, R.J., Cvorkov, N., Unpublished data.)

dria with ability for independent protein synthesis, the existence of self-replicating mitochondrial DNA (mDNA) and mitochondrial ribosomes, leads to interesting speculation on the position occupied in cellular hypertrophy by these organelles. The contribution of the elements and of the connective tissue cell nuclei to the increased total myocardial DNA pool in hypertrophy remains yet to be evaluated in both the exercise and pathological

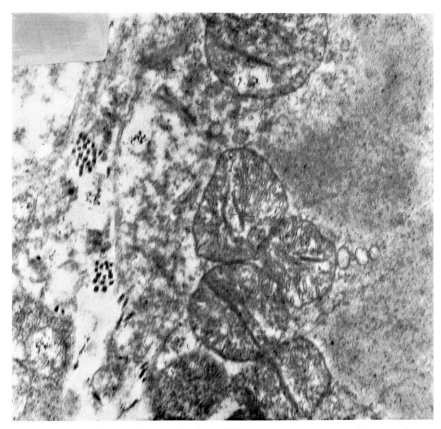

FIGURE 1-5. Electron-dense, thick, rodlike projections across the mitochondria from the right ventricle of a rat thirty minutes after exhaustive treadmill running. These changes are similar to those shown by Laguens and Gómez Dumm (68), which they have suggested as synthesised DNA. Magnification ×25,580. (Banister, E.W., Tomanek, R.J., Cvorkov, N., Unpublished data.)

models. Certainly, there is no contribution from an increased DNA content of the muscle cell nucleus itself (24, 77). If, as reported (4), the biosynthesis of mitochondrial proteins involves two independent cellular locations, one inside and one outside the mitochondria, then the synthetic activity of both of these centers could be stimulated by increased concentrations of substrate engendered (inside the mitochondrion by fragmentation of cristae and at the extramitochondrial location by the increased outward transport of mitochondrial constituents through swelling or a total disruption of their containing membrane).

Laguens and Gómez Dumm (68) have recently shown mitochondria structurally modified by exercise; these contain thick, electron-dense rods which have been postulated as newly synthesized DNA. This modification is similar to that shown in the micrograph of Figure 1-5.

The similarity between pathological and exercise-induced myocardial mitochondrial modifications is interesting, since their ultimate consequence can never be the same. Exercise, by nature of its intermittent acute action, can always allow the organism time for recuperation, whereas the chronic pathological condition is never alleviated. Thus, the successive stages of pathological involvement—a) transient breakdown, b) stable hyperfunction, and c) gradual exhaustion (9)—are not entirely representative of the exercise sequence, and it remains necessary to define this with regard to myocardial structure and function.

References

1. ABBOTT, B.C., BIGLAND, B., and RITCHIE, J.M.: The Physiological cost of negative work. *J Physiol (London)* 117:380-390, 1952.

2. ABBOTT, B.C., and MOMMAERTS, W.F.H.M.: Study of inotropic mechanisms in the papillary muscle preparation. *J Gen Physiol*, 42:533-551, 1959.

3. AUBERT, X., and MARÉCHAL, G.: Le bilan énergétique des contractions musculaires avec travail positif ou negatif. *J Physiol (Paris)*, 55:186-187, 1963.

4. BERGSTROM, J.: Local changes of ATP and phosphorylcreatine in human muscle tissue in connection with exercise. *Circ Res (Suppl. 1)*, 20 and 21:91-96, 1967.

5. BERNHARD, R.: Mitochondrial "genes": some gambles pay off. *Scientific Research*, February 19, 1969, p. 31.

6. BÖZNER, A., INCZINGER, F., and MRENA, E.: Ultrastructure of myocardium in physiological hypertrophy of the heart in rats. *Folia Morph*, 14:400, 1966.

7. BRADY, A.J.: Onset of contractility in cardiac muscle. *J Physiol (London)*, *184*:560, 1966.
8. BRADY, A.J.: The three element model of muscle mechanics: its applicability to cardiac muscle. *Physiologist, 10*:75-86, 1967.
9. BRAUNWALD, E., Ross, J., JR., and SONNENBLICK, E.H.: Mechanisms of contraction of the normal and failing heart. *New Eng J Med, 277*:794-799, 853-863, 910-920, 962-971, 1012-1022, 1967.
10. BRAUNWALD, E.: The determinants of myocardial oxygen consumption. *Physiologist, 12*:65-93, 1969.
11. BUCCINO, R.H., HARRIS, E., SPANN, J.F., JR., and SONNENBLICK, E.H.: Response of myocardial connective tissue to development of experimental hypertrophy. *Amer J Physiol, 216*:425-428, 1969.
12. BURDETTE, W.J., and ASHFORD, T.P.: Structural changes in human myocardium following hypoxia. *J Thorac Cardiovasc Surg, 50*:210, 1965.
13. BURTON, A.C.: *Physiology and Biophysics of the Circulation.* Chicago, Year Book Medical Publishers, 1966, p. 217.
14. CAPLAN, S.R.: A characteristic of self-regulated linear energy converters. The Hill force velocity relation for muscle. *J Theor Biol, 11*:63-86, 1966.
15. CAPLAN, S.R.: Autonomic energy conversion. II. An approach to the energetics of muscular contraction. *Biophys J, 8*:1167-93, 1968.
16. CARLSON, F.D., HARDY, D., and WILKIE, D.R.: The relation between heat produced and phosphorylcreatine split during isometric contraction of frog's muscle. *J Physiol (London), 189*:209-235, 1967.
17. CARLSON, L.A.: Lipid metabolism and muscular work. *Fed Proc, 26*:1755-59, 1967.
18. CAVAGNA, G.A., SÁBENE, F.P., and MARGARIA, R.: Effect of negative work on the amount of positive work performed by an isolated muscle. *J Appl Physiol, 20*:157-158, 1965.
19. CAVAGNA, G.A., and MARGARIA, R.: Mechanics of walking. *J Appl Physiol, 21*:271-278, 1966.
20. CAVAGNA, G.A., Dusman, B., and MARGARIA, R.: Positive work done by a previously stretched muscle. *J Appl Physiol, 24*:21-32, 1968.
21. CERRETELLI, P., DIPRAMPERO, P.E., and PIIPER, J.: Direct de-

termination of the energy equivalent of lactic acid formation *in vivo. Proc IUPS 25 Int Congr,* 7:79, 1968.

22. CHANCE, B., and LEGALLAIS, V.: A spectrofluorometer for recording of intracellular oxidation-reduction state. *IEEE Trans Biomed Electr, 10*:40-47, 1963.

23. CHANCE, B., SCHOENER, B., and SCHINDLER, F.: The intracellular oxidation-reduction state. In Dickens, F., and Neil, E. (Eds.): *Oxygen in the Animal Organism. I.U.B. Symposium Series.* Oxford Pergamon Press, 1964, vol. 31, p. 367.

24. CHERNUKH, A.M., ALEKSANDROV, P.N., ALEKHINA, G.M., PSHENNIKOVA, M.G., and MEERSON, F.Z.: DNA content of myocardial cell nuclei in the presence of compensatory hypertrophy of the heart. *Doklady (Biol Science), 178*:78, 1968.

25. Comparative Aspects of Muscle Contraction. *Amer Zool, 7*:433-699, 1967.

26. DAVIES, C.T.M.: Maximum power output in man. *Proc IUPS 25 Int Congr,* 7:101, 1968.

27. DAVIES, R.E.A.: A molecular theory of muscle contraction: calcium dependent contractions with hydrogen bond formation plus ATP dependent extensions of part of the myosin-actin cross-bridges. *Nature, 199*:1068-74, 1963).

28. DAVIES, R.E., KUSHMERICK, M.J., and LARSON, R.E.: ATP, Activation and the heat of shortening of muscle. *Nature, 214:* 148-151, 1967.

29. DIPRAMPERO, P.E., CERRETELLI, P., CUTTICA, F., and MARGARIA, R.: Kinetics of oxygen uptake in the adjustment to different exercise levels. *Proc IUPS 25 Int Congr,* 7:114, 1968.

30. DIPRAMPERO, P.E., and MARGARIA, R.: Relationship between oxygen consumption high energy phosphates and the kinetics of the O_2 debt in exercise. *Pflüeger Arch Ges Physiol 304:* 11-19, 1968.

31. DIPRAMPERO, P.E., CERRETELLI, P., and PIIPER, J.: Energy cost of isotonic tetanic contractions of varied force and duration in mammalian skeletal muscle. *Pflüeger Arch Ges Physiol, 305*:279-291, 1969.

32. DIPRAMPERO, P.E., and MARGARIA, R.: Mechanical efficiency of phosphagen (ATP+CP) splitting and its speed of re-synthesis. *Pflüeger Arch Ges Physiol, 308*:197-202, 1969.

33. DIPRAMPERO, P.E., CERRETELLI, P., and PIIPER, J.: O_2 consumption and metabolite balance in dog gastrocnemius at rest

and during exercise. *Pflüeger Arch Ges Physiol, 309*:38-47, 1969.

34. ERNST, E.: *Biophysics of the Striated Muscle.* Budapest, Publishing House of the Hungarian Academy of Sciences. 1963, pp. 301-303.

35. FALES, J.T.: Muscle heat production and work: effect of varying isotonic load. *J Appl Physiol, 216*:1184-87, 1969.

36. FENN, W.O.: A quantitative comparison between the energy liberated and the work performed by the isolated sartorius muscle of the frog. *J Physiol, (London) 58*:175-203, 1923.

37. GIBBS, C.L., RICCHIULI, H.H., and MOMMAERTS, W.F.H.M.: Activation heat in the frog sartorius muscle. *J. Gen Physiol, 49*: 517, 1966.

38. GIBBS, C.L., MOMMAERTS, W.F.H.M., and RICCHIUTI, N.V.: Energetics of cardiac contractions. *J Physiol (London), 191*:25-46, 1967.

39. GOLLNICK, P.D., and KING, D.W.: The effect of exercise and training on mitochondria of rat skeletal muscle. *Amer J Physiol, 216*:1502-1509, 1969.

40. GORDON, E.E., KOWALSKI, K., and FRITTS, M.: Adaptations of muscle to various exercises. *JAMA, 199*:139-144, 1967.

41. HANSEN, J., and LOWY, J.: Molecular basis of contractility in muscle. *Brit Med Bull, 21*:264-271, 1965.

42. HAVEL, R.J., NAIMARK, A., and BORCHGREVINK, J.: Turnover rate and oxidation of free fatty acids of blood plasma in man during exercise: studies during continuous infusion of palmitate-1-C^{14}. *J Clin Invest, 42*:1054, 1963.

43. HENGST, W., and KALTENBAD, M.: Comparative studies of positive and negative work by means of xenon clearance. *Kreislaufforsch, 57*:825-31, 1968.

44. HENRY, F. M., and DeMOOR, J.: Metabolic efficiency of exercise in relation to work load at constant speed. *J Appl Physiol 2*:481-487, 1950.

45. HERDSON, P.B., SOMMERS, H.M., and JENNINGS, R.B.: Comparative study on the fine structure of the normal and ischemic dog myocardium with special reference to early changes following temporary occlusion of the coronary artery. *Amer J Pathol, 46*:367, 1965.

46. HOES, M.J.A.J.M., BINKHORST, R.A., SMEEKES-KUYL, A.E.M.C., and VISSERS, A.C.A.: Measure of Forces Exerted on Pedal and

Crank during work on a bicycle ergometer at different loads. *Int Z Angew Physiol, 26*:33-42, 1968.

47. HOLLOSZY, J.O.: Biochemical adaptations in muscle. *J Biol Chem, 242*:2278, 1967.

48. HOLZER, H., and FREYTAG-HILF, R.: Zusammenwirken der garung-senzyme beim anaeroben und aeroben glucoseumsatz in hefezellen. *Hoppe Seyler Z Physiol Chem, 316*:7, 1959.

49. HILL, A.V.: The heat of shortening and the dynamic constants of muscle. *Proc Roy Soc [Biol], 126*: 136-195, 1938.

50. HILL, A.V., and HOWARTH, J.V.: The reversal of chemical reactions in contracting muscle during an applied stretch. *Proc Roy Soc [Biol], 151*:169-193, 1959.

51. HILL, A.V.: The effect of load on the heat of shortening muscle. *Proc Roy Soc [Biol], 159*:297-318, 1964.

52. HILL, A.V.: The ratio of mechanical power developed: total power expanded during muscular shortening. *Proc Roy Soc [Biol], 159*: 319-324, 1964.

53. HUXLEY, A.F.: Muscle. *Ann Rev Physiol, 26*:131-152, 1964.

54. HUXLEY, H.E.: The mechanism of muscular contraction. *Sci Amer, 213*:18-27, 1965.

55. INFANTE, A.A., KLAUPKIS, D., and DAVIES, R.E.: Adenosine triphosphate changes in muscles doing negative work. *Science, 144*:1577-1578, 1964.

56. JÖBSIS, F.F., and DUFFIELD, J.C.: Oxidative and glycolytic recovery metabolism in muscle. Fluorometric observations on their relative contributions. *J. Gen Physiol, 50*:1009-1047, 1967.

57. JÖBSIS, F.F., and DUFFIELD, J.C.: Force, shortening and work in muscular contraction: Relative contributions to overall energy utilization. *Science, 156*:1388-1392, 1967.

58. JÖBSIS, F.F., and STAINSBY, W.N.: Oxidation of NADH during contractions of circulated mammalian skeletal muscle. *Resp Physiol, 4*:292-300, 1968.

59. KEUL, J., DOLL, E., KEPPLER, D.: The substrate supply of human skeletal muscle at rest, during and after work. *Experientia, 23*:974-979, 1967.

60. KEUL, J.: Metabolism of skeletal muscle. I. Glucose, lactate, pyruvate and free fatty acids in arterial and venous blood of working muscles. Examinations of well trained athletes. *Pflüeger Arch Ges Physiol, 301*:198-213, 1968.

61. KING, H., HOPPER, B.J., and BANISTER, E.W.: Acceleration-

distance and acceleration-time curves as an expression of the total work performed in muscular exercise. Unpublished data, 1969.

62. KLOTZ, I.M.: *Energy Changes in Biochemical Reactions.* New York, Academic Press, 1967, pp.108.

63. KRAUS, H., KIRSTEN, R., and WOLFF, J.R.: Die Wirkung von Schwimm-und lauftraining auf die celluläre Funktion und Struktur des Muskels. *Pflüeger Arch Ges Physiol, 308*:57-79, 1969.

64. KUSHMERICK, M.J.: Energetics and efficiency of maximally working frog sartorius muscles at 0° C. *Fed Proc, 26*:727, 1967.

65. KYPSON, J., TRINER, L., VULLIEMOZ, Y., and NAHAS, G.G.: Effect of acidosis on glycolysis and pentose shunt in skeletal muscle. *Proc IUPS 25 Int Congr, 7*:250, 1968.

66. LAGUENS, R.P., LOZADA, B.B., GÓMEZ DUMM C.L., and BERAMENDI, A.R.: Effects of acute and exhaustive exercise upon the fine structure of heart mitochondria. *Experientia, 22*: 244, 1966.

67. LAGUENS, R.P., and GÓMEZ DUMM, C.L.: Fine structure of myocardial mitocondria in rats after exercise for one-half to two hours. *Circ Res 21*:271, 1967.

68. LAGUENS, R.P., and GÓMEZ DUMM, C.L.: Deoxyribonucleic acid synthesis in heart mitochondria after acute and exhaustive exercise. *Experientia, 24*:163, 1968.

69. LEHNINGER, A.L.: *Bioenergetics.* New York, Benjamin, 1965.

70. LINDEMAYER, G.E., SORDAHL, L.A., and SCHWARTZ, A.: Reevaluation of oxidative phosphorylation in cardiac mitochondria from normal animals and animals in heart failure. *Circ Res, 23*:439, 1968.

71, LOWENSTEIN, J.M.: The regulation of carbohydrate utilization, In Dickens, F., and Neil, E. (Eds.): *Oxygen in the Animal Organism. I.U.B. Symposium.* London, Pergamon Press, 1964, pp. 163-177.

72. MARGARIA, R., CERRETELLI, P., and MANGILI, F.: Balance and kinetics of anaerobic energy release during strenuous exercise in man. *J. Appl Physiol, 19*:623-628, 1964.

73. MASORO, E.J., ROWELL, L.B., MacDONALD, R.M., and STEIERT: Skeletal muscle lipids. II. Nonutilization of intracellular lipid esters as an energy source for contractile activity. *J Biol Chem, 241*:2626-34, 1966,

74. McCarter, R.J.M., and Ramsey, R.W.: Energetics of contraction of isolated frog muscles, as measured by their consumption of oxygen. *Proc IUPS 25 Int Congr, 7*:286, 1968.

75. Meerson, F. Z.: Compensatory hyperfunction of the heart. *Circ Res, 10*:250, 1962.

76. Meerson, F.Z., Zaletayeva, T.A., Lagutchev, S.S., and Pshennikov, M.G.: The structure and mass of mitochondria in the process of compensatory hyperfunction and hypertrophy of the heart. *Exp Cell Res, 36*:568, 1964.

77. Meerson, F.Z., and Alekhina, G.M.: Action of intensity of contractile function of muscle cells of the heart on the DNA synthesis of the intermediate connective tissue of the Myocardium. *Acta Anat [Basel], 70*:559, 1968.

78. Noble, M.I.M., Trenchard, D., and Guz, A.: Left ventricular ejection in conscious dogs: 1. Measurement and significance of the maximum acceleration of blood from the left ventricle. *Circ Res, 19*:139-147, 1966.

79. Noble, M.I.M., Trenchard, D., and Guz, A.: Left Ventricular ejection in conscious dogs: II. Determinants of stroke volume. *Circ Res, 19*:148-152, 1966.

80. Noble, M.I.M.: The contribution of blood momentum to left ventricular ejection in the dog. *Circ Res, 23*:663-670, 1968.

81. Opie, L.H.: Metabolism of the heart in health and disease I, II, III. *Amer Heart J, 76*:685-698, 1968. 77:100-122, 383-410, 1969.

82. Olson, R.E.: Excess lactate and anaerobiosis. *Ann Int Med, 59*: 960-963, 1963.

83. Olson, R.E.: Discussion. In *Proceedings of the International Symposium on Cardiovascular Respiratory Effects of Hypoxia.* Basel/New York, Karger, 1966, p. 108.

84. Packer, L.: In Dickens, F., and Neil, E. (Eds.): *Discussion, Oxygen in the Animal Organism. I.U.B. Symposium Series.* Oxford, Pergamon Press, 1964, vol. 31, p. 388.

85. Page, E.: Correlations between electron microscopic and physiological observations in heart muscle. *J Gen Physiol, 51 (Suppl)*: 211-220, 1969.

86. Parmley, W.W., and Sonnenblick, E. H.: Relation between mechanics of contraction and relaxation in mammalian cardiac muscle. *Amer J Physiol, 216*:1084-1091, 1969.

87. Parmley, W.W., and Sonnenblick, E.H.: Series elasticity in

heart muscles: Its relation to contractile element velocity and proposed muscle models. *Circ Res, 20*:112-123, 1969.

88. PEACHEY, L.D.: Muscle. *Ann Rev Physiol, 30*:401-440, 1968.

89. PELOSI, G., and AGLIATI, G.: The heart muscle in functional overload and hypoxia. *Lab. Invest, 18*:86, 1968.

90. PIIPER, J., DIPRAMPERO, P.E., and CERRETELLI, P.: Chemical-energetical basis of alactacid O_2 debt in mammalian skeletal muscle. *Proc IUPS 25 Int Congr, 7*:348, 1968.

91. POOL, P.E., COVELL, J.W., CHIDSEY, C.A., and BRAUNWALD, E.: Myocardial high energy phosphate stores in acutely induced hypoxic heart failure. *Circ Res, 19*:221, 1966.

92. PORTER, K.R., and BONNEVILLE, M.A.: Fine structure of cells and tissues. Philadelphia, Lea and Febiger, 1968, p.196.

93. PRINGLE, J.W.S.: Models of muscle. *Proc Soc Exp Biol Med, 14*: 41-68, 1960.

94. RUSHMER, R.F.: Initial Ventricular Impuse. A potential key to cardiac evaluation. *Circulation, 29*:268-283, 1964.

95. SANDOW, A.: Energetics of Muscular Contraction. In Shanes, A.M. (Ed.): *Biophysics of Physiological and Pharmalogical Actions.* Washington, Amer Assoc. Adv. Sci, 1961, pp.413-451.

96. SANDOW, A.: Excitation-contraction coupling in skeletal muscle. *Pharmacol Rev, 17*:265-320, 1965.

97. SAVULEV, YU.I.: Ultrastructure of the mitochondria and tigroid substance of neurons and the cerebral cortex of white rats after administration of blood serum from schizophrenic patients. *Ah Neuropatol psikhiatr, 67*:1033, 1967.

98. SIEGEL, J.H., and SONNENBLICK, E.H.: Isometric time-tension relationships as an index of myocardial contractility. *Circ Res, 12*:597-610, 1963.

99. SIEGEL, J.H., SONNENBLICK, E.H., JUDGE, R.D., and WILSON, W.S.: The quantification of myocardial contractility in dog and man. *Cardiologia, 45*:189-220, 1964.

100. SONNENBLICK, E.H.: Implications of muscle mechanics in the heart. *Fed Proc, 21*:975-990, 1963.

101. SONNENBLICK, E.H., and STAM, A.C.: Cardiac Muscle: Activation and contraction. *Ann Rev Physiol, 31*:647-674, 1969.

102. SPENCER, M.P., and GREISS, F.C.: Dynamics of ventricular ejection. *Circ Res, 10*:274, 1962.

103. SPIRO, D., and SONNENBLICK, E.H.: Comparison of ultrastructural

basis of contractile process in heart and skeletal muscle. *Circ Res, 15(Suppl. 2)*:14-37, 1964.

104. STARR, I.: Units for the expression of both static and dynamic work in similar terms, and their application to weight lifting experiments. *J Appl Physiol, 4*:21-29, 1951.

105. STEIGER, G.J., and RÜEGG, J.C.: Energetics and "efficiency" in isolated contractile machinery of an insect fibrillar muscle of various frequencies of oscillation. *Pflüeger Arch Ges Physiol, 307*:1-21, 1969.

106. SULKIN, N.M., and SULKIN, D.F.: An electron microscopic study of the effects of chronic hypoxia on cardiac muscle, hepatic and autonomic ganglion cells. *Lab Invest, 14*:1523, 1965.

107. TIPTON, C.M.: Training and bradycardia in rats. *Amer J Physiol, 208*:480-484, 1965.

108. VECCHIONI, R., and TARTARINI, A.: Comportamento delle frazioni collagene nella i pertrofia muscolare. *Boll Soc Ital Biol Sper, 36*:1415, 1960.

109. WHIPP, B.J., and WASSERMAN, K.: Efficiency of muscular work. *J Appl Physiol, 26*:644-648, 1969.

110. WILCKEN, D.E.L., BRANDER, D., MACDONALD, G.J., SHOREY, C.D., and HINTERBERGER, H.: Effect of Reserpine on the structure of heart mitochondria and the relation to catecholamine depletion. *Circ Res, 20* and *21(Suppl III)*:203, 1967.

111. WILKIE, D.R.: Facts and theories about muscle. *Progr Biophys, 4*:288-524, 1954.

112. WILKIE, D.R.: Man as a source of mechanical power. *Ergonomics, 1*:1-8, 1960.

113. WILKIE, D.R.: Muscle. *Ann Rev Physiol, 28*:17-38, 1966.

114. WILKIE, D.R., and WOLEDGE, R.C.: The application of irreversible thermodynamics to muscular contraction: comments on a recent theory of S.R. Caplan. *Proc Roy Soc [Biol], 169*:17-29, 1967.

115. WILKIE, D.R.: Heat work and phosphorylcreatine break-down in muscle. *J Physiol (London), 195*:157-183, 1968.

Chapter 2

MUSCLE GLYCOGEN STORES AND PROLONGED EXERCISE

Eric Hultman

I<small>T</small> <small>HAS</small> long been established that proteins are not concerned with energy production in muscle during exercise (42, 58). By 1920 respiratory quotient (RQ) determinations (37) had shown that both fat and carbohydrate are utilized during exercise. In a series of exercise studies where RQ determinations were made (15), it was shown that carbohydrate metabolism increased with increasing work load. It was also demonstrated that carbohydrate-rich food taken for some days before prolonged, severe exercise increased the subject's performance capacity. Subsequently, work capacity was thought to be related to the size of the glycogen store. However, calculations based on RQ and oxygen uptake are at best only approximate and give no information about which part of the body's carbohydrate store is utilized.

In the last few years fat has been reinvestigated as a potential source of energy for muscle during exercise (22, 23, 32, 57). In most of these studies constant rate infusions of labelled palmitate have been used to calculate the rate of utilization of free fatty acids (FFA). The results show a certain variance; this is due, in part, to differences in the method of calculation and in part to the fact that different work loads have been used. As was shown earlier and will be discussed further in following sections, the work load is very important for the muscle's choice of substrate for energy production.

The glucose uptake in working muscle has been studied by determining the arteriovenous glucose concentration difference of the working muscle together with concurrent measurements of the blood flow. The results are considered to indicate a considerable increase of glucose uptake by working muscle (14, 34).

37

In 1962 Bergström (5) introduced a biopsy needle which could be used to take repeated muscle samples from the lateral portion of the quadriceps femoris muscle in man. Six to 8 muscle samples can easily be taken from one subject during a single experiment; thus, changes in muscle composition can be followed sequentially. This biopsy technique has been used in a series of studies of local energy metabolism during exercise in man (2, 7, 8, 9, 10, 12, 24, 29, 31). Very few other quantitative attempts have been made to study the local metabolism of muscle glycogen in circulated skeletal muscle. However, in 1968 Chapler and Stainsby (14) did publish a paper on carbohydrate metabolism in contracting dog skeletal muscle *in situ,* and their results are in most respects similar to ours.

The Carbohydrate Store

The glycogen concentration in the human quadriceps femoris muscle has a mean value of 13.9 gm per kilogram wet tissue (28). Thus, if a subject has a body weight of 70 kg, 40 percent of which is muscle, there is a muscle glycogen store of about 390 gm. In a series of 230 normal men, 97 percent had glycogen concentrations between 9.5 and 20.0 gm per kilogram in samples taken from the quadriceps. There seem to be no significant variations with age or sex. In a survey on children three to ten years of age, the mean muscle glycogen concentration was 14.0, and the same value was found in a group of men sixty to eighty years of age (50). However, the glycogen concentration varies between different muscle groups; for example, in the deltoid muscle the glycogen content was significantly lower (mean 9.8 gm/kg) than in the quadriceps (28).

The muscle glycogen is not utilized at rest (4, 14, 28), and it is not appreciably affected by food intake, although it decreases slowly during fasting. One week of total starvation will decrease the muscle glycogen by 30 to 40 percent (30). The only physiological way of emptying the muscle of glycogen is by hard exercise. Glycogen cannot leave the muscle in any other form than as unphosphorylated metabolites and practically only as lactate. This means that only the local store in the working muscle group can be used during exercise. The glycogen content of a resting muscle is unchanged even if another muscle group in the same individual is subjected to exhaustive exercise (10).

The rate of resynthesis of glycogen after the store has been emptied is dependent on the type of food given. The rate is some ten times greater when a carbohydrate-rich diet is fed than if the diet is carbohydrate-free (30). It can take more than one week to refill the muscle stores when a carbohydrate-free diet is given, whereas a carbohydrate-rich diet will increase the glycogen stores very rapidly, not only to the basal level but beyond, to much higher values. The increase occurs only in the glycogen-depleted muscle, and values up to 60 gm per kilogram muscle have been observed (9), compared to the normal upper limit of 20 gm per kilogram muscle.

Carbohydrate Store in Liver

A survey (45) of the liver glycogen content in normal man following an overnight fast indicated a mean value of 44 gm per kilogram wet liver weight. Concentrations varied considerably, ranging from 15 to 80 gm per kilogram. Considering the same 70 kg subject as before, the glycogen store in the liver should amount to 66 gm (calculated on a 1.5 kg liver weight). This appears rather small in relation to the muscle glycogen store and in fact, it is still smaller when one considers that the liver is never completely emptied of glycogen. In an unpublished series of experiments (45) the glycogen content in the liver was determined after exhaustive work; at this point the muscle glycogen was less than 2 gm per kilogram in all subjects, while the mean liver glycogen was still 20 gm per kilogram (range 6-36 gm/kg). The amount of liver glycogen available as energy substrate during exercise therefore averages only 36 gm, less than 10 percent of the total muscle glycogen. Thus, it seems that muscle glycogen is the principle carbohydrate store available for exercise. On the other hand, it should be borne in mind that this is true only if a considerable part of the total muscle mass is working and the subject is fasting.

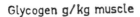

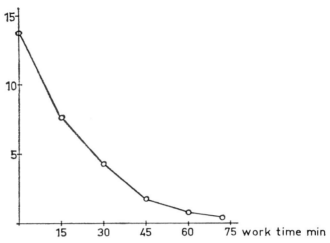

FIGURE 2-1. Glycogen content of the quadriceps femoris muscle during bicycle work. Mean values from eight subjects. Work load, 950 kpm per minute.

Muscle Glycogen Utilization during Prolonged Work

It has previously been shown that the muscle glycogen content decreases progressively during submaximal exercise. The rate of decrease is not constant but seems to be triphasic (10, 24) (Fig. 2-1). Initially there is a rapid decrease. This is followed by a second period when the rate of decrease is relatively constant. The third period begins when the glycogen store is low, and it is characterized by a slow rate of glycogen consumption. Of course, there are not three distinct periods but rather a progressive change from one to the other.

The three parts of the curve can be explained as follows: During the first period rapid glycogenolysis is stimulated by the initial muscle contraction, adrenalin release, and possibly a local decrease of oxygen tension. This period has long been recognized from the associated rapid increase in blood lactate. In the second period adaptation of the circulation to the work load and changes in enzymatic activities result in a decreased rate of glycogen consumption. In the third period there is a relative lack of glycogen substrate, and the muscle cells partially compensate for this by an increased uptake of blood glucose. During this period there is also an increase in the metabolism of plasma free fatty acids (FFA). This period was recognized earlier as showing a continuous decrease in blood sugar and a decrease of RQ (15).

The importance of FFA metabolism during the terminal period of work was investigated by Bergström *et al.* (12). They gave normal subjects nicotinic acid before and during exercise; nicotinic acid is known to inhibit the release of free fatty acids from adipose tissue (13). Their subjects operated a bicycle ergometer with one leg for ninety minutes while changes in plasma FFA and muscle glycogen were followed. Nicotinic acid was then given both intravenously and orally, and the experiment was repeated with the other leg. The results showed a pronounced decrease of plasma FFA in the presence of nicotinic acid. The glycogenolysis rate was the same initially, both with and without nicotinic acid. However, towards the end of the exercise, the glycogenolysis rate was significantly greater in the presence of nicotinic acid than in the control experiment.

In a further investigation (29) blood glucose was compared with local muscle glycogen as a potential source of carbohydrate for energy production. The glucose uptake of the muscle was not measured directly, but instead the output of glucose from the liver was calculated from its blood flow and the arteriohepatic venous glucose differences. As the arterial glucose concentration remained practically unchanged, the muscle glucose uptake could not be greater than the output from the liver. In this study the work load was about 70 percent of the subject's maximal oxygen uptake. The carbohydrate utilization ranged from 55 to 86 percent of the total energy consumption at the beginning of exercise and from 39 to 56 percent at the end. Glucose uptake by the muscle initially accounted for 10 to 15 percent of the total carbohydrate consumption, and during the last few minutes of work, it increased to as much as 50 percent. Thus, at the end of prolonged exercise, the liver glycogen can be important as an energy source for working muscle.

Muscle Glycogen Utilization in Relation to Work Load

The rate of muscle glycogen consumption not only varies with time but also with work load. This was shown indirectly by Christensen and Hansen (15), using RQ determinations, and it has also been demonstrated by direct measurement of muscle glycogen (24). Six well-trained men worked for one hour on each of three occasions; the work loads for the three tests were, respectively, 25, 54, and 78 percent of the individual's maximal oxygen uptake. The corresponding mean rates of glycogen consumption were 50, 140, and 260 mg per kilogram muscle per minute. A more recent investigation (3) is presented in Figure 2-2; the absolute work load is here related to muscle glycogen decrease per unit time. The subjects were six normal and relatively well trained men who each worked for four periods. Two different loads were used, 100 percent W_{170}[*] and 50 to 70 percent W_{170}, and work was performed at each load with and without continuous glucose infusion. The relationship between load and glycogen consumption is seen in Figure 2-2.

It can also be seen from Figure 2-2 that the rate of glycogenolysis in muscle is not affected by the infusion of glucose. Thus, it seems likely that for energy production during work muscle glycogen is a preferred substrate. This is valid only during the first thirty to sixty minutes of the exercise period. As discussed previously glucose is utilized during the last few minutes of hard exercise. During light work glycogen can even be synthesized, as will be discussed later.

Chapler and Stainsby (14) showed that in dogs, muscle contractions with a frequency of one tetanus per second resulted in no decrease of muscle glycogen, whereas a rate of five tetani per second gave a rapid decrease. Carbohydrate oxidation during the first ten minutes of "exercise" (5 tet/sec) was calculated to account for 94 percent of the oxygen uptake.

The load dependence of the glycogenolysis rate was also shown in an experiment with isometric work (1). A special chair was used to measure the isometric power (contractile force) of the m. quadriceps femoris. The load was varied between 30 and

---

[*]W_{170} = work load giving a constant pulse rate of 170 beats per minute.

Glycogen decrease mg/kg muscle/min

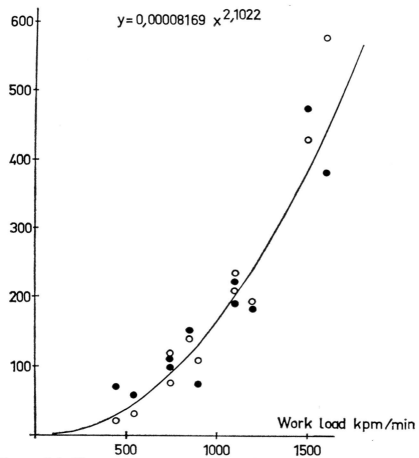

FIGURE 2-2. Glycogen consumption in mg glucosyl units per kg muscle per minute related to absolute work load. Every subject worked at two different loads, 100 percent of W_{170} and 50 to 70 percent of W_{170}. At each load the work was performed with ● and without ○ continuous glucose infusion.

100 percent of the subject's maximal power. The subjects worked at a predetermined load until exhaustion, that is, until the power could no longer be sustained. A biopsy was taken immediately and the tissue frozen and analyzed. The results can be seen in

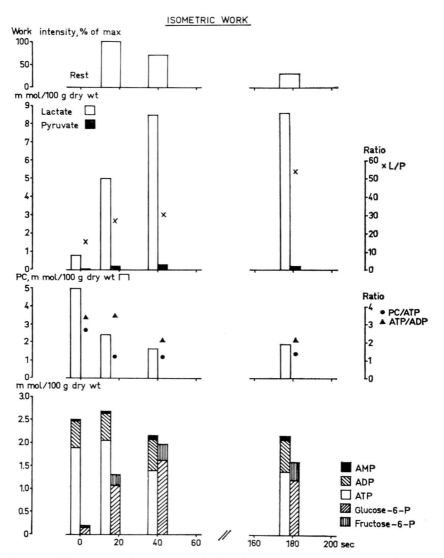

FIGURE 2-3. Active phosphates and glycolytic intermediates in muscle tissue before and immediately after isometric work. Mean values for six subjects. Work load 100, 70, and 30 percent of the subjects' maximal power. The work was continued till exhaustion, that is, until the power could no longer be sustained. Work time 13, 40, and 178 seconds.

Figure 2-3. Mean performance times at the different loads were 13 seconds, 40 seconds, and 179 seconds. All loads were so high that no blood flow through the "contracted" muscle should have occurred during the work period. The lactate formed should therefore be directly correlated to the total glycogenolysis. A very close correlation (r = 0.93) was found between lactate flux (measured as lactate produced per second) and the power produced (measured as a percentage of the subject's maximal power). A close correlation was also found between glucose 6-P, fructose 6-P, and lactate concentrations at the end of work. The rate of glycogenolysis in this series was calculated from the change in concentrations of lactate and other intermediary metabolites, divided by time. At 100 percent power the glycogenolysis rate in milligram glucosyl units per kilogram wet muscle per minute was 7387 mg; at 70 percent power it was 3419 mg, and at 30 percent it was 810 mg.

The rate of glycogenolysis found at 100 percent power is more than ten times the highest value recorded during the experiment with prolonged bicycle work (Fig. 2-2). In the latter case the maximum glycogenolysis rate recorded was 580 mg glucosyl units per kilogram wet muscle per minute at a work load of 1600 kpm per minute.

If the total glycogen store of the quadriceps femoris muscle had been used during isometric work, at a rate of 7387 mg glucosyl units per kilogram wet muscle per minute, the maximum permissible work time can be calculated as about two minutes. In fact, the mean work time in this series was thirteen seconds, which indicates that the limiting factor for this type of work is not the size of the glycogen store.

Muscle Glycogen and Performance Capacity

In the studies of muscle glycogen consumption during hard exercise, it was observed that when the glycogen content was very low or practically zero, the capacity to continue the exercise was lost. In order to investigate whether the glycogen store is really the factor limiting performance capacity during prolonged heavy exercise, the following experiment was conducted (7). Six

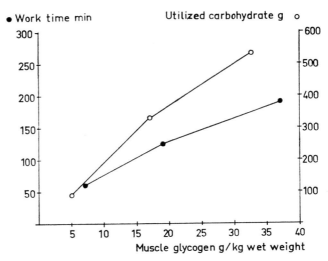

FIGURE 2-4. The relation between initial glycogen content of quadriceps femoris muscle and work time ●, and between glycogen utilized in the same muscle group and total carbohydrate utilized (the latter being calculated from O_2 uptake and RQ) ○.

subjects exercised on a bicycle ergometer at a work load that was 75 percent of their maximal oxygen capacity. They repeated the work three times with a three-day interval between each test. In every test they worked to complete exhaustion, and the performance time was measured. On the days between the tests different diets were given. Before the first exercise an ordinary mixed diet was used. After the first test the diet was changed to protein and fat with less than 5 percent carbohydrate. The third diet contained more than 95 percent carbohydrate. The caloric intake was normal and similar for all three diets. The results can be seen in Figure 2-4. The mean muscle glycogen after the normal mixed diet was 19.3 gm per kilogram (range 11.9-25.1). After the carbohydrate-free diet the glycogen content was 6.9 gm per kilogram (range 3.1-12.9), and after the carbohydrate-rich diet it was 37.0 gm per kilogram (range 26.6-46.8). It can be seen that a close correlation exists between the capacity for prolonged heavy exercise and the glycogen store in the muscle before exercise. From these results it was concluded that the muscle glycogen store is the factor limiting the subject's capacity to perform prolonged severe exercise. If the glycogen decrease per unit time is calculated for this series, values of 138, 85, and 173 mg glucosyl units per kilogram muscle per minute are obtained. This shows that after a carbohydrate-free diet other sources of energy apart from muscle glycogen are used, the most likely being fat. The RQ value after thirty minutes of exercise was 0.81 after the carbohydrate-free diet, 0.92 after the mixed diet, and 0.94 after the carbohydrate-rich diet (the corresponding glycogen consumption being 85, 138, and 173 mg glucosyl units per kilogram muscle per minute, respectively). Another difference is that the blood lactate concentration is higher after the carbohydrate-rich diet than after the carbohydrate-free diet. This would indicate a less efficient burning of carbohydrate when the muscle glycogen store is higher.

Biochemical Considerations

A detailed discussion of the biochemistry of glycogenolysis and glycolysis during exercise is beyond the scope of this chapter, though a few comments can be made here.

The conversion of muscle glycogen to glucose-phosphate is limited by the activity of phosphorylase (35, 43, 52). This enzyme exists in two forms, a and b. An increase in phosphorylase activity can be brought about by one of two means: a) the conversion of phosphorylase b to a (16, 18, 19, 35, 43, 52) or b) activation of phosphorylase b (43, 47).

Phosphorylase b is converted to the a form by a phosphorylation reaction. This is brought about either as a result of muscle contraction or by adrenaline which acts via 3' 5' cyclic adenosine monophosphate—AMP (33, 46, 49). The conversion of b to a is also stimulated by high levels of glycogen (36).

Phosphorylase b is activated by physiological concentrations of AMP. The AMP-induced stimulation is inhibited by physiological levels of ATP (43) and glucose 6-P, and this is thought to explain the low activity of phosphorylase b in resting muscle.

High levels of inorganic phosphate, on the other hand, decrease the requirement of phosphorylase b for AMP, thereby increasing the phosphorylase b activity at low levels of AMP.

Phosphorylase a is also stimulated by AMP in the presence of orthophosphate or glycogen (40).

Glycogen Conversion and Phosphorylase Activity

In the resting muscle most of the phosphorylase is in the b form (35). The level of ATP is high, whereas the levels of AMP, inorganic phosphate, and glucose 6-P are low. Under these conditions phosphorylase b activity is low, which is consistent with the previously mentioned observation that no glycogen is consumed at rest.

On contraction of the muscle the level of ATP falls, and the levels of AMP and inorganic phosphate increase. The level of glucose 6-P is initially unchanged. Under these conditions phosphorylase b is activated. Contraction also brings about the conversion of phosphorylase b to the more active a form, which is not inhibited by ATP or glucose 6-P. Further contractions with continuing glycogenolysis result in ATP being restored to its former level with an increase of glucose 6-P. These changes result in a decrease in phosphorylase b activity, even though AMP and inorganic phosphate levels are high. Phosphorylase a activity is unaffected by these changes in metabolites.

Adrenaline released during muscular exercise hastens the transformation of phosphorylase b to a.

Initial Glycogenolysis and Hard Work

The above mechanism would explain both the initial rapid decrease in glycogen during exercise and the load dependence of glycogen utilization. As shown earlier the utilization of phosphoryl creatine (PC), which results in the release of proportionate amounts of inorganic phosphate, is related to load (31). Similarly, at very high work loads the ATP level is decreased and AMP increased. All of these factors contribute to an increase of both phosphorylase a and b activity which is related to work load. This is illustrated in Table 2-I (6). It can be seen that after two minutes of exercise the concentrations of glucose 6-P, fructose

TABLE 2-I
MUSCLE METABOLITES BEFORE AND AFTER TWO-MINUTE
EXERCISE WITH DIFFERENT WORK LOADS
μmoles/100 gm Dry Muscle Tissue

Subject	Load kpm/min	Glucose	Glucose 6-P	Fructose 6-P	Lactate
CP	0	0.012	0.181	0.046	1.96
	750	0.380	0.590	0.149	6.42
	1100	0.551	0.830	0.225	8.49
	1500	0.760	1.087	0.296	13.28
SO	0	0.214	0.077	0.047	2.06
	600	0.208	0.378	0.076	4.87
	1200	0.616	0.632	0.130	6.77
BM	0	0.037	0.088	0.010	1.27
	750	0.098	0.334	0.080	2.63
	1500	0.261	0.467	0.156	3.34

6-P, and lactate all increase in proportion to work load. The concentration of individual metabolites increase proportionately with increasing load, but the ratios between them remain practically unchanged.

Steady State Glycogenolysis During Prolonged Submaximal Work

Although the rate of glycogen utilization during prolonged exercise is still dependent on phosphorylase activity, this activity is now regulated by feedback mechanisms involving the concentrations of glycolytic intermediates and adenosine phosphate levels. The first limiting step in the glycolytic pathway is mediated by phosphofructokinase (PFK) (20, 33, 44, 46) which is activated by fructose 6-P, ADP, AMP, and inorganic phosphate (P_i) (39, 41, 48) but inhibited by ATP, citrate, and PC (21, 38, 56). PFK is also very sensitive to cell pH (53). During steady state glycogenolysis, the levels of these activators and inhibitors remain fairly constant, and the PFK activity in turn regulates the phosphorylase b activity via the glucose 6-P level.

The second limiting step in the glycolytic pathway is the rate of pyruvate oxidation within the mitochondria. It is still unknown whether it is the rate of enzymic transformation of pyruvate, the rate of entrance of pyruvate into the mitochondria, or the availability of O_2 in the cell which limits the pyruvate oxidation rate. Holloszy (25) and Holloszy and Oscai (26) have shown that training of rats increases the oxidative capacity of the muscle mitochondria and that this is not due solely to changes in the number of mitochondria per cell. It has also been shown (54) that in well-trained subjects the arteriovenous O_2 difference across a working muscle is greater than in those who are untrained. It is also well known that even at the same relative work load (referred to maximum oxygen uptake or pulse rate), both the RQ and the lactate formation are lower in well-trained than in sedentary subjects (15, 24).

This could be explained by a more efficient oxidation of pyruvate in well-trained muscle, resulting in an increased rate of ATP resynthesis and citrate formation. This will in turn lead to a decrease in glycolytic flux (because of ATP increase, AMP decrease, citrate increase, and ultimately glucose 6-P decrease) with a subsequent decrease in lactate formation. Under these conditions the rate of FFA utilization can be increased.

During rapid glycolysis (for example, during hard work) or during anoxia, the rate of oxidation of pyruvate is low compared with the rate of pyruvate formation. For each mole of pyruvate formed, one mole of NADH is produced. The equilibrium constant for the interconversion of pyruvate and lactate under conditions where pyruvate oxidation is low or blocked favors lactate production with subsequent reoxidation of the NADH required for the continuation of glycolysis. The overall effects of this are that lactate accumulates and rephosphorylation of ADP is low. This gives a low energy yield (3 moles of ATP for every glucosyl unit metabolized from glucogen to lactate, compared with 38 moles of ATP for complete oxidative metabolism). Individual differences in this capacity to oxidize pyruvate could account for the main variations in the work load a subject can sustain during prolonged exercise.

Factors Contributing to Exhaustion and Cessation of Work

The most important factor contributing to exhaustion in prolonged heavy exercise is depletion of the glycogen store. As the glycogen content approaches zero, the phosphorylase a activity

TABLE 2-II

MUSCLE CONSTITUENTS BEFORE AND DURING EXERCISE IN THREE SUBJECTS

	0	5'	20'	0	5'	17'	0	5'	20'
Work time, min									
μmoles/100 gm Dry Muscle Tissue									
Glycogen*	26.4	18.6	4.9	24.6	7.1	2.5	34.2		7.7
Glucose	0.604	0.231	0.248	0.191	1.238	0.588	0.559	1.182	1.083
Glucose 6-P	0.276	0.461	0.311	0.151	0.743	0.082	0.170	0.697	0.293
Fructose 6-P	0.039	0.079	0.057	0.029	0.098	0.019	0.043	0.132	0.038
Lactate	1.38	3.86	4.76	0.60	11.53	10.45	0.59	9.30	6.70
ATP	2.50	2.25	2.15				1.82	1.58	1.07
PC	7.14	2.39	1.24				4.90	1.32	0.76
K	46.4	46.3	43.5	44.6	44.9	44.6	44.7	42.2	41.8
P total	30.7	31.3	29.2	28.8	30.4	31.3	29.5	28.1	28.7
ml/100 gm Dry Muscle Tissue									
H_2O_i	308	315	337	306	365	350	287	322	306
H_2O_e	21.9	27.7	55.8	26.7	34.6	45.5	32.6	61.0	90.9
Intracellular Concentration μmoles/liter Muscle Water									
Glucose	1.62	0.29	0	0.18	2.92	1.03	1.39	2.73	1.90
Lactate	4.4	12.0	13.0	1.9	31.0	28.0	1.7	27.0	19.0
K	150.5	146.8	129.8	145.4	122.9	127.1	155.3	130.9	136.2
Na	10.5	10.9	13.5	9.9	13.8	17.0	8.2	10.5	20.0
Intracellular Concentration μmoles/liter Blood									
Lactate	1.4	4.0	5.5	1.2	6.6	12.8	1.3	7.2	9.8

*Expressed as glucosyl units.

The work load was 1000 kpm/min for all three subjects. Subject No. 2 could not continue the exercise for more than 17 min. Determinations of electrolytes and fluid spaces were made according to Bergström (5).

decreases because of inactivation of phosphorylase b kinase. There is also a lack of substrate, and this decreases the glycolytic flux to a level insufficient to maintain the energy demands of the cell.

The decrease of glycogenolysis in turn leads to a reduction of the glucose 6-P level (Table 2-II). Phosphorylation of free glucose by hexokinase has been largely inhibited up to this point by the presence of high levels of glucose 6-P. With the fall in concentration of this metabolite, the inhibition of hexokinase is removed, and glucose can enter the glycolytic chain. As mentioned earlier, towards the end of work glucose uptake from the blood can account for 50 percent of carbohydrate metabolism.

The rapid accumulation of lactate during supramaximal or anoxic work could lead to changes of intracellular pH. In the series where subjects performed hard work on the bicycle ergometer (Table 2-II), the highest intracellular concentration of lactate recorded was 31 mEq per liter of intracellular water. This amount of lactate could easily lower the cell pH to values where PFK activity would be greatly decreased or abolished. This in turn could result in the cessation of work or a decrease of glycolytic flux. In the series performing maximal isometric work, the duration of work was only thirteen seconds, but as discussed previously it should theoretically have been two minutes. Rapid accumulation of lactate in this case may have resulted in a decrease of PFK activity with the result that the glycolytic flux was reduced to levels insufficient to meet energy demands. It is interesting that higher lactate concentrations were reached at exhaustion with a 70 percent than with a 100 percent load (Fig. 2-3).

Glycogen Resynthesis

Glycogen resynthesis is brought about by UDPG-glucosyl transferase (glycogen synthetase), which exists in two forms, I and D (17, 27, 51, 55). The D form is dependent on the presence of unphysiological levels of glucose 6-P and is inhibited by physiological levels of inorganic phosphate. Glycogen synthetase activity in the muscle cell is therefore assumed to depend solely on the activity of the I form, which is unaffected by these factors.

Glycogen synthetase I activity, % of total

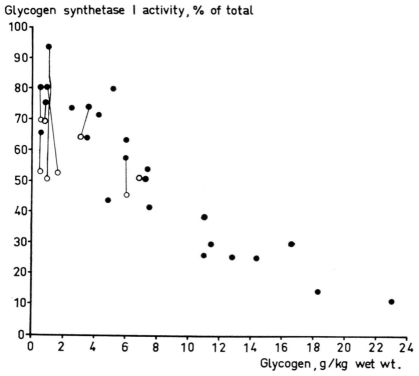

FIGURE 2-5. Glycogen synthetase I activity at rest ● and during exercise ○ in relation to muscle glycogen level.

The I form is converted to the D form by a phosphorylation reaction. Contraction of muscle or adrenalin release both of which stimulate the conversion of phosphorylase b to phosphorylase simultaneously effect an inactivation of glycogen synthetase by conversion of the I to D form.

The interconversion of the I and the D form is under the influence of various other factors, of which the glycogen concentration is the most important. High glycogen levels, which activate phosphorylase b kinase, also inhibit the transformation of D synthetase to the I form and therefore favor glycogenolysis. Low levels of glycogen have the opposite effect (17, 27, 55).

The changes in glycogen synthetase activity at different glycogen levels are illustrated in Figure 2-5. Muscle samples were

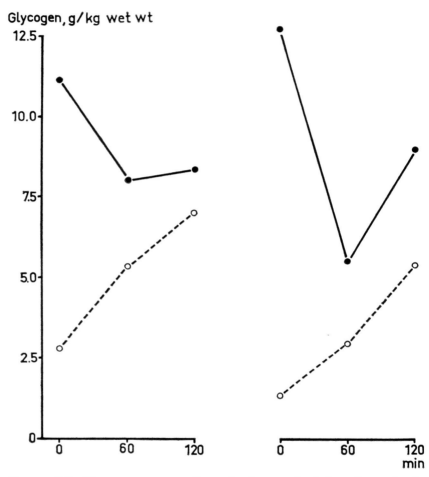

FIGURE 2-6. Glycogen content of previously exercised ○ and previously inactive ● leg muscle during a two-hour exercise with continuous glucose infusion.

taken during exercise and after ten to thirty minutes of subsequent rest. In most cases the glycogen synthetase activity was higher at rest than during exercise, indicating a relative inhibition of the transformation of the D to the I form during work. But even during exercise, a decrease of glycogen level concentration pronouncedly increased the synthetase I activity.

To demonstrate that low glycogen levels may also affect glycogen synthesis during exercise, a further experiment was performed (Fig. 2-6). Two subjects each worked with one leg on a bicycle ergometer until the glycogen store in that leg was very low. A second period of exercise was then begun in which both legs were used at a relatively low work load (pulse rate 140-150 beats/min). Glucose was simultaneously infused (4 gm glucose per kilogram BW, over a period of 2 hr). In the glycogen depleted leg glycogen resynthesis began immediately despite continuing exercise. In the other leg glycogenolysis proceeded for the first hour of exercise, after which time glycogen resynthesis began. It must be remembered that glucose phosphorylation is inhibited by high levels of glucose 6-P. As can be seen in Table 2-II, the level of glucose 6-P is decreased when the glycogen store is nearly empty. This leads to a difference between the two legs favoring an increase of glucose uptake by the previously active limb.

Summary

Muscle glycogen decreases progressively during prolonged exercise; the rate of utilization is directly proportional to work load.

At low work loads the local glycogen store is not decisive in determining the performance capacity; other energy substrates, for example, blood glucose and plasma FFA, appear acceptable to the muscle cells under these conditions.

At high submaximal loads muscle glycogen is the factor determining the long-term performance capacity of the individual.

At very high, supramaximal loads other factors such as substrate levels and possibly changes of intracellular pH appear to limit performance capacity.

The factor that determines the maximal work load at which an individual can perform prolonged exercise generally seems not the glycogen store but the local capacity to oxidize pyruvate in the working muscle.

56 *Frontiers of Fitness*

References

1. AHLBORG, B., BERGSTRÖM, J., EKELUND, L.-G., GUARNIERI, G., HULTMAN, E., and NORDESJÖ, L.-O.: Muscle metabolism during isometric work. To be published.
2. AHLBORG, B., BERGSTROM, J., EKELUND, L.-G., and HULTMAN, E.: Muscle glycogen and muscle electrolytes during prolonged physical exercise. *Acta Physiol Scand, 70*:129-140, 1967.
3. AHLBORG, B., BERGSTRÖM, J., EKELUND, L.-G., and Hultman, E.: Muscle glycogen consumption during prolonged exercise with and without glucose infusion. To be published.
4. ANDRES, R., CADER, G., and ZIERLER, K.L.: The quantitatively minor role of carbohydrate in oxidative metabolism by skeletal muscle in intact man in the basal state. Measurements of oxygen and glucose uptake and carbon dioxide and lactate production in the forearm. *J Clin Invest, 35*:671-682, 1956.
5. BERGSTRÖM, J.: Muscle electrolytes in man. Determined by neutron activation analysis on needle biopsy specimens. A study on normal subjects, kidney patients, and patients with chronic diarrhoea. *Scand J Clin Lab Invest (14 Suppl.), 68*:110, 1962.
6. BERGSTRÖM, J., GUARNIERI, G., and HULTMAN, E.: Glycolytic intermediates and electrolyte changes during short-term exercise. To be published.
7. BERGSTRÖM, J., HERMANSEN, L., HULTMAN, E., and SALTIN, B.: Diet, muscle glycogen and physical performance. *Acta Physiol Scand, 71*:140-150, 1967.
8. BERGSTRÖM, J., and HULTMAN, E.: The effect of exercise on muscle glycogen and electrolytes in normals. *Scand J Clin Lab Invest, 18*:16-20, 1966.
9. BERGSTRÖM, J., and HULTMAN, E.: Muscle glycogen synthesis after exercise. An enhancing factor localized to the muscle cells in man. *Nature (London), 210*:309-310, 1966.
10. BERGSTRÖM, J., and HULTMAN, E.: A study of the glycogen metabolism during exercise in man. *Scand J Clin Lab Invest, 19*:218-228, 1967.
11. BERGSTRÖM, J., and HULTMAN, E.: Glycogen synthetase activity in relation to muscle glycogen content and exercise in man. To be published.
12. BERGSTRÖM, J., HULTMAN, E., JORFELDT, L., PERNOW, B., and WAHREN, J.: The effect of nicotinic acid on physical working

capacity and metabolism of muscle glycogen in man. *J Appl Physiol, 26*:170-176, 1969.

13. CARLSON, L.A., and ORÖ, L.: The effect of nicotinic acid on the plasma free fatty acids. *Acta Med Scand, 172/6*:641-645, 1962.

14. CHAPLER, C.K., and STAINSBY, W.N.: Carbohydrate metabolism in contracting dog skeletal muscle *in situ. Amer J Physiol, 215*: 995-1004, 1968.

15. CHRISTENSEN, E.H., and HANSEN, O.: Zur Methodik der Respiratorischen Quotient-Bestimmungen Ruhe und Arbeit. *Scand Arch Physiol, 81*:137-151, 1939.

16. CORI, G. T., and ILLINGWORTH, B.: The effect of epinephrine and other glycogenolytic agents on the phosphorylase a content of muscle. *Biochim Biophys Acta, 21*:105-110, 1956.

17. DANFORTH, W.H.: Glycogen synthetase activity in skeletal muscle. *J Biol Chem, 240*:588-593, 1965.

18. DANFORTH, W.H., and HELMREICH, E.: Regulation of glycolysis in muscle. I. The conversion of phosphorylase b to phosphorylase a in frog sartorius muscle. *J Biol Chem, 239*:3133-3138, 1964.

19. DANFORTH, W.H., HELMREICH, E., and CORI, C.F.: The effect of contraction and of epinephrine on the phosphorylase activity of frog sartorius muscle. *Proc Nat Acad Sci USA, 48*:1191-1199, 1962.

20. DANFORTH, W.H., and LYON, J.B., JR.: Glycogenolysis during tetanic contraction of isolated mouse muscles in the presence and absence of phosphorylase a. *J Biol Chem, 239*:4047-4050, 1964.

21. GARLAND, P.B., RANDLE, P.J., and NEWSHOLME, E.A.: Citrate as an intermediary in the inhibition of phosphofructokinase in rat heart muscle by fatty acids, ketone bodies, pyruvate, diabetes and starvation. *Nature (London), 200*:169-170, 1963.

22. HAVEL, R.J., CARLSSON, L.A., EKELUND, L.G., and HOLMGREN, A.: Turnover rate and oxidation of different free fatty acids in man during exercise. *J Appl Physiol, 19*:613-618, 1964.

23. HAVEL, R.J., NAIMARK, A., and BORCHGREVINK, C.F.: Turnover rate and oxidation of free fatty acids of blood plasma in man during exercise: Studies during continuous infusion of palmitate-1-C^{14} *J. Clin Invest, 42/7*:1054-1063, 1963.

24. HERMANSEN, L., HULTMAN, E., and SALTIN, B.: Muscle glycogen during prolonged severe exercise. *Acta Physiol Scand, 71*:129-139, 1967.

25. Holloszy, J.O.: Biochemical adaptations in muscle. Effects of exercise on mitochondrial oxygen uptake and respiratory enzyme activity in skeletal muscle. *J Biol Chem, 242*:2278-2282, 1967.

26. Holloszy, J.O., and Oscai, L.B.: Effect of exercise on a-glycerophosphate dehydrogenase activity in skeletal muscle. *Arch Biochem, 130*:653-656, 1969.

27. Huijing, F., Nuttall, F.Q., Villar-Palasi, C., and Larner, J.: UDPglucose:α-1, 4-glucan α-4-glucosyltransferase in heart: regulation of the activity of the transferase *in vivo* and *in vitro* in rat. A dissociation in the action of insulin on transport and on transferase conversion. *Biochem Biophys Acta, 177*:204-212, 1969.

28. Hultman, E.: Muscle glycogen in man determined in needle biopsy specimens. Method and normal values, *Scand J Clin Lab Invest, 19*:209-217, 1967.

29. Hultman, E.: Studies on muscle metabolism of glycogen and active phosphate in man with special reference to exercise and diet. *Scand J Clin Lab Invest (Suppl. 19), 94*:63, 1967.

30. Hultman, E., and Bergström, J.: Muscle glycogen synthesis in relation to diet studied in normal subjects. *Acta Med Scand, 182*:109-117, 1967.

31. Hultman, E., Bergström, J., and McLennan Andersson, N.: Breakdown and resynthesis of phosphorylcreatine and adenosine triphosphate in connection with muscular work in man. *Scand J. Clin Lab Invest, 19*:56-66, 1967.

32. Issekutz, B., Paul, P., and Miller, H.J.: Metabolism in normal and pancreatectomized dogs during steady-state exercise. *Amer J Physiol, 213*:857-862, 1967.

33. Karpatkin, S., Helmriech, E., and Cori, C.F.: Regulation of glycolysis in muscle. II. Effect of stimulation and epinephrine in isolated frog sartorius muscle. *J Biol Chem, 239*:3139-3145, 1964.

34. Keul, J., Doll, E., and Keppler, D.: Metabolism of skeletal muscle. I. Glycose, lactate, pyruvate and free fatty acids in arterial and venous blood of working muscles. Examinations of well trained athletes. *Pflüeger Arch. Ges Physiol, 301*:198-213, 1968.

35. Krebs, E.G., and Fischer, E.H.: Phosphorylase activity of skeletal muscle extracts. *J Biol Chem, 216*:113-120, 1955.

36. Krebs, E. G., Love, D.S., Bratfold, G.E., Trayser, K.A., Meyers, W.L., and Fischer, E.H.: Purification and properties of rabbit skeletal muscle phosphorylase b kinase. *Biochemistry, 3*:1022-1033, 1964.
37. Krogh, A., and Lindhard, J.: The relative value of fat and carbohydrate as sources of muscular energy. With appendices on the correlation between standard metabolism and the respiratory quotient during rest and work. *Biochem J, 14*:290-363, 1920.
38. Krzanowski, J., and Matschinsky, F.M.: Regulation of phosphofructokinase by phosphocreatine and phosphorylated glycolytic intermediate. *Biochem Biophys Res Commun, 34*:816-823.
39. Lardy, H.A., and Parks, E., Jr.: In Gaebler, O.H. (Ed.): *Enzymes: Units of Biological Structure and Function.* New York, Academic Press, 1956, p. 584.
40. Lowry, O.H., Schulz, D.W., and Passonneau, J.V.: Effects of adenylic acid on the kinetics of muscle phosphorylase a. *J Biol Chem, 239*:1947-1953, 1964.
41. Mansour, T.E., and Mansour, J.M.: Effects of serotonin (5-hydroxytryptamine) and adenosine 3', 5'-phosphate on phosphofructokinase from the liver fluke, *Fasciola hepatica. J Biol Chem, 237*:629-634, 1962.
42. Margaria, R., and Foa, P.: Der Einfluss von Muskelarbeit auf den Stickstoffwechsel die Kreatin- und Säureausscheidung. *Arbeitsphysiol, 10*:553-560, 1939.
43. Morgan, H.E., and Parmeggiani, A.: Regulation of glycogenolysis in muscle. II. Control of glycogen phosphorylase reaction in isolated perfused heart. III. Control of muscle glycogen phosphorylase activity. *J Biol Chem, 239*:2435-2445, 1964.
44. Newsholme, E.A., and Randle, P.J.: Regulation of glucose uptake by muscle. Effects of anoxia, insulin, adrenaline and prolonged starving on concentrations of hexose phosphates in isolated rat diaphragm and perfused rat heart. *Biochem J 80*:655-662, 1961.
45. Nilsson, L.H., Bergström, J., and Hultman, E.: Changes in the liver glycogen content in man during short-time fasting and during heavy muscular work. To be published.
46. Özand, P., and Narahara, H.T.: Regulation of glycolysis in muscle. Influence of insulin, epinephrine, and contraction on phos-

phofrucktokinase activity in frog skeletal muscle. *J Biol Chem,* 239/10:3146-3152, 1964.

47. PARMEGGIANI, A., and MORGAN, H.E.: Effect of adenine nucleotides and inorganic phosphate on muscle phosphorylase activity. *Biochem Biophys Res Commun,* 9:252-256, 1962.

48. PASSONNEAU, J.V., and LOWRY, O.H.: P-frucktokinase and the control of the citric acid cycle. *Biochem Biophys Res Commun,* 13/5:372-379, 1963.

49. POSNER, J.B., STERN, R., and KREBS, E.G.: Effects of electrical stimulation and epinephrine on muscle phosphorylase, phosphorylase b kinase, and adenosine 3', 5' -Phosphate. *J Biol Chem,* 240:982-985, 1965.

50. ROCH-NORLUND, A. E., BERGSTRÖM, J., CASTENFORS, H., and HULTMAN, E.: Muscle glycogen in patients with diabetes mellitus. Glycogen content before treatment and the effect of insulin. To be published.

51. ROSELL-PEREZ, M., and LARNER, J.: Studies on UDPG: α-1, 4-glucan α-4-glucosyltransferase. Specificity and structural requirements for the activator of the D form of the dog muscle enzyme. *Biochemistry,* 3:773-778, 1964.

52. SUTHERLAND, E.W. The effect of the hyperglycemic factor and epinephrine on enzyme systems of liver and muscle. *Ann NY Acad Sci,* 54:693-706, 1951.

53. TRIVEDI, B., and DANFORTH, W.H.: Effect of pH on the kinetics of frog muscle phosphofructokinase. *J Biol Chem,* 241:4110-4112, 1966.

54. VARNAUSKAS, E., BERGMAN, H., HOUK, P., and BJÖRNTORP, P.: Haemodynamic effects of physical training in coronary patients. *Lancet, II:*8-12, 1966.

55. VILLAR-PALASI, C., and LARNER, J.: Feedback control of glycogen metabolism in muscle. *Fed Proc,* 25:583, 1966.

56. VINUELA, E., SALAS, M.L., and SOLS, A.: End-product inhibition of yeast phosphofructokinase by ATP. *Biochem Biophys Res Commun,* 12:140-147, 1963.

57. YOUNG, D.R., SHAPIRA, J., FORREST, R., ADACHI, R.R., LIM, R., and PELLIGRA, R.: Model for evaluation of fatty acid metabolism for man during prolonged exercise. *J Appl Physiol,* 23:716-725, 1967.

58. ZUNTZ, N.: Ueber die Bedeutung der verschiedenen Nährstoffe als Erzeuger der Muskelkraft. *Pflüeger Arch Ges Physiol,* 83:557-571, 1901.

Chapter 3

METABOLISM OF EXERCISING MUSCLE

R. F. MOTTRAM

O NE OF the major difficulties in any field of scientific exploration is the difference between the state required for experimental control of the factors affecting a function that is being studied and the normal performance of that function. Another is that of extrapolation from the controlled experimental situation to normal life.

Measurement of Muscle Metabolism *In Vivo*

In studies of metabolism of skeletal muscle, the differences between the *in vitro* and the *in vivo* states are obviously very great, and it is not possible to relate the former to the latter. The first attempt to study metabolism *in vivo* was performed by Chauveaux, who in 1887 performed some studies on the levator labii superioris muscle of the horse (5). He prefaced his report with an enunciation of the principles underlying such studies. These were "That one must be able to measure the rate of flow and collect samples of venous blood draining solely from the organ or tissue studied, to measure the volume or weight of this organ, also to measure the quantities in the blood, and in simultaneously drawn arterial blood of the substances to be studied." To these principles and to the Fick calculation which Chauveaux used, the last eighty years have seen the addition of only one major principle. This is the statement by Dr. Zierler, in 1962, that studies can only be performed when the metabolizing tissue is in equilibrium with the blood flowing through it (20).

Basically similar techniques to Chauveaux's were applied to man in the 1950's, and the experience gained by various teams was summarized by Butterfield and Mottram in 1961 (4). Briefly the forearm was immersed in a plethysmograph, and the whole forearm blood flow was measured by intermittent (5-10 sec) venous occlusion. Blood samples from deep muscle veins were withdrawn through catheters. These were inserted through needles in the superficial veins of the antecubital fossa and entered the deep forearm veins by communications that (almost) invariably exist in this region.

Problems of Interpretation

Two points are of immediate importance. The first is the relationship between the total forearm blood flow as measured with the plethysmograph and the blood actually flowing through the muscles of the forearm. The second is the source of the blood being sampled.

The first of these was tackled in the following way: In a series of studies the forearm blood flow was measured both before and after the skin blood flow had been abolished by iontophoresis of the skin with adrenaline (8). From these studies we calculated the relationship that would partition whole forearm blood flow into its cutaneous and muscular components when measured subsequently under similar conditions. The latter component may be converted to the blood flow per 100 ml muscle tissue. Dr. Edholm and Prof. Barcroft found by dissecting forearms that only about 65 percent of their bulk was muscle (8), and the figure obtained by these authors is used for this conversion.

The second point was brought to our attention rather dramatically in the following way: If a sample of blood was taken during a period of venous occlusion or when the cuff was alternately inflating and deflating, the oxygen content of the venous blood was frequently higher than when the venous blood flow was unimpeded (15). The explanation of this was that superficial vein blood, which normally has a higher oxygen content than deep vein blood, gets diverted by the block above the elbow and collects in the deep veins. This was first suggested by members of the Belfast Department of Physiology (17), who sampled blood from both types of vein simultaneously. We subsequently confirmed their findings by injecting dye and a radiopaque material into the cephalic vein at the wrist (7). The dye or contrast

TABLE 3-IA

MUSCLE O_2 UPTAKE AS DETERMINED BY DIFFERENT WORKERS

Mean Value (ml/100 ml Muscle/min)	Author	Remarks
0.19	Holling (1939)	Water at 30 C, skin flow assumed nil
0.24	Mottram (1955)	Water at 34 C
0.27	Mottram (1958)	Water at 34 C
0.27	Andres et al (1956)	Arm exposed to air at 25 C
0.28	Holling and Verel (1957)	Water at 34 C
0.21	Abramson et al (1958)	Water at 32 C
0.29	Baker and Mottram (1968)	Water at 34 C

TABLE 3-IB

EXCHANGES OF SOME OTHER METABOLICALLY IMPORTANT MATERIALS

Substance	Exchange /100 ml Muscle/min	Authors	Remarks
Glucose	0.07 mg	Andres et al (1956)	
	0.08 mg	Butterfield and Holling (1959)	Overnight fasted
	0.15 mg	Mottram and Brown (1963)	
	0.03 mg	Baker and Mottram (present work)	6-7 hr fasted (studied during afternoon)
	1.31 mg	Mottram and Brown (1963)	1-3 hr after breakfast
	0.50 mg	Baker and Mottram	2 hr after midday meal
Lactic acid	0.04 mg	Andres et al (1956)	
	0 mg	Baker and Mottram (present work)	
Carbon dioxide	0.19 ml	Andres et al (1956)	RQ = 0.74 fasted
	0.21 ml	Baker and Mottram	RQ = 0.70 fed and fasted

medium could be found in the deep veins only if the injection was followed immediately by venous occlusion above the elbow. The blood flow recording and sampling techniques therefore had to be modified to avoid any possibility of sampling deep vein blood when it might be contaminated by blood diverted from the superficial veins.

Table 3-I shows a selection of the results obtained using these techniques and Figure 3-1 shows the experimental preparation as described by Butterfield and Mottram (4).

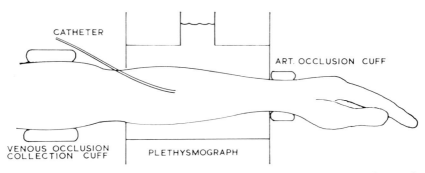

FIGURE 3-1. The human forearm preparation used in studies of muscle metabolism. The plethysmograph is water-filled, and the catheter tip is in a deep forearm vein.

Muscle Metabolism and Training

In my first group of subjects I found one in whom the O_2 uptake of resting forearm muscle was 0.36 ml per 100 ml of muscle per minute in the right arm and only 0.24 ml in the left arm. He was right-handed and a keen squash player. I persuaded him to train his left forearm muscles, and after seven weeks the O_2 uptake rose to 0.43 ml. Attempts were made to repeat this on six other subjects with results shown in Table 3-II.

Owing to the variability of these results and the amount of work required to obtain a single "yes" or "no" answer, the topic

TABLE 3-II
THE EFFECTS OF FOREARM MUSCLE TRAINING ON THE
O_2 UPTAKE OF THE FOREARM MUSCLES

Subject No.	Max. Exercise Rate (grips/day)	Period of Study (Days From Start of Study)	Muscle O_2 Uptake (ml/100 ml Muscle/min)		
			Before	During	
1	210	28-84	0.24	0.43	Significant increase
2	100	28-53	0.25	0.28	
3	360	47-54	0.24	0.42	Significant increase
4	360	41-95	0.17	0.27	Significant increase
5	360	16-86	0.35	0.32	
6	360	67-111	0.24	0.32	Significant increase
7	360	77-112	0.26	0.25	

was dropped in 1956, and these results have never hitherto been reported. It would obviously be of importance to discover whether "training" really increases basal muscle metabolism and whether this is related to the increases in muscle power or mass that may occur.

The Problem of Capillary Occlusion

When the basic method of studying muscle metabolism is applied to exercising muscle, a further difficulty arises. When muscles contract they normally alter their shape and obstruct capillaries carrying blood between adjacent muscle fibers. (The degree to which this occurs in the human forearm was originally studied by R.T. Grant in 1938; his experiments and reasoning in this field have inspired many subsequent workers (10). This produces a continually varying relationship between blood flow, exchanges between blood and tissue, and tissue metabolic activity. It is not possible to correct the errors that enter a calculation of metabolic activity when either metabolism or blood flow is altering as flow is measured and samples of venous blood are taken. For many of the materials of importance to muscle, there are large reserves either in tissue fluid or within the cells for example, the tissue fluid glucose content is 30 times the amount used per minute by resting muscle); the result is a varying time lapse before either blood flow or tissue metabolism affect each other or the composition of the venous blood. There are two solutions to this difficulty. One is that used by Zierler and his colleagues (21). The indicator dilution method of measuring blood flow that they use gives an integrated mean blood flow over a period of a few minutes. Blood samples are drawn over the same period and represent the similarly time integrated composition of muscle effluent blood. Dr. Zierler has thus found himself limited to mild intermittent exercise that can be maintained for many minutes at a time (21). His technique would also be unsuitable for studies of the vasodilator stimulus during exercise. The other solution lies in the development by Lind (6), of a method of performing sustained isometric contractions. Humphreys and Lind (13) showed that with contraction of up to 20 percent of a subject's maximal effort, the "vasodilator stimulus" was fully met and that the vasodilation was confined to the exercising muscle.

Design of a Hand-Grip Ergometer

The mechanical and electronic workshop staff of the Physiology Department at Cardiff built for me a form of Lind hand-grip ergometer. One of the grips is mounted on the frame of the machine and the other is attached to the free end of a spring-steel bar, also clamped at its opposite end to the frame of the machine. A maximal grip effort of a reasonably strong person approximates the hand grips by about 1 mm. Trick movements, such as using muscles other than those of the forearm, have been eliminated by mounting the ergometer on wheels. The deflection of the bar is detected by a strain-gauge dynamometer, the output of which is used for both recording and monitoring the strength of a contraction. The dynamometer has its own zeroing control clamped to the bar.

The amplified signal from the gauge is linearly related to bar deflection and to the load applied to the bar. This signal was recorded on one channel of the pen recorder which was also used to record the plethysmographic volume changes and thus the blood flow. The complete assembly, except the intravenous catheter, is shown on Figure 3-2. This figure also shows the galvanometer which enables the subject to control his grip strength. Initially I used this preparation for studies of blood-flow changes alone, expecting to define the conditions in which one might subsequently study metabolic activity.

The Circulatory Response to Isometric Muscular Activity

I found first that the blood-flow response to repeated contractions of the same strength was repeatable and that with mild contractions (5% or 10% of the subject's own maximal effort), the blood flow had settled to a new higher level within two minutes. A similar pattern of response occurred during 15 or 20 percent maximal contractions except that the blood flow was higher for the more powerful contractions. Despite the plateauing of blood

The Layout of the Apparatus

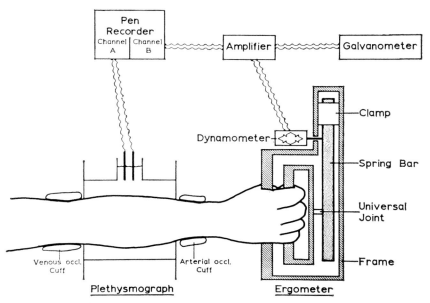

FIGURE 3-2. The plethysmograph and ergometer and the equipment used for recording blood flow and contraction strength; the galvanometer helps the subject to maintain a constant contraction.

flow during work, a large and persistent postcontraction hyperemia frequently occurred after these more powerful contractions. It took the form of an initial very high flow, followed by an exponential decline lasting three or more minutes.

If one assumes that this postexercise hyperemia is due to a gradual accumulation of some "metabolic vasodilator stimulus," then one might expect it to become larger the longer a contraction is maintained. This was tested in a number of subjects, the postexercise hyperemia being calculated as the number of milliliters of excess blood that passed through the limb segment before the blood flow returned to its resting level. The results of these studies were inconclusive. In some the hyperemia increased as the work period lengthened, and in some it was unaffected by the length of the contraction.

While performing these experiments, I came upon one curious phenomenon which needs further investigation, as does the whole subject of metabolically induced hyperemia. In these studies on postexercise hyperemia, the subjects are working near to their limits, and in fact some studies had to be abandoned before they were completed. One effect of a series of exhausting contractions is the development of progressively increasing hyperemia during the work phase as the experiment progresses. However, the resting flow remains unaffected by the contractions. Another effect of fatiguing contractions is to increase the blood-flow response to lesser loads. Thus, if one studies the response to two 10 percent contractions, one made before and the other after the subject has attempted a series of 15 percent contractions, the resting blood flow again remains unaltered, but the response to the second 10 percent contraction may be much larger than that to the first. It is as if the "vasodilator mechanism" but not the blood flow to resting muscle has become sensitized in some way to the effects of increased metabolism.

At this stage, I suppose the wise physiologist would have stopped and investigated these circulatory phenomena further by continuous measurement of key constituents in the venous blood; he might then have elucidated the cause of exercise hyperemia and the odd behaviors of the postexercise hyperemia and blood flow in tired muscle. Other workers are currently studying these questions. O_2, CO_2, H^+, K^+, lactic acid, and ATP breakdown products have all been implicated, and some have also been rejected on either theoretical or experimental grounds (for current reviews see References 2 and 12). For example, lactic acid is not formed in McArdle's disease, an inborn error of metabolism in which the glycogen phosphorylase of muscle is deficient, but exercise hyperemia is brisk in this condition.

However, if one is careful never to fatigue muscles and to avoid contractions that produce postexercise hyperemia, one can proceed straight to the study of metabolism in exercising muscle and leave these other topics alone. This in fact, is what I have done.

Conditions for the Study of Muscle Metabolism

Most of my studies have been done with subjects contracting at 5 percent of their maximal efforts, this maximum being determined with the arm positioned as it would be during metabolic studies. The maximum force varied between 25 and 50 kg and was not related obviously to the limb volume. A given subject had similar maxima when studied on repeated occasions.

Individual studies have taken the following form: One minute prior to the onset of flow recording, the hand was excluded from the circulation. Blood flow was measured three times a minute, using six-second periods of venous occlusion. Venous blood samples were obtained in the last nine seconds of each fourteen-second interval between successive venous occlusions. In this way we managed to avoid contaminating our deep vein blood samples with blood diverted from superficial veins during the venous occlusion, a problem that I have already mentioned. Sustained contractions were maintained during the second through the fifth minutes of flow recording, and recording was continued for a further three minutes after conclusion of the four-minute-long contraction period. Pooled blood samples were collected for the first minute of flow recording, in the third and fourth minutes of exercise, and in the third minute of the recovery period.

In each study I attempted to perform three replicates of this procedure at twenty-minute intervals. Quite apart from the obvious value of duplicating one's observations in a steady state, this plan of study has enabled me sometimes to follow the changes in muscle metabolism that accompany changes in general body metabolism, as, for instance, the glucose absorbed from the gut is stored in the tissues.

The Sampling of Arterial Blood

The problem of arterial blood sampling must now be mentioned. When I began this work in 1952, I studied oxygen alone, and it was sufficient to determine the oxygen-carrying capacity of a venous sample from the Hb concentration and then to take the arterial content as 95 percent of this value. For substances other than oxygen there is no substitute for arterial blood except "arterialized" venous blood. A technique for obtaining such blood was developed by Goldschmidt and Light in 1922 (9), who put a hand in hot water and sampled from the veins on the back of the wrist. This method was checked by Ellen Brown and myself (16) and under somewhat less stringent conditions, by Victor Wynn (3) at St. Mary's Hospital in London. In the present studies we have used this method throughout, using initially a water bath at 45 C and later an electric heating pad wrapped around the subject's spare hand. Haemoglobin determinations have been performed on many of the "arterial" samples to compare their oxygen content with the theoretical oxygen capacity of these bloods.

The method is not ideal but is a compromise arising out of practical and ethical considerations, on the one hand, and scientific desirability on the other.

Storage and Biochemical Analysis of Blood

In as many studies as possible each period of blood-flow recording, sampling, and work was bracketed by "arterial" samples taken before and afterwards. Samples for blood gas and glucose analysis were collected anaerobically into paraffined syringes, the dead spaces of which were previously filled with a mixture of potassium fluoride solution and heparin. They were then sealed and stored in ice-water mixture until they were analyzed. Blood for determinations of lactic and pyruvic acids was collected into paraffined syringes with dead spaces filled with heparin alone; a measured quantity of this blood was immediately mixed with perchloric acid and subsequently centrifuged, the being supernatant stored in the refrigerator until analyzed.

Blood gases were determined on the manometric Van Slyke analyzer, since direct determinations of the volumes of oxygen and carbon-dioxide were required. Glucose was analyzed on the Technicon Autoanalyzer, using $K_3Fe(CN)_6$ reduction. Lactic and pyruvic acids were determined by the lactic dehydrogenase enzyme method.

In the oxidation of glucose 30 mg of glucose are chemically equivalent to 22.4 ml of oxygen or carbon dioxide, so that 1 mg of

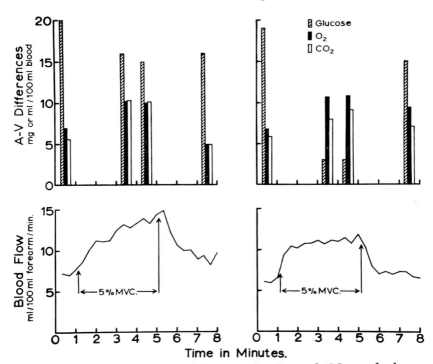

FIGURE 3-3. The arteriovenous differences for O_2, and CO_2, and glucose and the blood flow before, during and after four-minute contractions at 5 percent of maximum effort in two subjects (each contraction was performed in triplicate and results were averaged). Equilibrium is reached in the experiment shown on the right but not in that on the left.

glucose is roughly equivalent to 0.75 ml of oxygen. With no method can glucose be determined to an accuracy much greater than the nearest 1 mg per 100 ml blood. While blood gas analysis on the Van Slyke apparatus can be performed to an accuracy of 0.02 vol%, I do not think it it practicable to expect a routine accuracy greater than 0.1 vol%. Even so, in chemically equivalent terms the gas analysis technique is several times more discriminant than the blood glucose method that we have used.

Typical Successful and Unsuccessful Experiments

Figure 3-3 shows the average observations obtained from three replicate four-minute long contractions from two subjects.

Above are the arteriovenous differences for glucose, oxygen, and carbon-dioxide. Below are the blood flow records. The arterio-venous difference for glucose invariably fell during the hyperemia of contraction (unless it was already undetectable at rest), while the differences for oxygen and carbon dioxide invariably rose. The left-hand study is a good example of failure to reach equilibrium, as the blood flow is rising throughout the period of sampling. The right-hand study is successful in that both blood flow and arteriovenous differences were virtually the same in the third and fourth minutes of exercise. Studies like the left-hand one of this figure have had to be discarded from any quantitative consideration of the results.

The Calculation of Muscle Blood Flow

Until now I have considered raw observations—whole forearm blood flow and arteriovenous differences of the blood as sampled. In order to proceed further in the resting state, one need only convert the blood flow to flow per 100 ml muscle and assume a uniformity of both local blood flow and of metabolism before applying the Fick equation. During the exercise that we have been studying, things are very different. Humphreys (personal communication) states that 50 percent is a reasonable estimate of the proportion of forearm muscle that is active in these studies. It is also reasonable to assume that skin blood flow and flow through inactive muscle would be unaltered by the strength of effort used. The very extensive circulatory adjustments that Lind and his colleagues have been studying over the last seven years are not usually apparent at the level of grips we have studied. Alteration, which would almost certainly be downwards, of blood flow through skin and inactive muscle or an overestimate of the percentage of active muscle would result in the values for the increases in metabolic activity that I am reporting being too small.

Blood flow through resting and active muscle are estimated from the recorded whole forearm flow by the following method:

Total forearm blood flow at rest = 5 ml per 100 ml forearm per minute

∴ skin blood flow = 1.5 ml per 100 ml forearm per minute
and residual (muscle) blood flow = 3.5 ml per 100 ml forearm per minute
∴ muscle blood flow = 3.5 x 100 per 65 or
5.4 ml per 100 ml mus-
cle per minute

Total forearm blood
flow during exercise = 10 ml per 100 ml forearm per minute
blood flow through skin = 1.5 ml per 100 ml forearm per minute
and blood flow through
resting muscle = 1.75 ml per 100 ml
forearm per minute
∴ blood flow through
active muscle = 6.75 ml per 100 ml
forearm per minute
= 6.75 x 100 per 32.5 or
20.8 ml per 100 ml ac-
tive muscle per min-
ute

The skin flow is obtained from the adrenaline iontophoresis observations as described earlier. The Barcroft and Edholm values
for the percentage muscle are used. Small corrections have also to
be applied to the observed venous blood contents during work
because some of this blood comes from inactive muscle.

The Resting Metabolism of Muscle

The metabolic exchanges of oxygen, carbon-dioxide, and glucose were determined for each of fifteen subjects in the fed state
and in four subjects fasted for six hours. Most subjects had three
replicate sets of observations made at twenty to twenty-five minute intervals, and the average of these was obtained.

Metabolic exchanges of the resting muscle are shown in Table

TABLE 3-III
METABOLIC ACTIVITY OF RESTING MUSCLE
(21 Subjects, 3 Determinations on Each)

	O_2 Uptake *ml/100 ml Muscle/min*	CO_2 Prodn. *ml/100 ml Muscle/min*	*RQ*	*Glucose* Uptake *ml/100 ml Muscle/min*
Mean	0.30	0.21	0.70	0.50
Range	0.22-0.42	0.10-0.36	0.32-1.04	0.0-1.14

3-III. The average values for oxygen uptake, carbon dioxide production, and the respiratory quotient (RQ) are similar to those of Andres *et al.*, (1), but the glucose uptake of the tissue is very much higher, as the subjects are all in the absorptive phase after their normal midday meals. The average glucose uptake is considerably lower than that found by Mottram and Brown (16) for similar subjects who were studied after breakfast. This difference is paralleled by the difference in glucose tolerance curves found by Jarrett and Keen (personal communication); both indicate a difference in the tissues' handling of glucose between the morning and the afternoon. I mention this here because it is possible that these differences in glucose uptake might affect the muscles' ability to perform high levels of work when the main source of energy is the anaerobic breakdown of the stored glycogen of the muscles. Unlike Zierler *et al.* (21) but as Taylor *et al.* have also found (18), we did not find any production of lactic acid in these studies of resting muscle. In spite of the high

TABLE 3-IV
THE EFFECTS OF EXERCISE ON MUSCLE IN THE FED AND FASTED
STATES. DATA ON THE METABOLISM OF O_2, CO_2, AND GLUCOSE
AND ON THE BLOOD FLOW THROUGH THE ACTIVE MUSCLE

		O_2	CO_2	*Glucose*	*Blood Flow*
		15 Fed Subjects			
Rest	Mean	0.29	0.25	0.60	4.2
	Range	0.21-0.37	0.11-0.36	0.17-1.14	3.0-6.4
Work	Mean	2.21	1.87	1.35	20.6
	Range	0.93-3.18	0.77-2.72	0-3.37	14.5-31.6
		Four 7-Hour Fasted Subjects			
Rest	Mean	0.28	0.23	0.03	4.2
	Range	0.20-0.41	0.15-0.36	0-0.13	3.5-5.1
Work	Mean	1.52	1.07	0	15.4
	Range	1.03-1.93	0.79-1.29		9.2-21.4

glucose uptake (1.25 times the chemically equivalent oxygen uptake), the muscle RQ suggests that the main use of the oxygen is in oxidizing fatty acids. Zierler has direct evidence of fatty acid uptake by muscle in the amounts required to satisfy this suggestion (21).

Muscle Metabolism During Exercise

The mean effects of exercise in the fed and the fasted subjects are shown in Table 3-IV. Blood flow through active muscle sustaining a force of 5 percent of its maximal effort has increased by five times the resting flow rate. Arteriovenous differences for both oxygen and carbon dioxide have increased by 50 percent. The resultant products, oxygen uptake and carbon dioxide production, both therefore increased by seven times resting values. In terms of whole-body exercise and oxygen uptake, this increase over basal oxygen uptake would be achieved by level treadmill running at 8.5 km per hour and would take about two minutes to achieve (14).

Glucose uptake only doubled, though this average figure conceals some studies in which glucose uptake rose as much as did the gas exchange and some in which it apparently fell. This was due to arteriovenous differences becoming undetectable. No change was seen in the lactic acid content of the venous blood. In view of the previously published work on glucose uptake and exercise from Butterfield and his colleagues (19), I was surprised at our results.

Figure 3-4 analyzes the observations with respect to glucose a little further. On the left are the arteriovenous differences for glucose at rest and during contraction. The shaded areas indicate the limit of the chemical analysis. It can be clearly seen how the increase in blood flow during work has caused the extraction of glucose from a given volume of blood to shrink. It is clear that blood flow, or the supply of glucose to the tissue in the blood, is not the limiting factor determining glucose uptake by the muscles —a situation very different from that of oxygen where the increase in blood flow is always accompanied by a simultaneous increase in the extraction rate or arteriovenous difference for oxygen. On

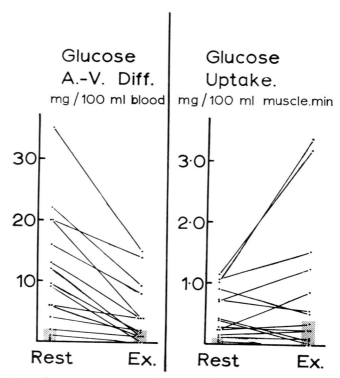

FIGURE 3-4. The arteriovenous glucose differences and derived muscle glucose uptake at rest and work. The shaded areas indicate the size of errors that could be introduced by the limits of the chemical analysis methods.

the right-hand side of the figure, showing the effect of exercise on glucose uptake, the shaded areas again indicate the limits set by the autoanalyzer. One can again see that in many subjects the effect of activity on the glucose extraction from the blood is very small.

References

1. ANDRES, R., ZIERLER, K.L., ANDERSON, H.M., STAINSBY, W.N., CADER, G., GHRAYYIB, A.S., and LILIENTHAL, J.L. JUN: Measurement of blood flow and volume in the forearm of man with notes on the theory of indicator dilution and on production of

turbulence, haemolysis and vasodilatation by intra-vascular injection. *J Clin Invest, 33*:482-504, 1954.

2. BARCROFT, H.: Circulatory changes accompanying the contraction of voluntary muscle. *Aust J Exp Biol Sci, 42*:1-16, 1964.
3. BROOKS, D., and WYNN, V.: Use of venous blood for pH and Carbon-dioxide studies. *Lancet, (i)*:227-230, 1959.
4. BUTTERFIELD, W.J.H., and MOTTRAM, R.F.: The human forearm as a preparation for metabolic investigations. *Proc Roy Soc Med, 54*:549-552, 1961.
5. CHAUVEAU, M.A., and KAUFFMAN, M.: Expériences pour la détermination du coefficient d'activité nutritive et respiratoire des muscles en repôs et en travail. *C R Acad Sci (Paris), 104*:1126-1132, 1887.
6. CLARKE, R.S.J., HELLON, R.F., and LIND, A.R.: The duration of sustained contractions of the human forearm at different muscle temperatures. *J Physiol (London), 143*:454-473, 1958.
7. COLES, D.R., COOPER, K.E., MOTTRAM, R.F., and OCCLESHAW, J.V.: The source of blood samples withdrawn from deep forearm veins via catheters passed upstream from the median cubital vein. *J Physiol (London), 142*:323-328, 1958.
8. COOPER, K.E., EDHOLM, O.G., and MOTTRAM, R.F.: The blood flow in skin and muscle in the human forearm. *J Physiol (London), 128*:258-267, 1955.
9. GOLDSCHMIDT, S., and LIGHT, A.B.: A method of obtaining from veins blood similar to arterial blood in gaseous content. *J Biol Chem, 64*:53-58, 1925.
10. GRANT, R.T.: Observations on the blood circulation in voluntary muscle in man. *Clin Sci, 3*:157-173, 1938.
11. HOCKADAY, T.D.R., DOWNEY, J.A., and MOTTRAM, R.F.: A case of McArdle's syndrome with a positive family history. *J Neurol, 27*:186-197, 1964.
12. HUDLICKA, O. (Ed.): *Circulation in Skeletal Muscle.* Oxford, Pergamon, 1968, pp. 121-225.
13. HUMPHREYS, P.W., and LIND, A.R.: The blood flow through active and inactive muscles of the forearm during sustained hand-grip contractions. *J. Physiol (London), 166*:120-135, 1963.
14. MARGARIA, R., EDWARDS, H.T., and DILL, D.B.: The possible mechanisms of contracting and paying the oxygen debt and the role of lactic acid in muscular contraction. *Amer J. Physiol, 106*:689-715, 1933.

78 *Frontiers of Fitness*

15. MOREIRA, M.F., MOTTRAM, R.F., and WERNER, A.Y.: Effect of venous pressure on the oxygen content of venous blood in the deep forearm veins. *J Physiol (London)*, *133*:255-265, 1956.
16. MOTTRAM, R.F., and BROWN, E.: Influence of local cooling on the glucose and oxygen uptake of the human forearm muscle. *Clin Sci*, *25*:249-262, 1963.
17. RODDIE, I.C., SHEPHERD, J.T., and WHELAN, R.F.: Evidence from venous oxygen saturation measurements that the increase in forearm blood flow during body heating is confined to the skin. *J Physiol (London)*, *134*:444-450, 1956.
18. TAYLOR, S.H., LIND, A.R., STAUNTON, H.P., HUMPHREYS, P.W., and DONALD, K.W.: Changes in constituents of the venous effluent from muscles engaged in sustained contractions. Unpublished work cited by K.W. Donald *et al.* Cardiovascular Responses to sustained (static) contractions. *Circ Res, 20 (Suppl. 1)*:15-43, 1967.
19. WHICHELOW, M.J., BUTTERFIELD, W.J.H., ABRAMS, M.E., STERKY, G., and GARRATT, C.J.: The effects of mild exercise on glucose uptake in human forearm tissues in the fasting state and after oral glucose administration. *Metabolism, 17*:84-96, 1968.
20. ZIERLER, K.L.: Theory of the use of arteriovenous concentration differences for measuring metabolism in steady and non-steady states. *J Clin Invest, 40*:2111-2125, 1961.
21. ZIERLER, K.L., MASERI, A., KLASSEN, G., RABINOWITZ, D., and BURGESS, J.: Muscle Metabolism during exercise in Man. *Trans Assoc Amer Phys, 81*:266-273, 1968.

Chapter 4

ISOMETRIC MUSCULAR STRENGTH IN WOMEN

W. Rohmert and P. Jenik

THIS PAPER reports measurements of isometric muscular strength in women, with particular reference to research methods and the classification of work loads. To this end, three tasks have been closely studied; each requires a selected type of isometric muscular activity.

Introduction

The growing number of women employed outside the home increases the need for the scientific study of this subject. The most important reasons for such a study are as follows:

1. A large number of women, including a growing percentage of married women, are in employment. The latter increasingly wish to resume employment after their children have grown up.

2. Nearly 90 percent of female industrial workers are regarded as unskilled or semiskilled, but so-called "typical women's work" is more exacting for the most part than the usual work on a production line.

3. Industry does not yet have at its disposal sufficient experience of the work loads tolerated by the female.

4. Work organization and the division of labor are such that monotonous mechanical tasks predominate especially with respect to female labor. No opportunities are given for counterbalancing such tasks with those that are more diverse.

5. Women often control machines which were originally designed to suit men.

6. The ability of a woman to undertake work outside the home is limited by the sex-specific role which she plays.

7. The female is not able to pursue her work in so stable a fashion as the male.

8. The woman has a dual responsibility for work, both inside and outside the household. Work organization too often fails to avoid conflict between these two responsibilities.

Factory design and the organization of work need to take into account the growing role which women are playing in the industrial work force. These topics come within the competence of Ergonomics, and one of the first steps to their intelligent discussion is to discover the exact extent of women's isometric muscular strength within arm reach. These are numerous reports of maximum muscle strength of the hand and foot in the male, and there are also reports concerning machine controls and equipment in the same context. However, despite a need for similar research on the isometric strength of women, such studies have seldom been undertaken. The usual practice has been to estimate women's strength as about two-thirds that of men. "A review of the literature substantiates the estimate that general muscle strength in women is about two-thirds that in men. This is only an average figure which we can use for general circulation; it does not apply to every muscle group." (1).

Definitions

The strength of the human body can only be determined, in practical terms, through the measurement of what it can effect externally. Maximum isometric muscular strength may be defined as "the force of reaction achieved when the greatest possible effort is intentionally brought to bear in an isometric muscle contraction of from two to six seconds duration" (8). A definite body posture and a predetermined limb position are adopted. Body supports of various types are provided. The force is exerted in a definite direction and at a preselected point of application. Two types of load may be distinguished: the exertion of maximum isometric muscular strength and the exertion of a torque moment with a definite direction. The loading case may be defined as the type of load relative to a precisely determined point of application.

Relevant Factors

Isometric muscular strength is dependent on a number of variables which may be divided as follows:

1. Type of mechanical load.
2. Personal characteristics.
3. Working conditions.

The first factor has the greatest interest for the present research. However, the last two are briefly considered for the sake of completeness.

The working conditions for our experiments consisted essentially of a normal environment (room Temperature: circa 20 C, with normal humidity). The usual sports clothes were worn by the subjects. With respect to personal characteristics, we may note the following: Our subjects were ten young females. Positive motivation was provided through the stimulation of interest in the experiment and through payment. Nutrition, health, and bodily conditions were normal. The state of training corresponded to that of any normal young person. Occupation included laboratory assistants and university students. Anthropometric data is summarized in the following:

Measurement	Dimension	Range From	Range To	Mean	Standard Deviation	Coefficient of Variation
Age	year	17.2	24.7	20.5	—	—
Body weight	kp	52.0	73.0	64.1	20.0	31.2
Height	cm	158.1	172.5	167.5	14.0	8.3
Arm reach	cm	69.6	76.0	72.3	10.7	6.8
Length of thigh	cm	34.6	43.9	38.4	8.5	22.3
Length of leg	cm	39.1	43.5	40.6	5.0	12.2

Method

Isometric muscle strengths were measured on the right limbs. The subjects were in a resting position, with both feet placed parallel to one another and about 30 cm apart. The floor surface was the usual laminated wood, with a coefficient of friction of about 0.70. Where appropriate the subject sat on an ordinary chair with a back rest. The height of the seat was 46 cm and the depth 40 cm. The lower edge of the back rest was 20 cm, and the upper edge was 40 cm above the seat. The seat had a glazed surface and was inclined towards the back at an angle of about 2 degrees. The subjects were required to sit in an upright position with their backs supported, their knees apart, and their feet about 30 cm from one another.

The measured arm strengths were exerted on the vertically positioned, cylindrical wooden hand grip of a dynamometer. The diameter of the grip was 30 mm. It was assumed that the point of application was identical with the center of gravity of the clenched hand. In most experiments the arm was spontaneously held in a manner optimal for the exertion of maximum strength. However, this was not the case in some experiments where the lower and upper arms were intentionally held in the horizontal plane.

The subjects made three successive isometric contractions for each limb position studied. Measurements of isometric strength were used in this study, as they possess the almost exclusive advantage of being repeatable. The arithmetic mean of the three readings was calculated and taken as the measure of strength. Each contraction lasted about one second; this timing permitted the recording of a steady state value. There was a pause between each contraction to prevent progressive muscle fatigue. As a rule, after each contraction in one direction the subjects exercised a contraction of the antagonistic muscles in the opposite direction.

Strain gauges were used in this survey; they were fitted to dynamometers as previously described by Rohmert (2, 3). Vertical strength and torque were measured by a dynamometer modified by Rohmert and Neuhaus (8). All measurements followed an experimental order which has been described previously (3).

Statistical analysis included calculation of the arithmetic mean, the standard deviation, and the coefficient of variation for each loading case.

A total of over 3590 individual measurements of maximum isometric strength were made. This number included 2340 measurements of arm strengths, 840 measurements of arm torque moments, 180 measurements of lifting strengths, and 230 measurements of foot pressure. This research into the strength of women thus supplements other publications of the author (9) and can be considered in conjunction with the strength atlas for men (10), since both experiments were carried out using the same method and experimental design (9, 10).

Figure 4-1 shows the isometric strengths studied. The point of application lay in a vertical plane, passing through the mid-point of the shoulder joint, and rotated 60 degrees outwards to a sagittal plane. In the diagram, arrows are used to indicate the direction of force: a) vertical isometric strength: VZ—vertical pull, VD—vertical push. b) horizontal isometric strength: SZ—sagittal pull, SD—saggital push both parallel to a sagittal direction; FZ—frontal pull, FD—frontal push, parallel to a frontal direction; AD—adduction pull, AB—abduction push, perpendicular to a vertical plane through the midpoint of the shoulder joint and the point of application. The following are also indicated in Figure 4-3: ZZ—central pull, ZB—central push in the direction of a line joining the midpoint of the shoulder joint and the point of application. In addition to isometric measurements, maximum torque was measured in both directions, that is, forwards and backwards with supination and pronation around a sagittal axis.

The position of the point of exertion relative to the body is one of the most important determinants of isometric strength. In order to permit comparisons, a uniform system of space coordinates was established. Each point of application was specified by three polar coordinates with the origin at the hypothetically fixed point of the shoulder joint: 1. Angle of elevation α between the radius vector of the point of application and the horizontal plane; 2. Angle of yaw β between the symmetrical plane of the body and the vertical plane through the radius vector; and 3. Radius vector R of the point of application measured as the length of the line joining the center point of the shoulder joint and the point of application, stated as a percentage (50%, 75%, and 100%) of the maximum arm reach.

Results

Representative measurements of the body musculature will

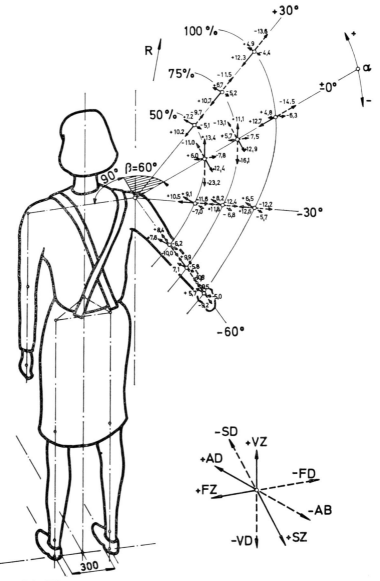

FIGURE 4-1. The maximum isometric strength of the right arm in women. The point of application was in a vertical plane rotated 60 degrees outwards in a sagittal plane (strengths expressed in kiloponds, kp, where 1 kilopond is the force exerted by a mass of 1 kg in unit gravitational field).

be given here, with the aim of characterizing, as simply as possible, the total muscle strength of the female.

The measurements selected are

1. The lifting strength of both arms, representing the capacity of the total body musculature.

2. The foot pressure exerted from a sitting position, representing the capacity of the leg musculature.

3. The isometric strength of the right arm in an upright position, representing the capacity of the arm musculature.

4. The central pull and push of the arm.

5. The adduction pull and abduction push of the arm.

The Maximum Lifting Strength of Both Arms

This type of load was chosen as an example of maximum isometric strength for two reasons: a) The task employs almost all of the body musculature and so, to a certain extent, is characteristic of total mechanical capacity. b) There is a frequent need to carry or move articles in industry. We may instance the lifting or lowering of articles from the work bench, the feeding and removal of articles from conveyor belts, and the carrying of loads from one work place to another to and from stores and shelves. It is thus important to know the maximum weight which a person is capable of moving when various postures are held. In our case these postures are characterized by the position of the point of exertion relative to the body, the height of the grip above floor level, and the grip distance, that is, the horizontal distance between the heel of the foot and the line of force of the vertical lift. The palm of the hand was used in all of these tasks. The knee was sometimes bent and sometimes straight; the latter resulted, for the most part, in a somewhat smaller lifting strength. Similar research has been carried out by Whitney (11).

Table 4-I compares the maximum lifting strengths of both women and men at different grip heights and distances and with different postures of the knee; their ratios are also given. The female values range from 64.5 to 73.0 percent of the male, with an average of 67.3 percent. This is in accord with the expected result that women have about two-thirds the strength of men.

TABLE 4-I
MAXIMUM LIFTING STRENGTH OF BOTH ARMS IN WOMEN AND
MEN AND COMPARISON OF THESE VALUES AT DIFFERENT
GRIP HEIGHTS AND DISTANCES AND WITH DIFFERENT
POSITIONS OF THE KNEE

Grip Height cm	Grip Distance cm	Knee Position	Max. Lifting Strength Women kp	Max. Lifting Strength Men kp	Comparison of Lifting Strength in Women and Men %
12.5	30	d*	86	123	70.0
		a †	100	138	72.5
	40	d	82	120	68.5
		a	91	129	70.5
	50	d	74	115	64.5
		a	80	123	65.0
25	30	d	86	122	70.5
		a	90	127	73.0
	40	d	82	116	70.7
		a	83	119	69.8
	50	d	78	110	70.8
		a	75	109	68.8
50	30	d	79	116	68.0
		a	80	124	64.5
	40	d	76	112	67.8
		a	77	115	67.0
	50	d	74	105	70.5
		a	71	109	65.2
Arithmetic mean for knee bent					68.4
Arithmetic mean for knee straight					69.0
Arithmetic for combined data					67.25

*Knee straight.
†Knee bent

The Foot Presure Exerted From a Sitting Position by the Right Leg

This strength was measured in a sagittal plane through the hip joint. The direction of force lay in the required line joining the center point of the hip and the ankle. The force was exerted by the ball of the foot acting on a foot pedal (even surface, area 10 x 20 cm). The heel of the foot was not stressed.

Pedal positions are characterized in terms of pedal distances and heights. Data for various pedal distances ("R") are given as percentages of the maximum pedal distance when the leg was extended. The pedal distances studied were 95, 80, and 65 percent

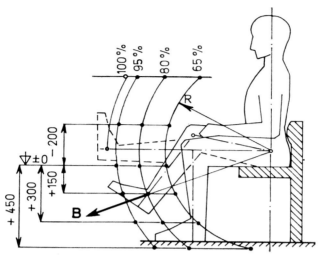

FIGURE 4-2. Illustration of measurement of maximum foot pressure.

for women, and 95, 90, and 85 percent for men. Pedal height ("h") means the height of the foot pedal (ankle joint) above or below the horizontal plane of the seat surface.

Figure 4-2 illustrates the points of reference from which the pedal pressures exerted by the women were determined. When the pedal distance was 95 percent, the mean of the female/male (F/M) ratios was about 55 percent. When the distance was 90 percent, the F/M ratio was about 80 percent. It may be that when the leg is extended, the factor determining foot pressure is the muscular capacity; hence the lower ratio under these conditions. The mean ratio was about 80 percent when pedal distances were relatively smaller. It is possible that the weight of the leg is also brought into play with shorter distances. The weight of the leg plays a more important role in the foot pressure exercised by women than in that exercised by men. The mean ratio for all pedal positions was 67.5 percent, again corresponding to the classical ratio of isometric strengths between women and men. However, it should be emphasized that this ratio is not valid in every case; the example given clearly shows this point.

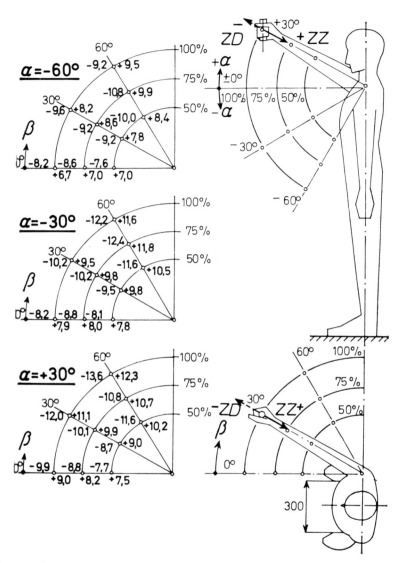

FIGURE 4-3. Total values of maximum Central Push ZD and Central Pull ZZ within the reach of the right arm in women for different points of application (strength expressed in kiloponds).

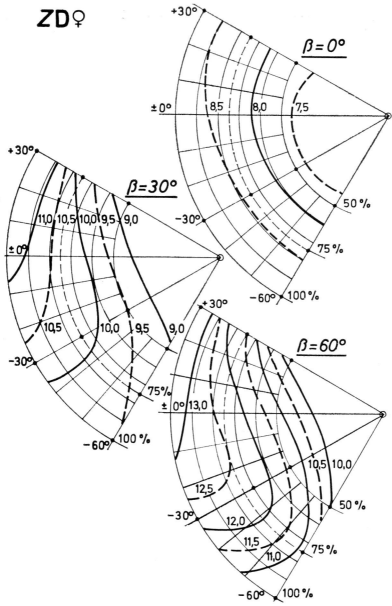

FIGURE 4-4. Isodynes of the maximum Central Push ZD in a vertical plane with angle of yaw (β) = 0, 30, and 60 degrees (strengths expressed in kiloponds).

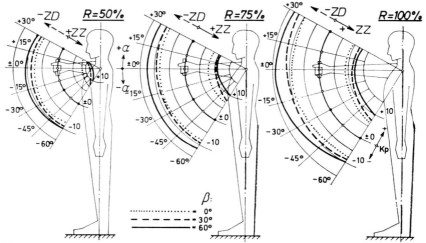

FIGURE 4-5. Polar diagrams of the maximum Central Push ZD and Central Pull ZZ for different angles of elevation ($\alpha = +30$ to -60 degrees), different angles of yaw ($\beta = 0$, 30, 60 degrees) and different arm reaches ($R = 50\%$, 75%, 100%) (strengths expressed in kiloponds).

Central Pull and Push of Arm

This type of load relates to the isometric strength within the reach of the right arm. The line of application joins the point of application with the center point of the shoulder joint. The central push is in an outwards direction (ZD), and the central pull is inwards (ZZ). Figure 4-3 shows the isometric strengths as determined for different points of application in accordance with methods mentioned above.

On the basis of these initial results, isodynes* were drawn as polar diagrams for various angles of yaw ($\beta = 0$, 30, and 60 degrees). These coincided with a vertical plane through the center point of the shoulder joint. (Figure 4-4). Figure 4-5 shows the central pull and push, respectively, in the form of three polar diagrams for arm reaches, $R = 50$, 75, and 100 percent. The curves in this particular diagram coincide with the angles of yaw $\beta = 0$, 30, and 60 degrees. They join the final

---

*Isodynes are curves which join points within arm reach and which indicate strengths of the same type and amount.

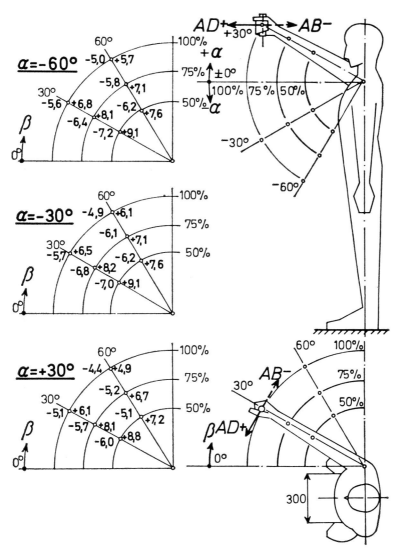

FIGURE 4-6. Measured values of maximum Abduction Push AD and Adduction Pull AZ within the reach of the right arm in women for different points of application (strengths expressed in kiloponds).

points of the radius vectors in the direction of the relevant angle of elevation on which the appropriate points of application lie.

This type of description demonstrates that the ratio of central push to pull remains practically constant for a particular arm reach. It is interesting to note that the ratio of central push to pull, ZD:ZZ, does not deviate far from a value of 1 under the conditions of this experiment. The mean ratio of ZD:ZZ was 1.06, and the range was from 0.95 to 1.22. This type of load, in contradistinction to vertical lift, adduction, abduction, and frontal strength, exerts only a slight torque on the longitudinal axis of the body. Therefore, these results are determined almost exclusively by the strength of the arm musculature.

Adduction Pull and Abduction Push

In this type of load the direction of force is perpendicular to the palm and the back of the hand. Figure 4-6 shows the isometric strengths which were determined for different points of application in accordance with the methods mentioned above. On the basis of these initial results, isodynes were drawn on polar diagrams. These coincided with a vertical plane through the center point of the shoulder joint for angles of yaw $\beta = 30$ and 60 degrees (Figs. 4-7 and 4-8). Not only are the absolute values of interest but so also are the ratios. The values for adduction are greater than those for abduction; the ratios range from 1.1 to 1.4, with a mean of about 1.28.

The mean ratio between women and men with respect to this type of strength is 0.61. The range was from 0.44 to about 0.72, and again the mean approached the classical value of two-thirds. However, the wide range prohibits the use of this figure as an estimate for all subjects. Adoption of this average result could lead to a gross overstressing (66:46, implying that the permissible value could be overstepped by as much as 44 percent).

Discussion of Results

Few generalizations can be made because of the limited scope of the examples quoted. The data was collected from comparatively young subjects. In this context it should be noted that

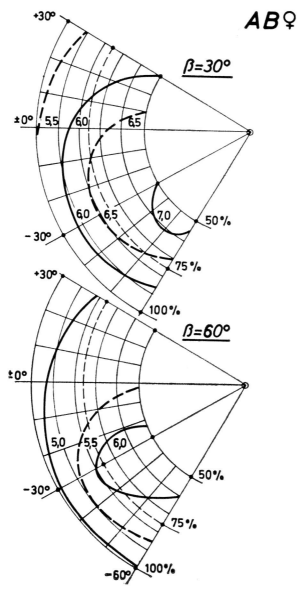

FIGURE 4-7. Isodynes of the maximum Abduction Push AB in a vertical plane with angle of yaw β = 30 and 60 degrees (strengths expressed in kiloponds).

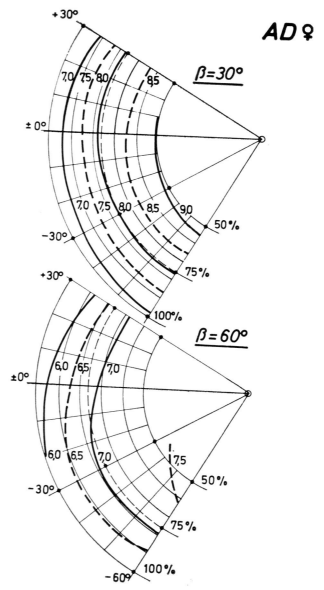

FIGURE 4-8. Isodynes of the maximum Adduction Pull AD in a vertical plane with angle of yaw $\beta = 30$ and 60 degrees (strengths expressed in kiloponds).

many experiments have confirmed that the maximum strength of the female does not begin to decline until she has reached the age of fifty-five; this in marked contrast with the deterioration in performance over a long time span. Throughout the course of active life, her maximum strength remains practically constant.

The second important point of discussion concerns the constant vertical position of the hand grip of the dynamometer and the close relationship between adjustment of the longitudinal axis of the hand grip relative to the axis of the forearm and the value of isometric strength reached. In most of the arm reaches studied, the chosen orientation of the hand grip corresponded to the transmission of force (with the exception of certain cases of vertical strength). At this point another question emerges, namely the optimal limb posture and the optimal hand grip for the most effective exertion of strength. There is a need for further basic research before these problems can be solved satisfactorily. This research is needed in order to determine the correlation between each point of application and the corresponding performance of each task, that is, the optimal limb and grip positions. Experiments relating to this topic have been started, but they are not sufficiently advanced to indicate what the results may be. At present an attempt is being made to secure uniformity and comparability by keeping the position of the hand grip unchanged throughout the complete range of arm movements that are being studied.

There are indications that the biomechanical criteria mentioned above are not the sole determinants of the capacity of women for physical work. Other factors include fatigue, training, motivation, and so on.

Summary

The foregoing results are based on measurements of the strength of ten females between seventeen and twenty-four years of age. This paper discusses the method used as well as the results obtained for several typical types of load: maximum lifting strength of both arms, foot pressure exerted by the right leg from a sitting position, central push and pull of the arm, and adduction pull and abduction push of the arm within arm reach and from a standing position. The results have been compared with data previously obtained on men using identical methods. The coefficients of variation for women correspond with those for the men. The results have been analyzed from both theoretical and practical viewpoints, and the data obtained have confirmed the value of standard and comparable research methods.

A knowledge of the maximum isometric strength of women has great significance for two reasons. On a theoretical level it establishes a basis for further research into biomechanics and provides a survey of the mechanical capacity of the musculature in women. On a practical level the endurance under static stress can be determined by assuming it is a fixed percentage (15%) of the maximum value (4).

Ergonomics applies such knowledge of maximum strength to a number of ends. In general, the effort required for work is matched to the capacity available. The demands made by work are apportioned and estimated on the basis of the known maximum strength. The appropriate organization of work over time with suitable rest pauses is also based on a knowledge of maximum strengths. The same applies to the choice of correct body posture and optimal working methods. The efficient layout of the work place and the design of machine controls all require that the biomechanical capacity of the human body should be taken into account.

References

1. HETTINGER, TH. MD: *Physiology of strength.* Springfield, Charles C Thomas, 1961.

2. ROHMERT, W.: Ermittlung von Erholungspausen für Statische Arbeit des Menschen. *Int Z Angew Physiol, 18*:122-164, 1960.

3. ROHMERT, W.: Die Armkräfte des Menschen im Stehen bei verschiedener Körperstellung. *Int Z Angew Physiol, 18*:175-190, 1960.

4. ROHMERT, W.: Statische Haltearbeit des Menschen. Sonderheft der *REFA-Nachrichten.* Berlin, Köln, Frankfurt (Main), Beuth-Vertrieb GmbH, 1960.

5. ROHMERT, W.: Untersuchung statischer Haltearbeiten in achtstündigen Arbeitsversuchen. *Int Z Angew Physiol,* 19:35-55, 1961.

6. ROHMERT, W., and HETTINGER, TH.: Körperkräfte im Bewegungsraum. *RKW-Reihe "Arbeitsphysiologie—Arbeitspsychologie."* Berlin, Köln, Frankfurt(Main), Beuth-Vertrieb GmbH, 1963.

7. ROHMERT, W., and HETTINGER, TH.: Arbeitsgestaltung und Muskelermüdung. *RKW-Reihe "Arbeitsphysiologie—Arbeitspsychologie."* Berlin, Köln, Frankfurt(Main), Beuth-Vertrieb GmbH, 1963.

8. ROHMERT, W., and NEUHAUS, H.: Der Einfluß verschiedener Ruhelänge des Muskels auf die Geschwindigkeit der Kraftzunahme durch isometrisches Training. *Int Z Angew Physiol,* 20:498-514, 1965.

9. ROHMERT, W.: *Maximalkräfte von Männern im Bewegungsraum der Arme und Beine.* Köln und Opladen, Westdeutscher Verlag, 1966.

10. ROHMERT, W.: Untersuchung über Muskelermüdung und Arbeitsgestaltung. *Schriftenreihe "Arbeitswissenschaft und Praxis"* Berlin, Köln, Frankfurt(Main), Beuth-Vertrieb GmbH, 1967.

11. WHITNEY, R.J.: The strength of the lifting action in man. *Ergonomics,* 1:101-128, 1958.

Chapter 5

ISOMETRIC EXERCISE AND GAINS OF MUSCLE STRENGTH

Phillip J. Rasch

In the late 1920's and early 1930's students at Springfield College conducted a number of studies which demonstrated that it was possible to increase strength by the use of short static contractions. This theory was also the rationale for a highly advertised mail-order course in strength development. Otherwise, isometric training received little attention in the United States until publication of a paper by Müller (29), in 1957, in which he stated that there was no better way to increase muscular strength than by exerting a short contraction of about one-half a muscle's maximal strength once a day. Actually this same argument had been expressed in a more prescriptive form in an earlier article in German, in which Hettinger and Müller contended that a single daily effort maintained for six seconds at about two-thirds the muscle's maximal strength would increase strength at an average rate of 5 percent per week. This outcome could not be improved by the use of greater force, frequency, or duration.

They attributed this training effect to the fact that static work created particularly unfavorable conditions for oxygen metabolism and suggested that this was the stimulus to which the muscle responded. Later, Hettinger wrote that "the maximum improvement in the strength of the muscle group being trained can be obtained by giving daily one maximum voluntary isometric muscle contraction against a resistance for one or two seconds" (17). However, he conceded that the results are affected by the muscle group involved and by the age and sex of the subjects.

Note: The opinions or assertions contained herein are the private ones of the writer and are not to be construed as official or reflecting the views of the Navy Department or the naval service at large.

Muscles which are used the most strenuously in day-to-day work respond to training by increasing in muscular strength more slowly than the muscles that are used less frequently; the response is also slower in women and older individuals than in men and younger people (30).

These pronouncements received a very mixed reception. Those who saw in them a method of getting strong with almost no effort and entrepreneurs who recognized an opportunity to sell courses, books, or apparatus welcomed them as a revelation. The scientific community, however, was critical of the lack of satisfactory physiological bases, controlled studies, and statistical evaluation. It would appear that their scepticism was justifiable, since work by other scientists largely failed to confirm Hettinger and Müller's original claims.

Morehouse, Rasch, and O'Connell (27) demonstrated that oxygen deficit was not an agent in increasing strength. They favored the theory that the development of muscular tension was the stimulus to increase of strength. These conclusions have since been accepted by Hettinger (17). However, the "development of tension" theory seems to involve problems of its own. During an isotonic movement the tension developed gradually diminishes as the muscle shortens, presumably resulting from the manner in which energy is liberated during contraction. Accordingly, the tension developed by a muscle is greatest at zero-velocity shortening. If tension is the controlling factor in the development of strength, it is difficult to account for the fact that many subjects make no gains or actually lose strength while on an isometric regimen. Of Hislop's (18) ninety-one subjects approximately twenty showed no improvement after six weeks of training. Of Morehouse's (26) 104 subjects, 24 made no measurable strength gains in nine weeks of training; in fact, 10 of them actually showed losses in strength.

Müller (31) now argues that contraction causes a lasting excitation of an unknown nature in the muscle. This does not diminish in less than twenty-four hours, and it leads to a gradual increase in the cross section and strength of the muscle. Others (13, 16, 18) incline to the opinion that the source of any observed change is within the central nervous system and emphasize the role of motor learning. This is supported by Rose's (39) contention that the amount which can be added at each training period is constant, regardless of the initial strength or weakness of the muscle, and he feels this limitation of response is neurogenic in origin.

Rasch and Morehouse (36) compared the effect of pressing and curling movements with dumbbells with a static movement exerted for the same time (15 sec) at two-thirds of the subject's strength. Strength was measured a) by the use of strain gauges in both exercised and non-practiced positions and b) by a modified Martin breaking-point technique. It was reported that the strength gains in the subjects practicing isotonically were significantly greater than in those employing static contractions; however, in all cases the apparent gains were considerably larger when the subject was tested in a manner similar to that in which he had exercised than when the test was conducted in a position or by a technique that was unfamiliar to him. This emphasizes the effects of learning and of test procedures on the observed results. Brodin likewise found better results with DeLorme-type exercises than with isometric training, and he attributed this to the fact that the absence of movement "might mean an absence of valuable activating stimuli" (9). The problem of the training stimulus and the effect of various other factors on training results remain unresolved.

Repeated bouts of isometric exercise have been shown to be more effective than single bouts. Several investigators have employed as many as 20 to 150 repetitions a day with varying degrees of effectiveness, while a number of others have shown that their subjects improved more when a resistance greater than two-thirds of the muscle's strength was employed.

Morehouse (26) holds that the intensity of the contractions performed is of greater importance than the frequency, although he believes that some individuals must perform ten or more contractions at least four times a week in order to gain strength. Others have demonstrated that a five-day-a-week program is superior to a lesser number in the development of strength.

As a result of studies such as those cited above, Müller and Rohmert (32) now agree with the following:

1. The rate of strength increase is significantly slower with one-a-day contractions at 67 percent of maximal strength and five to forty-five seconds duration than at 100 percent of maximal strength for one second duration.

2. Five to ten daily maximal contractions of four to six seconds each increase strength faster and to a greater extent than do one-a-day contractions of one second.

The Concept of Trainability

One other shift in Müller's concepts has not been fully appreciated by some recent investigators and has been the source of a certain amount of confusion in the literature. He originally defined "trainability" as the increase in strength resulting from training. He now holds that "trainability" is the disposition of a muscle "to respond to repeated contractions of a certain strength, duration, and frequency with an increase in strength" (31). By focusing on the ability of the individual muscle to respond, Müller is able to say that trainability is not influenced by age, sex, or muscle group. This has enabled Müller and Rohmert (32) to argue that investigators who did not observe a significant improvement in strength from static exercise had studied muscles with low trainability. It probably also explains much of the reason why Ward and Fisk (44) found that the increase in strength of the biceps as a result of training was less than half that of the quadriceps and that the latter was more markedly affected by the type of training. The increase in strength was slower when the muscle was trained isotonically, and they attributed this to the fact that it was required to learn a more complex pattern of activity. When extremes of strength are considered, it is certainly true that the closer a muscle approaches its maximal strength, the less the potential development still remaining. Were it otherwise, there would be no limit to a weightlifter's development of strength. It has not been shown, however, that this is necessarily true in the middle and lower ranges of strength. In fact, it is directly contradicted by Morehouse's conclusion that "individuals with diverse initial strength levels increase in strength at the same rate and make about the same gains in isometric strength" (26).

Fleishman's Fitness Factors

The fact that the theory and practice of isometric exercise have undergone such drastic change in the few years since it first became popular has created a problem for the reviewer, since a study conducted under the older concepts might have a different outcome if undertaken today. A second difficulty is that the term "physical fitness" is not a well-defined concept. Asmussen (1) comments that it is an Anglo-Saxon expression which is difficult even to translate into other languages. Most fitness tests are designed to determine objectively how qualified a person is to perform a specific task, but some respected physiologists view fitness as a general condition of the human mechanism and reject any measures of isolated performance. For the purposes of this review it was concluded that an acceptable approach would be to examine the effects of isometric exercise on the fitness factors identified by the analytical and testing procedures of Fleishman (12). These consist of the following:

1. Dynamic Strength—the strength of the limb muscles applied to moving or supporting the weight of the body repeatedly over a given period of time.
2. Static Strength—the ability to exert a maximum force for a brief period of time. Typically this force is exerted against an immovable external object, such as a dynamometer.
3. Explosive Strength—the ability to expend a maximum of energy in one explosive act, as in jumping or projecting some object as far as possible.
4. Trunk Strength—this appears to be a dynamic strength factor specific to the trunk muscles.
5. Extent Flexibility—the ability to flex or stretch the trunk and back muscles as far as possible in either a forward, lateral, or backward direction.
6. Dynamic Flexibility—the ability to make rapid and repeated movements involving muscle flexibility.

7. Gross Body Equilibrium—the ability to maintain body equilibrium without the aid of visual clues.
8. Balance—the ability to maintain balance with the aid of visual clues.
9. Speed of Limb Movement—the speed with which an individual can make rapid ballistic or adjustive movements of arms or legs when accuracy and force requirements are not involved.
10. Gross Body Coordination—the ability of the whole body to perform gross movements. This may depend on central or cortical nervous system activity, and Fleishman concedes that it is not well defined at the present time.
11. Stamina—cardiovascular endurance, represented by the ability to maintain prolonged exertion of the whole body.

Static Strength

Probably the best data we have on the isometric strength of individual muscle groups are those collected by Asmussen and Heebøll-Neilsen (2). There is evidence that static strength tends to be a specific rather than a general phenomenon. Knowledge of one strength does not permit accurate predictions of contralateral or ipsilateral strengths.

Variations in the muscles tested, the sex and physical status of the subjects, training programs, and techniques of testing have been so great that evidence on the training response is often thoroughly confusing. By far the greater part of the research on isometric training has been conducted with dynamometers or other static measuring devices. The majority of studies have compared isometrics with some other form of training. In general, researchers have found that similar increases in muscle strength result from comparable "doses" of isometric and isotonic exercise. For example, Lorback (22) compared a group of subjects participating in a standard weight-training course with a second group who held static contractions for six seconds at two-thirds of their maximal force. He reported that the two methods of training were equally effective. A study by Morgan (28) produced inconclusive results; the subjects exercised one arm with a dumbell and the other with a static pull against a tensiometer. It is possible that cross education was a factor in these experiments. Mathews and Kruse (25) obtained better results from isometric exercise than from a Kelso-Helebrandt ergometer which they used as a training aid.

In spite of some disagreement and the inexplicable failure of some subjects to show strength gains, researchers in general have reported that isometric training produces an increase of strength, particularly when the latter is measured isometrically.

Dynamic Strength

The picture is less clear when strength is measured by dynamic methods. Most investigators agree that dynamic strength measurements are more highly related to motor performance than are static strength measurements. Some, in fact, have questioned the validity of isometric measurements as criteria of the functional activity of skeletal muscle. However, it appears that in any given individual there is a moderate correlation between static and dynamic strength. Correlation coefficients of $r = 0.67$ for quadricep femoris strength (38), $r = 0.62$ for the lower back muscles (7) and $r = 0.77$ for arm flexion (24) have been reported in the literature. Asmussen *et al.* (3) found a correlation of $r = 0.8$ between a person's isometric and dynamic strength, regardless of his state of physical fitness. Part of the reason they are not more closely correlated may be that maximal forces are developed in differing positions with isometic and concentric efforts (41).

It has also been suggested that the development of isometric tension depends on the cross-sectional area of the muscles, whereas isotonic strength and endurance are more closely related to circulatory adaptations. Another factor lies in the technique of the tests themselves. Isometric tests measure force, whereas, isotonic tests measure work; these two factors are obviously not identical.

Most of the studies of dynamic strength have been conducted using dumbells or other weights to provide the resistance. This, of course, fails to meet Fleishman's definition of dynamic strength in that external weights are moved rather than the weight of the body, but it is a reasonable assumption that the two are closely related.

Berger (5) has stated that improvements in static strength do not result in improvement in dynamic strength and vice versa. This is consistent with Orban's (33) finding that dynamometer strength tests do not predict ability in weightlifting. However, other investigators have found little difference in the effectiveness of isometric and isotonic exercise as means of developing strength (8, 23, 28, 35). The available evidence suggests that the practice of isometric exercises will increase dynamic strength but that the increase is less marked when strength is tested by dynamic methods than when static strength tests are used.

Explosive Strength

In physical fitness testing, explosive strength is commonly measured by use of a short run, the vertical jump, or the standing broad jump. All studies (4, 6, 21, 45) known to the reviewer agree that the practice of isometric exercise does not improve either the vertical jump or the standing broad jump, although several investigators reported an increase in strength of the muscles involved. Perhaps the factor evaluated by these jumping tests does not reflect the strength of the muscles measured by the investigators in question.

Trunk Strength

Studies of the effects of isometric exercise on trunk strength are few indeed. Plinske (35) measured abdominal strength by the number of sit-ups that could be performed in two minutes; he reported that weight training produced a significantly greater improvement in strength than isometric exercise. Shefcyk (40) also found that isometric exercises were superior to calisthenics for this purpose. These findings are puzzling, since there seems no reason to assume that the muscles of the trunk would respond to isometric strength exercises any differently than would limb muscles. One is left with the annoying question of whether sit-ups are a satisfactory measure of trunk strength.

Extent Flexibility and Dynamic Flexibility

There is almost nothing in the literature examining the effect of static training on flexibility. Some coaches and team physicians have contended that any exercise done against a resistance that is fixed or which moves only slightly will result in functional shortening of the muscle harmful to the athlete, but the writer knows of no controlled studies to support this claim. Harvill (15) reported that for the most part there was no difference in the effects of isometrics and calisthenics on flexibility or agility.

Speed of Limb Movement

Many investigators have concluded that the speed of movement has little relationship to strength and that the two are reasonably separate entities. In their view, it would seem unlikely that isometric exercise would increase the speed of limb movement unless the resistance to movement was such that strength became a factor. Several studies of isometric exercise support this expectation. Tucker (43) for example, found that isometric training which increased strength had no effect on maximal power, acceleration, or velocity of either resisted or free horizontal movements: Kerns (20) reported similar findings in the case of flexion, extension, and rotary movements of the forearm. Dissenting voices are those of Chui (10) and workers at Louisiana State University and Agricultural and Mechanical College; both argue that gains in isometric strength are accompanied by gains in speed. Swegan (42), on the contrary, observed that the practice of isometrics resulted in a significant loss of speed in flexion and extension of both the elbow and knee, while Rector (37) reported that the practice of isometric contractions significantly improved the speed of lower leg extension but not of lower leg flexion. At the present time it is impossible to reconcile these differences.

Stamina

Müller himself was the first to note that "Heart and circulation are not stressed by static training" (29). Accordingly, it is to be anticipated that tests of stamina would show little or no improvement from isometric training. Hansen reported that the increase in endurance after isometric exercise was relatively small compared with dynamic exercise. He suggested that this form of activity did not increase vascularization (13).

Fleishman's factor analysis failed to reveal the existence of separate muscle endurance factors, and he concluded that it was not "necessary to provide separate measures of muscle endurance in the strength area" (12). Nevertheless, a number of investigators have measured "muscle endurance," interpreted by them as the ability to hold a prolonged contraction against a dynamometer or other immovable external object. Various authors (8, 11, 19) have reported improvement in muscular endurance following isometric training although Swegan had only inconclusive results (42). Since such dynamic exercises as chinning and dipping, riding a bicycle ergometer, and using weights were used to test endurance, Fleishman would probably classify these as tests of dynamic strength rather than of stamina.

Both Marley (23) and Hansen (14) believe that isometric exercise is more effective in the development of isometric endurance and isotonic exercise is more effective in the development of isotonic endurance.

Gross Body Equilibrium, Balance, and Gross Body Coordination

No investigations of the effect of isometric exercises on these factors were found during this review.

Hazards of Isometric Training

Like any other form of exercise, a certain amount of judgment is required when one is attempting to improve fitness by the use of isometric exercises. Some investigators (8, 14, 34) have found that improper use of this type of exercise may result in muscular trauma and decreased performance.

Conclusions

Evaluation of the effects of isometric exercises on physical fitness is confused by differences in the type and intensity of the exercises performed, the age and sex of the subjects, the trainability of the muscles involved, and other variables. Accordingly, conclusions must be drawn with considerable caution, and exceptions to any of them will be easy to cite. While recognizing the hazards of making generalizations, it appears to the reviewer that the following summary can be justified on the basis of the evidence quoted:

Isometric exercise in general

1. Will increase static strength

2. Will increase dynamic strength but to a lesser degree than static strength.

3. Does not affect explosive strength.

4. Probably increases trunk strength.

5. Has no known effect on extent flexibility or dynamic flexibility.

6. Questionably affects speed of limb movement.

7. Does not improve stamina (cardiovascular condition).

8. Has not been studied in relationship to gross body equilibrium, balance, and gross body composition.

9. May result in muscular trauma if improperly used.

References

1. Asmussen, E.: The Physiological Background of Physical Fitness. *Theorie a Praxe Telesné Výchovy.* Supplement to No. 6, Vol. 16, 1968.

2. Asmussen, E., and Heebøll-Nielsen, K.: Isometric Muscle Strength of Adult Men and Women. *Communications from the Testing and Observation Institute of the Danish National Association for Infantile Paralysis, No. 11.* Hellerup, Denmark, 1961.

3. Asmussen, E., et al.: The Relation Between Isometric and Dynamic Muscle Strength in Man. *Communications from the Testing and Observation Institute of the Danish National Association for Infantile Paralysis, No. 20,* Hellerup, Denmark, 1965.

4. Ball, J.R., et al.: Effects of Isometric Training on Vertical Jumping. *Res Quart,* 35:231-235, 1964.

5. Berger, R.A.: Comparison of Static and Dynamic Strength Increases. *Res Quart,* 33:329-333, 1962.

6. BERGER, R.A.: Effects of Dynamic and Static Training on Vertical Jumping Ability. *Res Quart*, 34:419-424, 1963.

7. BERGER, R.A., and BLASCHKE, L.A.: Comparison of Relationships Between Motor Ability and Static and Dynamic Strength. *Res Quart*, 38:144-146, 1967.

8. BRIGHAM, R.J.: The Relative Effectiveness of Three Methods of Muscle Contractions in Developing Muscular Strength and Endurance of the Triceps Muscle. Unpublished Doctor of Physical Education dissertation, Indiana University, 1963.

9. BRODIN, H.: Evaluation of Two Methods for Increasing Muscle Strength. *Acta Orthop Scand*, 33:208-219, 1963.

10. CHUI, E.F.: Effects of Isometric and Dynamic Weight-Training Exercises Upon Strength and Speed of Movement. *Res Quart*, 35:246-257, 1964.

11. DENNISON, J.D., *et al.*: Effect of Isometric and Isotonic Exercise Programs Upon Muscular Endurance. *Res Quart*, 32:348-352, 1961.

12. FLEISHMAN, E.A.: *The Structure and Measurement of Physical Fitness*. Englewood Cliffs, Prentice-Hall, Inc., 1964.

13. HANSEN, J.W.: The Training Effect of Repeated Isometric Muscle Contractions. *Int Z Angew Physiol*, 18:474-477, 1961.

14. HANSEN, J.W.: The Effect of Sustained Isometric Muscle Contraction on Various Muscle Functions. *Int Z Angew Physiol*, 19:430-434, 1963.

15. HARVILL, A.H.: The Relative Effects of Selected Warm-up Experiences on Strength, Agility, Flexibility, and Power. Unpublished Doctor of Physical Education dissertation, Indiana University, 1966.

16. HELLEBRANDT, F.A.: Application of the Overload Principle to Muscle Training in Man. *Amer J Phys Med*, 37:278-283, 1958.

17. HETTINGER, T.: *Physiology of Strength*. Springfield, Charles C Thomas, 1961, pp.31-32.

18. HISLOP, H.J.: Quantitative Changes in Human Muscular Strength During Isometric Exercise. *J Amer Phys Ther Assoc.*, 43:21-38, 1963.

19. HOWELL, L., *et al.*: Effect of Isometric and Isotonic Exercise Programs Upon Muscle Endurance. *Res Quart*, 33:536-540, 1962.

20. KERNS, R.D.: The Effect of an Isometric Training Program Upon Speed of Forearm Muscle Contractions. Unpublished Master's

thesis, South Dakota State College of Agriculture and Mechanic Arts, 1964.

21. LINDEBURG, A., *et al.*: Effect of Isometric Exercise on Standing Broad Jumping Ability. *Res Quart, 34*:478-483, 1963.

22. LORBACK, M.M.: A Study Comparing the Effectiveness of Short Periods of Static Contraction to Standard Weight Training Procedures in the Development of Strength and Muscle Girth. Unpublished Master's thesis, Pennsylvania State University, 1955.

23. MARLEY, W.P.: The Comparative Effectiveness of Isometric Exercise and Isotonic Exercise in the Development of Muscular Strength, Endurance, and Girth. Unpublished Master's thesis, University of Maryland, 1962.

24. MARTENS, R., and SHARKEY, B.J.: Relationship of Phasic and Static Strength and Endurance. *Res Quart, 37*:435-437, 1966.

25. MATHEWS, D.K., and KRUSE, R.: Effects of Isometric and Isotonic Exercise on Elbow Flexor Muscles. *Res Quart, 28*:26-37, 1957.

26. MOREHOUSE, C. A.: Development and Maintenance of Isometric Strength of Subjects With Diverse Initial Strengths. *Res Quart, 38*:449-456, 1967.

27. MOREHOUSE, L.E.: *Physiology of Exercise,* 3rd ed. St. Louis, C. V. Mosby Co., 1959, pp.200-201.

28. MORGAN, W.P.: The Effectiveness of Static Exercise as Opposed to Phasic Exercise for Increasing Muscular Strength and Size. Unpublished Master's thesis, University of Maryland, 1961.

29. MÜLLER, E.A.: The Regulation of Muscular Strength. *J Assoc Phys Ment Rehab, 11*:41-47, 1957.

30. MÜLLER, E.A.: Training Muscle Strength, *Ergonomics, 2*:216-223, 1959.

31. MÜLLER, E.A.: Physiology of Muscle Training. *Rev Canad Biol, 21*:303-313, 1962.

32. MÜLLER, E.A., and ROHMERT, W.: The Speed in Increase of Muscle Strength Through Isometric Exercise. *Int Z Angew Physiol, 19*:403-419, 1963. Office of Naval Intelligence Translation No. 987.

33. ORBAN, W.A.R.: Dynamometer Strength Tests and Performance of Weight Lifters in International Competition. *J Sport Med, 2*:12-16, 1962.

34. PIERSON, W.R., and RASCH, P.J., Injurious Consequences of Max-

imal Isometric Arm Exercises. *J Amer Phys Ther Assoc, 43*:582-583, 1963.

35. PLINSKE, M.D.: A Comparison of the Effects of an Isometric Program A Weight Training Program and an Isometric-Weight Training Program on Strength Development. Unpublished Master's thesis, South Dakota State College of Agriculture and Mechanic Arts, 1963.

36. RASCH, P.J., and MOREHOUSE, L.E.: Effect of Static and Dynamic Exercises on Muscular Strength and Hypertrophy. *J Appl Physiol, 11*:29-34, 1957.

37. RECTOR, L.G.: The Effect of an Isometric Training Program on the Speed of Selected Leg Movements. Unpublished Master's thesis, South Dakota State University, 1964.

38. RICHARDS, D.B.: A Comparison of Cable Tensiometer Strength, 1-RM, and 10-RM Values Obtained in Knee Extension. Unpublished Master's thesis, Michigan State University, 1965, Cited in Berger: Comparison of Static and Dynamic Strength Increases. *Res Quart, 33*:329-333, 1962.

39. ROSE, D.L.: Brief Maximal Isotonic Exercises in the Treatment of Knee Injuries. *JAMA, 171*:1673-1675, 1959.

40. SHEFCYK, D.L.: The Effect of Isometric Contraction and Calisthenic Exercises on Strength Development of Male College Freshmen. Unpublished Master's thesis, South Dakota State College of Agriculture and Mechanic Arts, 1963.

41. SINGH, M., and KARPOVICH, P.V.: Isotonic and Isometric Forces of Forearm Flexors and Extensors. *J Appl Physiol, 21*:1435-1437, 1966.

42. SWEGAN, D.B.: The Comparison of Static Contraction With Standard Weight Training in Effect on Certain Movement Speeds and Endurance. Unpublished Doctoral dissertation, Pennsylvania State University, 1957.

43. TUCKER, R.M.: Effects of Isometric Strength Development on Speed and Power of Resisted and Non-resisted Horizontal Arm Flexion. Unpublished Master's thesis, Pennsylvania State University, 1967.

44. WARD, J., and FISK, G.H.: The Difference in Response of Quadriceps and the Biceps Brachii Muscles to Isometric and Isotonic Exercise. *Arch Phys Med, 45*:614-623, 1964.

45. WOLBERS, P., and SILLS, D.: Development of Strength in High School Boys by Static Muscle Contractions. *Res Quart, 27*:446-450, 1956.

Chapter 6

CELLULAR ADAPTATIONS TO EXERCISE

Philip D. Gollnick

T HE ABILITY to adapt to environmental and metabolic changes is a characteristic common to most animals and particularly mammals. Thus, during cold acclimatization heat production increases and heat loss decreases. Conversely, the mechanisms for heat loss are augmented during heat acclimatization, and heat production declines. Exercise places heavy demands upon several systems that are needed for sustained work. The purpose of this paper is to examine some of the adaptations that occur at the cellular level during chronic exposure to exercise (training); some of these changes may result in an improved capacity of the organism to meet the challenges of heavy work.

Muscular Hypertrophy

One of the most overt responses to training can be an increase of muscle bulk. This phenomenon has been reported in both skeletal and cardiac muscle. Muscular hypertrophy does not occur during all types of training, but only when the work intensity (work/unit time) exceeds that normally experienced by the muscle. One result of the increased size is an increase of strength. Another is that during submaximal contractions the force developed per unit of muscle is reduced. Increases in strength can occur without hypertrophy, probably as a result of an improved ability to recruit individual muscle fibers.

One of the earliest attempts to determine what changes occur in skeletal muscle to produce the increased size was the classical investigation of Morpurgo (39), published in 1897. He was unable to find any change in the number of fibers in the sartorius muscle of dogs after a three-month training program of arduous

112

running. He did, however, demonstrate that the average diameter of the fibers had increased by 55 percent. These findings were subsequently confirmed by Karsner, Saphir, and Todd (31) for cardiac muscle and by Thorner (48) for both heart and skeletal muscle. It was generally concluded from these experiments that the increase in cross-sectional area of muscle was due to an increase in the size of the muscle cells rather than in their number. An early suggestion was made that this increase in size was the result of an increase in the sarcoplasmic fraction of the muscle. In this regard, Holmes and Rasch (29) were unable to find any change in the number of myofibrils per fiber in the sartorius muscle of exercised rats. However, these authors also failed to present clear evidence of muscular hypertrophy after a rather mild seven-week training program.

Helander (25) provided the first indication that changes in muscular components other than the sarcoplasm might account for the increased muscular size after training. He found a 15 percent increase in the myofilamental protein in the gastrocnemius muscle of guinea pigs after a four-month training period of running 1 km per day. Subsequently Denny-Brown (10) reported that a twofold increase in myofibrillar count accompanied a 25 percent hypertrophy of the soleus muscle of the cat after surgical removal of the gastrocnemius. Similarly Goldspink (13) found a threefold to fourfold increase in myofibrillar count in the work-induced hypertrophied biceps brachia of mice.

Comparisons of normal and hypertrophied heart muscle have revealed that the increases in size are the result of both an enlargement of the individual myofibrils as well as by the addition of new myofibrils (46). Richter and Kellner (46) concluded from an examination of the geometrical arrangement of the myofilaments of normal and hypertrophied myocardium that the size of the filaments of the myofibrils was not altered by hypertrophy. They suggested that the increase in myofibrillar size occurs from an addition of new filaments around the periphery of the pre-existing functional units. A direct measurement of the myosin filaments of normal and hypertrophied rat heart muscle by Carney and Brown (7) has also established that there is no increase in the size of these filaments during hypertrophy.

Investigations with heart and skeletal muscle have revealed that there is a rapid synthesis of protein during the process of hypertrophy (12, 19). Goldberg (12) has shown that the protein formed during compensatory hypertrophy in the soleus and plantaris muscles of rats after sectioning of the gastrocnemius tendon is evenly distributed among all of the muscle fractions such as sarcoplasm, myofilaments, and mitochondria. Thus, the newly formed muscle has all the functional capacity of the preexisting muscle.

The stimulus for inducing hypertrophy in muscle, skeletal or cardiac, appears to be an increased tension per unit time (2). Just how this initial stimulus is passed on to the genetic apparatus for protein synthesis is unknown at the present time. However, it is known that the DNA and RNA concentrations of hypertrophied muscle are greater than those of normal muscle (20). In addition, microsomes isolated from hypertrophied muscle have greater RNA concentrations and can support a faster rate of *in vitro* protein synthesis than those from normal muscle (20). Induction of hypertrophy does not appear to be mediated by growth or other hormones, since it can occur equally well in muscles of normal and hypophysectomized animals (11). The specific inducer of hypertrophy, irregardless of its nature, must remain localized within the individual muscle cells, since only the muscles that experience the elevated work load respond with increases in size.

Identification of Hypertrophy

Although hypertrophy of the heart and of other organs is a criterion frequently used to identify the existence of the trained state in animals, it is a phenomenon not easily demonstrated. The principal difficulty arises when fairly wide differences in body weight exist between two experimental groups. A technique that is commonly used to overcome this problem is the use of an

Note: ADP = adenosine diphosphate, ATP = adenosine triphosphate, DNA = deoxyribonucleic acid, RNA = ribonucleic acid, FFA = free fatty acids, and DPNH = reduced diphosphopyridine nucleotide.

organ weight-body weight ratio (organ weight/body weight). The unfortunate choice and wide application of this technique has lead to a great deal of confusion in the exercise literature concerning the effect of exercise on various organs. The organ weight-body weight ratio incorrectly implies that a linear relationship exists between the weight of the body and its organs. This can easily be disproved for an animal such as the rat from the fact that the hearts (or other organs) of 400 gm animals are not twice as large as those of 200 gm animals. This problem becomes especially important in the light of the fact that trained animals frequently are lighter and have less body fat than sedentary controls. In many instances the hearts of two groups of animals may be nearly identical, but because the trained animals are lighter, their organ weight ratios are greater and they are declared to have cardiac hypertrophy. This problem has been discussed at some length by Heroux and Gridgeman (26), who have suggested the use of regressed rather than actual or ratio weights. Another and perhaps better technique is to make a log-log plot of the organ weight against body weight for the control group and then determine whether similar plots for the experimental group fall outside the confidence limits of this regression line. The readers are referred to an excellent paper by Stahl (47) for additional material concerning the relationship of body weight to organ weight in mammals.

Metabolic Changes in Muscle

Investigations concerning possible adaptative responses in the metabolic capacity of heart and skeletal muscle to training have produced conflicting results. The earliest investigations in this area, conducted in the Soviet Union (see Reference 40 for review to 1945), described rather dramatic increases in the capacity of both the aerobic and anaerobic pathways after training. These studies reported that the succinic dehydrogenase (8) and alpha glycerophosphate (9) activities of the oxidative system and the lactic dehydrogenase (50) and hexokinase activities (40) of the anaerobic system of both heart and skeletal muscle of rabbits and rats were significantly enhanced by a regular program of exercise.

The exercise used for these studies was electrical stimulation of individual muscle groups for some experiments and running or swimming for others. Subsequent experiments by Hearn and his co-workers (14, 21, 22) and by Gould and Rawlinson (18) could not confirm these early findings. In the later experiments training programs composed of various durations of swimming failed to produce any changes in the succinic dehydrogenase, malic dehydrogenase, aldolase, phosphorylase, and creatine phosphokinase activities of rat skeletal muscle. Some small changes in the enzymatic activities of heart ventricle muscle were observed in some of these experiments. The differences in the duration and intensity of the exercise programs used by the Russian workers and those of Hearn and associates and of Gould and Rawlinson could have been responsible for the lack of agreement. Gould and Rawlinson also suggested that the differences might have been due to the methods used for the enzyme assays. In most instances the Russian workers performed their assays with large samples of tissue brei, incubated for long periods of time. In contrast, present-day enzyme assays are usually conducted under optimal conditions for short periods of time. The use of large samples of tissue brei and prolonged incubation may have caused the results to reflect not enzyme concentrations but rather the concentrations of endogenous substrates or other substances in the tissue that produced either activation or inhibition of the enzymes.

Recently Holloszy (27) has reinvestigated the effect of training on the oxidative capacity of rat skeletal muscle. He found that with pyruvate as a substrate and in the presence of non-limiting amounts of ADP and inorganic phosphate, the oxygen uptake by the mitochondrial fraction (mitochondria from 1 gm of fresh muscle) of the animals that had completed a program of strenuous treadmill running was twice that of sedentary control animals. This training program also produced a 70 percent increase in mitochondrial protein per gram of muscle, while the content of cytochrome c and the activities of several enzymes including succinate dehydrogenase, reduced diphosphopyridine nucleotide dehydrogenase, DPNH, cytochrome c reductase, succinate oxidase, and cytochrome oxidase were doubled. The respiratory control index and P/O ratios were not affected by training. Holloszy, however, did not find any change in the succinate dehydrogenase activity of skeletal muscle of rats that had been exercised for six weeks by swimming thirty minutes per day, five days per week. This confirmed the earlier report of Hearn and Wainio (21). It also provided clear evidence that the functional capacity of the oxidative system only responds when it is severely stressed.

In contrast to the earlier report of Chepinoga (9), Holloszy and Oscai (28) have reported that alpha glycerophosphate dehydrogenase activity of rat skeletal muscle does not increase during training. In fact, the activity of the trained animals per unit of protein was less than that of the sedentary controls. These authors have interpreted this as a demonstration that the adaptive response in muscle is specifically related to an increase in the components of the mitochondrial cristae and that the increase in mitochondrial protein following training is not due to a general increase in the size or number of mitochondria. This does not, however, preclude the possibility of an increase in the number of mitochondria during training.

Laguens and associates (32, 33) have demonstrated that a single bout of exercise can produce increases in the mitochondrial mass of dog and rat myocardium. In some instances they observed changes suggesting to them that new components were being added to the existing mitochondria. Gollnick and King (16) have recently presented evidence indicating that both an increase in the size and number of mitochondria occur in rat muscle following a program of strenuous treadmill running. Morgan and co-workers (38) have concluded from changes in the lipid composition of human skeletal muscle following a long-term exercise program that a similar increase in size or number of mitochondria occurs in human muscle.

A point that should be emphasized from the experiments of Holloszy is that the changes in oxygen uptake and enzymatic activities following training closely parallel the increases in mitochondrial protein per gram of fresh muscle. Little or no difference exists between the trained and untrained groups when their oxidative capacities are expressed as activities per milligram of mitochondrial protein. Thus, the increases in oxidative capacity do not result from changes in the specific activity of the existing metabolic apparatus but rather from the addition of more of this material possessing similar characteristics. This is consistent with the knowledge that enzymes are proteins of genetically established functional capacity and that increases in the total capacity of tissue from normal animals occurs by increasing the amount of these materials contained within its cells.

Arcos *et al.* (1) have studied the effects of a prolonged program of group swimming (10-12 rats in a 2-foot diameter tank, swimming continuously for up to 6 hours, 6 days per week) on the mitochondrial mass and metabolic capacity of rat myocardium. They found that after an average of seventy-three hours of swimming, there were no changes in mitochondrial mass (milligram of protein per gram of heart) or respiratory rate (O_2 uptake per milligram of mitochondrial dry weight per hour in the presence of various substrates). For rats that had completed an average of 161 hours swimming, mitochondrial mass was 52 percent greater than that of the controls. Respiratory control had also increased by 62 percent. Although mitochondrial respiration for this group was unchanged when considered per gram of fresh tissue, the combination of an increased mitochondrial protein and the increased respiratory control strongly suggests that the oxidative system of the heart can be increased when the metabolic demands are sufficiently high. When the swimming program was prolonged to an average of 610 hours, the mitochondrial mass, respiratory control, and respiratory rate were similar to that of untrained controls. This latter condition may be synonymous with the stable phase of cardiac hypertrophy described by Meerson (37).

From the results of the experiments described above, it is apparent that the oxidative capacity of both heart and skeletal muscle can be significantly increased by training. However, it is important that these results be correctly interpreted when related to the intact organism. Although it has been demonstrated that the oxidative capacity of skeletal muscle can be doubled, similar changes in total body oxygen consumption do not occur following training. The question might be asked as to whether the ability of the muscle to extract oxygen from the blood limits its total consumption in the untrained organism during maximal work. This does not seem to be the case, since the extraction of oxygen from the blood that perfuses the working muscles is nearly maximal during heavy exercise, both before and after training. Thus, additional oxygen must be provided by the circulatory system if a muscle is to increase its oxidative rate during work. It is known that cardiac output is enlarged by training and that increases in total body oxygen uptake closely parallel this change. What then, is the importance of the increase in oxidative capacity of the skeletal muscle? It would seem most likely that such increases would allow individual functional units of the oxidative apparatus to work at a lower percentage of their total capacity during maximal exercise. This would be consistent with the generally accepted hypothesis that during adaptation to a given stress the capacity of the specific system is increased so that when the stress is reencountered, it can be met by an expenditure of a smaller percentage of its total capacity than was previously required.

At the present time there is no definite evidence to indicate that the capacity of the anaerobic system is increased by training. Peter *et al.* (43) have reported that the hexokinase activity of guinea pig muscle is higher after a program of treadmill running. However, more recent experiments by Barnard and Peter (4) reveal that this response, while occurring early in training, does not persist, and after about nine days of running the activity of this enzyme begins to decline. They conclude that this change in hexokinase activity is not a good criterion for the existence of the trained state. Furthermore, Holloszy (personal communication) has not been able to find any change in the phosphofructokinase (a rate-limiting enzyme of glycolysis) activity of rat skeletal muscle after a strenuous training program of treadmill running.

It is not particularly surprising to find that the glycolytic pathway is not augmented by training. After all, even in untrained individuals this system has the capacity to produce very high concentrations of lactate in blood and tissue during heavy work. Further development of such a system would seem unnecessary. The often reported capacity of trained individuals to develop higher blood lactate levels than their untrained counterparts probably is merely a reflection of an improved tolerance to the physical discomforts of heavy exercise.

Myosin Adenosine Triphosphatate Activity

Markarova (36) has reported that the calcium-activated adenosine triphosphatase activity of myosin prepared from rat skeletal muscle can be elevated by training and by various types of exercise. Studies by Hearn and Gollnick (23) and Rawlinson and Gould (45) in which tissue homogenates were used did not confirm this finding. In a subsequent experiment (unpublished data) I was unable to find any significant change in the adenosine triphosphatase activity per unit of myosin protein prepared from trained and untrained rats killed either at rest or after exercise. The purity of these myosin preparations was evaluated from their molecular weights as determined by ultracentrifugation.

Adipose Tissue

Adipose tissue plays a key supportive role by providing substrate in the form of FFA to working muscles during exercise; however, there have been very few investigations to determine its adaptability to training. Parizkova and Stankova (41) have shown that the *in vitro* release of FFA in response to epinephrine is greater for adipose tissue obtained from trained than from untrained rats. In a recent study we (17) have also observed that the responsiveness of isolated fat cell to various concentrations of norepinephrine is enhanced by training. This adaptation is the result of an increased sensitivity of the beta receptor site of the fat cells. Isolated fat cells from the adipose tissue of trained animals also have a greater total lipolytic capacity than those from the adipose tissue of sedentary rats.

Intracellular Components

Glycogen

The concentration of glycogen in the skeletal muscle of man (5) and of animals (44) has been reported to be increased by training. In dogs, muscle glycogen levels are elevated early in the training program and then decline towards normal levels as training is continued. This is similar to the change in hexokinase activity observed by Barnard and Peter (4). This could be indicative of a greater reliance upon oxidative metabolism as the training program is continued. In man the greatest muscle glycogen levels have been observed after heavy exercise followed by a high carbohydrate diet (5). In these experiments only those muscles that were active during the exercise responded with increased glycogen levels. The specific enhancing factor producing the elevation of muscle glycogen during training is unknown. However, Jeffress *et al.* (30) have reported that the glycogen synthetase activity in red and white fibers of guinea pig muscle is elevated after three weeks of treadmill running. The importance of the increased store of glycogen within the muscle is to provide an immediately available substrate for the metabolic apparatus of the muscle.

Phosphocreatine

Phosphocreatine levels in muscle have also been reported to be elevated by training (40). This compound fills the role in muscle of providing a reserve pool of high energy phosphate that can be transferred to ADP to replenish the supply of ATP. Increases in this energy reserve would be important during periods of high intensity work when normal metabolic pathways cannot keep pace with energy consumption.

Minerals

Elevated muscle concentrations of several ions, including calcium and magnesium, have been reported following training (40). The importance of these changes has not been fully elucidated; however, the role of these ions in the initiation of contraction and relaxation could indicate that this is an important phenomenon. Since most of the calcium is sequestered in the sarcoplasmic reticulum of muscle and this tubular system is intimately associated with the control of muscular activity, it would appear that this might be a fruitful area for future research.

Myoglobin

In 1926 Whipple (49) reported that the myoglobin of several muscles of hunting dogs was greater than that of sedentary house dogs. Lawrie (34) subsequently demonstrated that this was not due to differences in the breeds of the dogs but to exercise; he showed that the skeletal muscles of rats that had been trained by running for periods ranging from seventeen to sixty days also contained significantly more myoglobin than did those of sedentary controls. He further demonstrated that this component of muscle could be reduced by prolonged immobilization. Pattengale and Holloszy (42) have recently reported a similar response to training in the skeletal muscle of rats and have shown that the response is restricted to those muscles actually used for the exercise. It has been suggested that one result of an increased myoglobin content of muscle following training is to facilitate the transport of oxygen from the blood into the muscle.

Liver Cholesterol

Chronic exposure to exercise can reduce the concentration of cholesterol in the livers of rats (3, 6, 15). Whether a similar effect occurs in man is unknown. This, however, would appear to be an important effect, since the rate of synthesis, oxidation, and excretion of cholesterol by the liver is the major factor controlling its level in the blood. The hypocholesteremic effect of exercise on the liver is dependent upon the intensity of effort; the training program must be quite vigorous for it to be effective. However, when sufficiently intense, exercise can reduce the liver cholesterol levels of rats fed diets specifically designed to produce either high or low liver cholesterol levels in sedentary animals (15). The mechanism(s) by which exercise influences liver cholesterol concentration is not fully understood. However, it is known that both the excretion and the oxidation of this compound are elevated by exercise (24, 35). Barnard and co-workers (3) have shown that thyroid hormone may be necessary, at least in a permissive manner, for the hypocholesteremic effect of exercise to occur.

References

1. ARCOS, J.C., SOHAL, R.S., SUN, S., ARGUS, M.F., and BURCH, G.E.: Changes in ultrastructure and respiratory control in mitochondria of rat heart hypertrophied by exercise. *Exp Molec Pathol,* 8:49-65, 1968.

2. BADEER, H.S.: The stimulus to hypertrophy of the myocardium. *Circulation, 30*:128-136, 1964.

3. BARNARD, R.J., TERJUNG, R.L., and TIPTON, C.M.: Hormonal involvement in the reduction of cholesterol associated with chronic exercise. *Int Z Angew Physiol,* 25:303-309, 1968.

4. BARNARD, R.J., and PETER, J.B.: The effect of various training regimes and of exhaustion on hexokinase activity of skeletal muscle. *J Appl Physiol,* In Press.

5. BERGSTRÖM, J., and HULTMAN, E.: Muscle glycogen synthesis after exercise: an enhancing factor localized to the muscle cells in man. *Nature, 210*:309-310, 1966.

6. CARLSON, L.A.: Lipid metabolism and muscular work. *Fed Proc* 26:1755-1759, 1967.

7. CARNEY, J.A., and BROWN, A.L.: Myofilament diameter in the normal and hypertrophic rat myocardium. *Amer J Pathol, 44*:521-529, 1964.

8. CHEPINOGA, O.P.: Muscle tissue dehydrogenases in training and fatigue. I. Succinic dehydrogenase. *Ukr Biokhim Zhur, 14*:0-15, 1939.

9. CHEPINOGA, O.P.: Muscle tissue dehydrogenases in training and fatigue. II. Alpha glycerophosphate dehydrogenase. *Ukr Biokhim Zhur, 14*:15-26, 1939.

10. DENNY-BROWN, D.: Experimental studies pertaining to hypertrophy, regeneration, and degeneration. In Adams, R. P., Eaton, L. M., and Shy, A. M.: *Neuromuscular Disorders: Proceedings of Association for Research in Nervous and Mental Disease.* Baltimore, Williams and Wilkins, 1964, pp.147-196.

11. GOLDBERG, A.L.: Work-induced growth of skeletal muscle in normal and hypophysectomized rats. *Amer J Physiol, 213*:1193-1198, 1967.

12. GOLDBERG, A.L.: Protein synthesis during work-induced growth of skeletal muscle. *J Cell Biol, 36*:653-658, 1968.

13. GOLDSPINK, G.: The combined effects of exercise and reduced food intake on skeletal muscle fibers. *J Cell Comp Physiol,* 63:209-216, 1964.

14. GOLLNICK, P.D., and HEARN, G.R.: Lactic dehydrogenase activities of heart and skeletal muscle of exercised rats. *Amer J Physiol,* 201:694-696, 1961.

15. GOLLNICK, P.D., and TAYLOR, A.W.: Effects of exercise on hepatic cholesterol of rats fed diets high in saturated or unsaturated fats. *Int Z Angew Physiol,* 27:144-153, 1969.

16. GOLLNICK, P.D., and KING, D.W.: Effect of exercise and training on mitochondria of rat skeletal muscle. *Amer J Physiol, 216:* 1502-1509, 1969.

17. GOLLNICK, P.D., and WILLIAMS, C.: The effect of training on the lipolytic response of isolated fat cells to norepinephrine. *Physiologist,* In Press.

18. GOULD, M.K., and RAWLINSON, W.A.: Biochemical adaptation as a response to exercise. I. Effect of swimming on the levels of lactic dehydrogenase, malic dehydrogenase, and phosphorylase in muscles of 8-, 11-, and 15-week old rats. *Biochem J,* 73:41-44, 1959.

19. GUDBJARNASON, S., TELERMAN, M., and BING, R.J.: Protein metabolism in cardiac hypertrophy and heart failure. *Amer J Physiol,* 206:294-298, 1964.

20. HAMOSH, M., LESCH, M., BARON, J., and KAUFMAN, S.: Enhanced protein synthesis in a cell-free system from hypertrophied skeletal muscle. *Science, 157:*935-937, 1967.

21. HEARN, G.R., and WAINIO, W.W.: Succinic dehydrogenase activity of the heart and skeletal muscle of exercised rats. *Amer J Physiol, 185:*349-350, 1956.

22. HEARN, G.R., and WAINIO, W.W.: Aldolase activity in the heart and skeletal muscle of exercised rats. *Amer J Physiol, 190:*206-209, 1957.

23. HEARN, G.R., and GOLLNICK, P.D.: Effects of exercise on the adenosine triphosphatase activity in skeletal and heart muscle of rats. *Int Z Angew Physiol, 19:*23-26, 1961.

24. HEBBLINCK, M., and CASIER, H.: Effect of muscular exercise on the metabolism of 4-C^{14} labelled cholesterol in mice. *Int Z Angew Physiol, 22:*185-189, 1966.

25. HELANDER, E.A.S.: Influence of exercise and restricted activity on

the protein composition of skeletal muscle. *Biochem J*, 78:478-482, 1964.

26. Heroux, O., and Gridgeman, N.T.: The effect of cold acclimation on the size of organs and tissues of the rat, with special reference to modes of expression of results. *Canad J Biochem Physiol*, 36:209-216, 1958.

27. Holloszy, J.O.: Effects of exercise on mitochondrial oxygen uptake and respiratory enzyme activity in skeletal muscle. *J Biol Chem*, 242:2278-2282, 1967.

28. Holloszy, J.O., and Oscai, L.B.: Effect of exercise on α-glycerophosphate dehydrogenase activity in skeletal muscle. *Arch Biochem*, 130:653-656, 1969.

29. Holmes, R., and Rasch, P.J.: Effect of exercise on number of myofibrils per fiber in sartorius muscle of the rat. *Amer J Physiol*, 195:50-52, 1958.

30. Jeffress, R.N., Peter, J.B., and Lamb, D.R.: Effects of exercise on glycogen synthetase in red and white skeletal muscle. *Life Sci*, 7:957-960, 1968.

31. Karsner, H.T., Saphir, O., and Todd, T.W.: The state of the cardiac muscle in hypertrophy and atrophy. *Amer J Pathol*, 1:351-373, 1925.

32. Laguens, R.P., Lozada, B.B., Gomez-Dumm, C.L.A., and Ruiz-Beramendi, A.L.: Effect of acute and exhaustive exercise upon the fine structure of heart mitochondria. *Experientia*, 22:244-246, 1966.

33. Laguens, R.P., and Gomez-Dumm, L.A.: Fine structure of myocardial mitochondria in rats after exercise for one-half to two hours. *Circ Res*, 11:271-279, 1967.

34. Lawrie, R.A.: Effect of enforced exercise on myoglobin concentration in muscle. *Nature*, 171:1069-1070, 1953.

35. Malinow, M.R., McLaughlin, P., and Perley, A.: Cholesterol: Treadmill activity accelerates oxidation in rats. *Science*, 160:1239-1240, 1968.

36. Markarova, A.F.: Effect of types of muscular activity on ATPase activity of myosin. *Ukr Biokhim Zh*, 30:230-239, 1959.

37. Meerson, F.Z.: Compensatory hyperfunction of the heart and cardiac insufficiency. *Circ Res*, 10:250-258, 1962.

38. Morgan, T.E., Short, F.A., and Cobb, L.A.: Effect of long-term exercise on skeletal muscle lipid composition. *Amer J Physiol*, 216:82-86, 1969.

39. MORPURGO, B.: Ueber Activitats-Hypertrophie der willkurlichen Muskeln. *Virchow Arch Path Anat, 150*:522-554, 1897.

40. PALLADIN, A.V.: The biochemistry of muscle training. *Science, 102*:576-578, 1945.

41. PARIZKOVA, J., and STANKOVA, L.: Influence of physical activity on a treadmill on the metabolism of adipose tissue in rats. *Brit J Nutr, 000*:325-332, 1964.

42. PATTENGALE, P.K., and HOLLOSZY, J.O.: Augmentation of skeletal muscle myoglobin by a program of treadmill running. *Amer J Physiol, 213*:783-785, 1967.

43. PETER, J.B., JEFFRESS, R.N., and LAMB, D.R.: Exercise: Effects on hexokinase activity in red and white skeletal muscle. *Science, 160*:200-201, 1968.

44. PROCTOR, H.A., and BEST, C.H.: Changes in muscle glycogen accompanying physical training. *Amer J Physiol, 100*:506-510, 1932.

45. RAWLINSON, W.A., and GOULD, M.K.: Biochemical adaptation as a response to exercise. II. Adenosine triphosphatase and creatine phosphokinase activity in muscles of exercised rats. *Biochem J, 73*:45-48, 1959.

46. RICHTER, G.W., and KELLNER, A.: Hypertrophy of the human heart at the level of fine structure: an analysis and two postulates. *J Cell Biol, 18*:195-206, 1963.

47. STAHL, W.R.: Organ weights in primates and other mammals. *Science, 150*:1039-1042, 1965.

48. THORNER, S.H.: Trainingsversuche an Hunder-3. Histologishe Beobachtungen an Herz and Skeletmuskel. *Arbeitsphysiologie, 8*:359-370, 1935.

49. WHIPPLE, G.H.: The hemoglobin of striated muscle. I. Variations due to age and exercise. *Amer J Physiol, 000*:693-707, 1926.

50. YAMPOLSKAYA, L.I.: Biochemical changes in the muscle of trained and untrained animals under the influence of small loads. *Sechenov J Physiol USSR, English Transl, 39*:91-99, 1952.

SECTION TWO

PHYSIOLOGY AND BIOCHEMISTRY
OF WORK

Chapter 7

THE OXYGEN CONDUCTANCE EQUATION

Roy J. Shephard

Introduction

Wнат LIMITS the rate of aerobic metabolism during maximum exercise? Is there a specific "bottleneck" to the several closely linked processes that transport oxygen from the atmosphere to the working tissues or is the supply of energy to the active muscles limited rather by the rate of some biochemical process within the structure of the individual cell? This question has important practical implications for the direction of both research effort and training emphasis, and it has intrigued exercise scientists for several generations. The oxygen conductance equation (5, 41, 42) now offers an interesting theoretical solution to this question under a variety of environmental conditions. The present article surveys the development of the oxygen conductance concept and discusses its practical validity when applied to individual patients; a more detailed review of the magnitude of individual links in the oxygen transport chain is available elsewhere (35, 43).

The Conductance Concept

A conductance ($\dot{G}$) is the reciprocal of the corresponding resistance (R):

$$\dot{G} = \frac{1}{R} \tag{1}$$

For a given flow (I) through the conductance, there is a corresponding pressure gradient (ΔP):

$$I = \dot{G}(\Delta P) \tag{2}$$

If a number of conductances, $\dot{G}_1$, $\dot{G}_2$, $\dot{G}_3$ . . . $\dot{G}_n$ are arranged in

Note: The work of this laboratory is supported in part by research grants from the Directorate of Fitness and Amateur Sport, the Ontario Heart Foundation, and the World Health Organization.

series, then the overall conductance ΣG is given by

$$\frac{1}{\Sigma G} = \frac{1}{G_1} + \frac{1}{G_2} + \frac{1}{G_3} \cdots \frac{1}{G_n} \qquad (3)$$

Further, since the flow through all conductances must be the same, ΔP distributes itself between the individual conductances in inverse proportion to their size; if ΔP_1 is large, this implies that the conductance $\dot{G}_1$ is small.

Applications to Foreign Gas Uptake

The late Dr. Hatch, an engineer with a strong interest in physiology, suggested that the overall process of gas transport could usefully be represented by the mechanical or electrical anology of a series of conductances (16, 17). Hatch was particularly concerned with the uptake of foreign gases such as acetylene and ether, and he partitioned the overall conductance $\dot{G}_{C_2H_2}$ into three series components corresponding to alveolar ventilation ($\dot{V}_A$), the pulmonary diffusing capacity for acetylene ($\alpha\dot{D}_{L,C_2H_2}$), and blood transport

$\dfrac{r}{\lambda\dot{Q}}$, respectively:

$$\frac{1}{\dot{G}_{C_2H_2}} = \frac{1}{\dot{V}_A} + \frac{1}{\alpha\dot{D}_{L,C_2H_2}} + \frac{r}{\lambda\dot{Q}} \qquad (4)$$

In this equation $\lambda_{C_2H_2}$ is the solubility of acetylene in unit volume of blood. $\dot{Q}$ is the effective pulmonary blood flow, and r is equal to $(1 - e^{-\alpha\dot{D}_{L,C_2H_2}\lambda_{C_2H_2}\dot{Q}})$. If concentration gradients are expressed in milliliters per liter of gas, then the uptake of acetylene in unit time ($\dot{V}_{C_2H_2}$) is given by

$$\dot{V}_{C_2H_2} = \dot{G}_{C_2H_2}\,(C_{I,C_2H_2} - C_{\bar{v},C_2H_2}) \qquad (5)$$
$$= \dot{V}_A\,(C_{I,C_2H_2} - C_{A,C_2H_2}) \qquad (6)$$
$$= \alpha\dot{D}_L\,(C_{A,C_2H_2} - C_{\overline{p.c.},C_2H_2}) \qquad (7)$$
$$= \lambda_{C_2H_2}\dot{Q}\,(C_{\overline{p.c.},C_2H_2} - C_{\bar{v},C_2H_2}) \qquad (8)$$

where C_{I,C_2H_2}, C_{A,C_2H_2}, $C_{\overline{p.c.},C_2H_2}$, and $C_{\bar{v},C_2H_2}$ are the respective concentrations of acetylene in inspired gas, alveolar gas, pulmonary capillary blood, and mixed venous blood, and α is a factor converting diffusing capacity from the traditional units of pulmonary physiology (milliliters per minute per millimeter Hg) to the units applicable to the conductance equation (milliliter per liter).

In the case of very soluble foreign gases such as acetylene and ether, $\alpha \dot{D}_L$ is quite large, and to a first approximation this term may be neglected. Furthermore, the ratio $r = \dfrac{C_{p.c.} - C_{\bar{v}}}{C_a - C_{\bar{v}}}$ is close to unity, and in the initial ten seconds or so (4, 27), problems of recirculation may be neglected (in other words, $C_{\bar{v}, c_2 H_2} = 0$).

Application to Metabolic Gas Exchange in Exercise

Equation (4), simplified by assuming $r = 1$ and $C_V = 0$, has found useful application in describing the uptake of foreign gases such as acetylene and ether, both in health (30, 31, 33) and in disease (32). Unfortunately, such simplifications are not possible when describing the respiratory exchange of oxygen and carbon dioxide in maximum exercise. The diffusing capacity is finite, r is substantially less than unity, and we must consider the process of gas transport from the tissue capillaries to the metabolically active sites within the individual cells. An alternative manner of partitioning the overall conductance is thus more appropriate to the respiratory gas exchange (5, 41, 42). It is derived from the basic differential rate equation; this states in simple terms that the rate of gas transfer $\dfrac{\delta m}{\delta t}$ in unit length of capillary is proportional on the one hand to the conductance of this segment $(\delta \alpha \dot{D}_L)$ and the corresponding concentration gradient $(C_A - C_{p.c.})$ and on the other hand to the product of effective pulmonary blood flow $(\lambda \dot{Q})$ and the change of gas concentration within this segment $(\delta C_{p.c.})$. Thus, we may write

$$\frac{\delta m}{\delta t} = \delta \alpha \dot{D}_L \, (C_A - C_{p.c.}) = \lambda \dot{Q} \delta C_{p.c.} \qquad (9)$$

Rearranging equation (9), we obtain

$$\int_0^{\dot{D}_L} \frac{\delta \alpha \dot{D}_L}{\lambda \dot{Q}} = \int_{C_{\bar{v}}}^{C_a} \frac{\delta C_{p.c.}}{C_A - C_{p.c.}} = -\int_{C_{\bar{v}}}^{C_a} \frac{\delta (C_A - C_{p.c.})}{C_A - C_{p.c.}} \qquad (10)$$

Integrating both sides of equation (10) between venous and arterial points, we may write

$$\int_0^{\dot{D}_L} \frac{1}{\lambda} \frac{\alpha D_L}{\dot{Q}} = - \, \mathrm{Log_e} \, \frac{C_A - C_a}{C_A - C_V} \tag{11}$$

and thus

$$\frac{C_A - C_a}{C_A - C_V} = e^{\displaystyle \int_0^{\dot{D}_L} \frac{1}{\lambda} \left(\propto \frac{\dot{D}_L}{\dot{Q}} \right)} = B \tag{12}$$

so that

$$\frac{B}{1 - B} = \frac{C_A - C_A}{C_a - C_{\bar{v}}} \tag{13}$$

In the case of oxygen transport we know from the Fick equation (equation [8]) that

$$\dot{V}_{O_2} = \lambda \, \dot{Q} \, (C_a - C_{\bar{v}}) \tag{14}$$

and by combination with equation (13) we may also write

$$\dot{V}_{O_2} \qquad = \left(\frac{1 - B}{B} \right) \lambda \, \dot{Q} \, (C_A - C_a) \tag{15}$$

A parallel mathematical exercise may be applied to diffusion in the active tissues. By analogy with equation (12) an expression K is derived such that

$$K = e^{\displaystyle \int_0^{\dot{D}_t} \frac{1}{\lambda} \left(\propto \frac{\dot{D}_t}{\dot{Q}} \right)} \tag{16}$$

where $\alpha \, \dot{D}_t$ is the average diffusing capacity of the tissues, considered as a single homogenous oxygen sink. Again, by analogy with equation (13)

$$\frac{K}{1 - K} = \frac{C_{\bar{v}} - C_t}{C_a - C_{\bar{v}}} \tag{17}$$

Combining equations (14) and (17) we obtain

$$\dot{V}_{O_2} = \left(\frac{1 - K}{K} \right) \lambda \, \dot{Q} \, (C_{\bar{v}} - C_t) \tag{18}$$

It is then a simple matter to partition the overall conductance $\dot{G}_{O_2}$ into four series components representing, respectively, alveolar ventilation, the interaction between pulmonary diffusion and blood transport, blood transport, and the interaction between tissue diffusion and blood transport:

$$\frac{1}{\dot{G}_{O_2}} = \frac{1}{\dot{V}_A} + \left(\frac{B}{1-B}\right)\frac{1}{\lambda\dot{Q}} + \frac{1}{\lambda\dot{Q}} + \left(\frac{K}{1-K}\right)\frac{1}{\lambda\dot{Q}} \quad (19)$$

Limitations of the Oxygen Conductance Theory

There are many limitations to such a simplified representation of the cardiorespiratory system. As in many other areas of human physiology, body mechanisms are more complex than any practical physical analogy to which they can be constrained. Some of the more obvious problems may be listed as follows:

1. Gas is not necessarily transferred between the terminal points of individual conductances. Thus, much of the oxygen leaves the tissue capillaries before the end-point of blood transport ($C\bar{v}_{,O_2}$) is reached.

2. The lungs are represented as a single equivalent chamber with effective values of $\dot{V}_A$ and $\lambda\dot{Q}$ determined by the spatial and temporal matching of ventilation and perfusion. Application of the conductance equations to a more complicated ("nine slice") model of the lung is considered later in this chapter.

3. Both $\alpha\dot{D}_L$ and $\alpha\dot{D}_t$ are complex quantities that include components relating to a) the rate of reaction θ between the gas and the capillary blood volume V_c and b) the membrane characteristic $\alpha\dot{D}_M$. Thus,

$$\frac{1}{\alpha\dot{D}_L} = \frac{1}{\alpha\dot{D}_M} + \frac{1}{\theta V_c} \quad (20)$$

Further, neither $\alpha\dot{D}_L$ nor $\alpha\dot{D}_t$ are independent of $\dot{Q}$. An increase of cardiac output may distend existing capillaries or it may open up new vessels. In either case there may be an increase in both the surface available for diffusion ($\alpha\dot{D}_M$) and the capillary blood volume (V_c).

4. The tissues are assumed to behave as a single oxygen "sink," represented by an equivalent "diffusing capacity" and terminal oxygen concentration. The magnitude of the conductance term describing the interaction between tissue diffusion and blood transport is large during exercise (see below), and accordingly,

errors incurred by the assumption of a homogenous tissue sink
are small.

5. The solubility factor λ is a constant for most gases. However, the properties of hemoglobin are such that λ changes continuously during the passage of blood through the pulmonary and tissue capillaries. This has two consequences: a) The value of λ required for calculation of the blood transport conductance $\lambda \dot{Q}$ is the average slope of the oxygen dissociation curve between arterial and mixed venous points; to the extent that the arterial point is displaced by changes in alveolar ventilation, $\dot{V}_A$ and $\lambda \dot{Q}$ are thus interdependent. b) The value of λ needed for the calculation of B and of K is an integral related, respectively, to diffusion in the pulmonary and the tissue capillaries ($\int_0^{\dot{D}_L} \dfrac{1}{\lambda}$ and

$\int_0^{\dot{D}_t} \dfrac{1}{\lambda}$, respectively). A nomogram is now available (42) that

permits the estimation of $\int_0^{\dot{D}_L} \dfrac{1}{\lambda}$ from a knowledge of the ratio

$\dot{D}_L/\dot{V}_{o_2}$ and the alveolar gas tension.

6. There is no guarantee that a large value of $\dot{G}_{o_2}$ is a desirable objective in terms of physical performance. If it is achieved at the expense of a gross increase in respiratory or cardiac work, there is at least a theoretical possibility that the oxygen available for the performance of external work may be less than during more modest respiratory and cardiac efforts.

Despite these limitations the conductance equations provide a convenient framework on which to examine the various factors limiting cardiorespiratory performance.

The Tissue Oxygen Sink

Conditions in the tissue oxygen sink deserve attention for two reasons:

1. Equation (19) is technically difficult to calculate. However, computation becomes much easier if it can be shown that the final (tissue) term is of minor significance.

2. The fourth term of equation (19) is in the zone of demarcation between the traditional physiologist and the biochemist.

If the tissue oxygen pressure is high, then the main limitation to metabolism is presented by biochemical mechanisms; on the other hand, if the tissue oxygen pressure is low relative to ambient air, this implies that performance is limited by physiological rather than by biochemical conductances.

Information on the pressure of oxygen within the active tissues comes from several sources. Millikan (23) observed the behavior of myoglobin pigment during tetanic stimulation of the soleus muscle, and from the reported saturation of the pigment, it has been concluded that the oxygen pressure in the muscle cytoplasm is 3 (22) or 5 (3) mm Hg. Others (7) have excited the DPNH fluorescence and from the oxidation/reduction status of this and other components of the respiratory chain, have concluded that in the resting state cellular metabolism drops to 50 percent of its maximum value when the oxygen pressure is ∼ 1 mm Hg. Experiments with isolated muscle preparations originally indicated a somewhat higher critical oxygen pressure. However, this result was probably due to inadequate perfusion of the muscle; if the flows used are expressed per kilogram of muscle tissue, they fall far below the flows found in exercising human muscle. More recently Whalen and Nair (49) have reported an intracellular pO_2 of 1 to 4 mm Hg in the resting gracilis muscle of the pig, while Stainsby (45,46) has found a venous effluent Po_2 of 6 to 10 mm Hg in muscle consuming 150 ml O_2 per gram of tissue per minute; in a man using 20 kg of muscle tissue, this would be equivalent to an oxygen consumption of 3 liters per minute. Stainsby commented that owing to the relatively slow rate of dissociation of oxygen in the tissue capillaries, the plasma Po_2 may have been somewhat lower than the experimentally recorded value. Others (9) also report an effluent Po_2 of about 6 mm Hg in experiments on the isolated dog gastrocnemius muscle. Somewhat surprisingly, Keul *et al.* (10) found a femoral venous oxygen tension of 22 mm Hg during maximum leg exercise in man; this corresponds to an oxygen content of about 6 ml per 100 ml of blood. In several recent studies the oxygen content of *mixed* venous blood has dropped to 3 to 4 ml per 100 ml during maximum exercise (29, 38); the oxygen content of the mixed venous speci-

men is of course enriched by blood that has perfused the skin
vessels, and an oxygen content of 1 to 2 ml per 100 ml would be
anticipated in blood leaving the active muscles (38). It must
be presumed that the femoral vein receives a substantial proportion of its total blood flow from the superficial veins during
maximum exercise.

It is difficult to establish a simple model to describe tissue
diffusion. A common approach is to assume the validity of
Krogh's simple cylinder (21); this permits either a calculation
of the minimum intercapillary distance compatible with metabolism or (given the intercapillary distance) the mean tissue Po_2.
An alternative is to apply the Bohr integration procedure as used
in the lungs; it is then necessary to assume a uniform tissue Po_2
determined by cellular metabolism.

The present author has used the second (Bohr integration)
approach. To the extent that the tissue Po_2 is nonuniform, the
tissue-diffusing capacity is *under*estimated; however, since the
underestimate is itself larger than the other conductances in the
oxygen transport chain, this is not a great problem. Let us consider a typical exercising man. The pulmonary venous oxygen
tension is 115 mm Hg, the oxygen tension in the muscle veins is
5 mm Hg, and equilibration between the tissue capillaries and the
peripheral oxygen sink is fairly complete, so that a tissue oxygen
tension of 4.5 mm Hg may be assumed. Applying a modified*
Bohr integration procedure, the mean oxygen tension in the
tissue capillaries is about 17.5 mm Hg, implying an average
gradient of some 13 mm Hg between the tissue capillaries and
the first link of the oxygen transport chain within the cytoplasm
of the active tissues. For a relatively sedentary young man with
a maximum oxygen intake of 3.3 liters per minute STPD, the
maximum diffusing capacity of the tissues is thus about 256 ml
per minute per millimeter Hg or in the conductance units, 181

liter per minute STPD. The integral $\int_{0}^{\dot{D}_t} \dfrac{1}{\lambda}$ amounts to about

---

*A modified Bohr integration takes account of a) the *in vivo* "physiological"
oxygen dissociation curve and b) the effect of oxygen tension on the rate of reaction θ and thus the diffusing capacity.

0.57, and since some 75 percent of the maximum cardiac output of perhaps 21 liters per minute is directed to the active tissues, we may put

$$K = e^{-\int_0^{\dot{D}_t} \frac{1}{\lambda}\left(\frac{\alpha \dot{D}t}{\dot{Q}}\right)} = e^{-0.57\left(\frac{181}{16}\right)} = 0.0016$$

Evidently, $\left(\frac{K}{1-K}\right)\frac{1}{\lambda\dot{Q}}$ is a negligible fraction of $\frac{1}{\lambda\dot{Q}}$, and this term may be discounted in subsequent calculations.

The total gradient of oxygen pressure from the atmosphere to the working tissues is normally 150 mm Hg. Since at least 145 mm of this total is developed across physiological conductances, it seems fair to conclude that the maximum oxygen intake is normally limited by physiological rather than by biochemical processes. This view is not negated either by displacement of the DPN/DPNH system in the direction of an increased redox potential by exercise (19) and physical training (11) or by an increase in muscle mitochondria with training (11, 18, 20). An improvement of muscle perfusion secondary to exercise or training could increase the biochemical component of oxygen impedance from (say) 3 to 5 percent of the whole, while leaving it a small percentage of the total impedance. Further, it can be argued that an increased mitochondrial density is of benefit to the body even if the biochemical component of oxygen impedance is small; there is a small gain in overall oxygen conductance, and (perhaps more importantly) glycolytic mechanisms would be spared in just submaximal work.

A Nomogram for the Integration of λ

If the basic conductance equation is reduced from four to three terms, we are left with the awkward nonlinear function B

$$= e^{-\int_0^{\dot{D}_L} \frac{1}{\lambda}\left(\frac{\alpha \dot{D}_L}{\dot{Q}}\right)}$$

, describing the interaction between diffusion and blood transport within the lungs. Fortunately, a nomogram

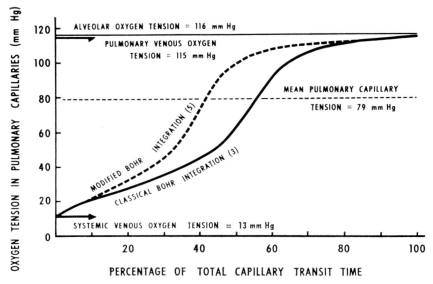

FIGURE 7-1. Oxygen tension within the pulmonary capillary plotted in relation to percentage of the total capillary transit time (42). (Courtesy of the editor and publisher, *Int Z Angew Physiol.*)

is now available for the estimation of $\int_0^{\dot{D}_L} \frac{1}{\lambda}$ (42). This is based on the fact that each curve of pulmonary capillary oxygen tension against percentage of total capillary transit time (**Fig. 7-1**), and the corresponding curve of $\frac{1}{\lambda}$ against percentage of total transit time (Fig. 7-2) may be equated with certain specific values of alveolar, pulmonary venous, and systemic venous oxygen tension. It is further assumed that in maximum exercise the mixed venous oxygen tension approaches a low and relatively constant limiting value of 12 to 13 mm Hg determined by the relative perfusion of skin and muscle and that the end-capillary gradient is small, so that to a first approximation, alveolar and pulmonary venous gas tensions may be assumed equal. The

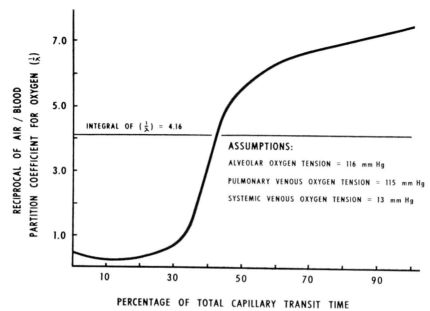

FIGURE 7-2. The reciprocal of the slope of the oxygen dissociation curve $\frac{1}{\lambda}$ plotted in relation to percentage of the total capillary transit time (42). (Courtesy of the editor and publisher, *Int Z Angew Physiol.*)

prime determinant of $\int_{0}^{\dot{D}_{L}} \frac{1}{\lambda}$ is thus the alveolar oxygen tension. Each integral also corresponds to a unique mean pulmonary capillary oxygen tension and thus to a unique ratio of $\dot{D}_{L}$ to $\dot{V}_{O_2}$ max. It is thus possible to plot isopleths of $\int_{0}^{\dot{D}_{L}} \frac{1}{\lambda}$ —or more conveniently its reciprocal—against the corresponding ratio of diffusing capacity to maximum oxygen intake ($\dot{D}_{L}/\dot{V}_{O_2}$ max) for a series of alveolar oxygen tensions, as illustrated in Figure 7-3.

Typical Sea-Level Conductances

We will now consider values appropriate to the oxygen

conductance equation under conditions of maximum performance at "sea-level." The majority of physiologists have been content to submit their colleagues and other experimental subjects to rather modest levels of exercise, and there is surprisingly little data that refers to maximum effort (35, 43).

The maximum ventilatory conductance (36) is greater than the ventilation normally seen in maximum exercise and may amount to as much as 75 percent of the fifteen-second maximum voluntary ventilation (about 105 liters/min STPD in a sedentary young man, and about 130 liters/min STPD in a young athlete[*]). Alveolar ventilation is normally some 75 percent of external ventilation in maximum exercise but may drop to about 70 percent if ventilation is increased to the maximum level that can be sustained (Shephard, To be published). Thus, the appropriate values of alveolar ventilation for the conductance equation are 70 percent of 105 and 130 liters per minute, about 73 liters per minute STPD in a sedentary young man, and about 91 liters per minute STPD in an athlete.

The pulmonary diffusing capacity increases with work load to the highest levels of exercise (2). During maximum effort we have found a carbon monoxide diffusing capacity ($\dot{D}_{L,co}$) of some 40 ml per minute per millimeter Hg in sedentary subjects and 62 ml per minute per millimeter Hg in athletes. The corresponding values for oxygen diffusion expressed in conductance units ($\alpha \dot{D}_{L,o_2}$) are 35 and 54 liters per minute STPD, respectively. The $\dot{D}_L/\dot{V}_{o_2}$ ratio thus amounts to about 14 in both sedentary and athletic subjects. The corresponding alveolar oxygen tensions are about 115 and 112 mm (42); given this information it is a simple

matter to read the corresponding integrals of $\displaystyle\int_0^{D_L} \frac{1}{\lambda}$ (0.32 and 0.38) from Figure 7-3.

The maximum cardiac output of sedentary subjects is about 20 to 25 liters per minute, while that of athletes is 30 to 35 liters per minute. Only a small part of this total is "wasted" in frank

_____

[*]Note that for the purpose of the conductance equation, gas volumes are expressed as liters per minute STPD and *not* liters per minute BTPS.

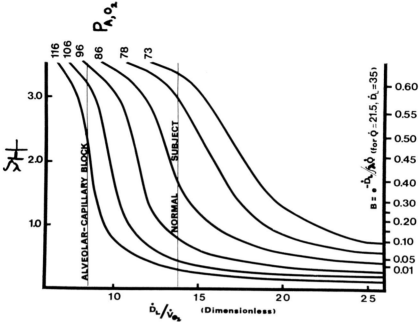

FIGURE 7-3. The relationship between the reciprocal of $\int_{0}^{D_L} \dfrac{1}{\lambda}$ and the ratio of diffusing capacity to maximum oxygen intaxe $(\dot{D}_L/\dot{V}o_2$ max$)$. Normal curves for selected alevolar oxygen tensions (42). (Courtesy of editor and publisher, *Int Z Angew Physiol.*)

venous-arterial shunts and overperfusion of underventilated alveoli; since arterial oxygen saturation rarely drops below 90 percent, we may arbitrarily set the amount of such shunts at 6 to 7 percent of the cardiac output.

The average value of the solubility factor λ between arterial and venous points of the oxygen dissociation curve is about 1.16:

$$\frac{197\text{-}30 \text{ ml/liter}}{115\text{-}13 \text{ mm Hg}} \times \frac{(760\text{-}47)}{1000} = 1.16 \qquad (21)$$

This figure is based on an arterial oxygen content of 197 ml per liter, a mixed venous oxygen content of 30 ml per liter, an arterial oxygen tension of 115 mm Hg, a mixed venous oxygen tension of 13 mm Hg, and a barometric pressure of 760 mm Hg.

Taking equation (19) and omitting the final term, we are now in a position to insert normal values for maximum exercise under "sea level" conditions. In the sedentary subject

$$\frac{1}{\dot{G}_{O_2}} = \frac{1}{73} + \frac{0.0061}{24.9} + \frac{1}{24.9}$$

$$(\dot{V}_{O_2} \text{ max} = 3.55 \text{ liter/min STPD} \tag{22}$$

and in the athlete

$$\frac{1}{\dot{G}_{O_2}} = \frac{1}{91} + \frac{0.0104}{35.9} + \frac{1}{35.9}$$

$$(\dot{V}_{O_2} \text{ max} = 48.8 \text{ liters/min STPD}) \tag{23}$$

It is immediately apparent that the main limitation to oxygen transport in both classes of subject is the third term $(\lambda \dot{Q})$; the first term (maximum alveolar ventilation) has a much smaller influence on oxygen conductance, and the second term (describing the interaction between pulmonary diffusion and blood transport) plays a negligible role. The equations suggest that the overall conductance can be increased either by an increase of λ (increased blood hemoglobin concentration) or by an increase of $\dot{Q}$ (an increase of stroke volume with little change of maximum heart rate). However, such an analysis ignores certain complications, particularly the influence of an increased red cell count on blood viscosity and thus maximum cardiac output. It also leaves unanswered such questions as the relative importance of central factors (cardiac power, depressor reflexes) and peripheral limitations ("nipping" of major vessels by the fascia of contracting muscles, adequacy of the intramuscular capillary bed, pooling of blood in the veins of inactive limbs) as determinants of the maximum cardiac output.

Validity of the Oxygen Conductance Equation

The values for maximum oxygen intake calculated by the conductance equations (22) and (23) (3.55 liters/min STPD in a sedentary young man, 4.88 liters/min STPD in a young athlete) are obviously of the correct general order. We must now consider how accurately the calculated value corresponds with the directly measured maximum oxygen intake of individual subjects. In children ten to twelve years of age, there is a fair scatter about

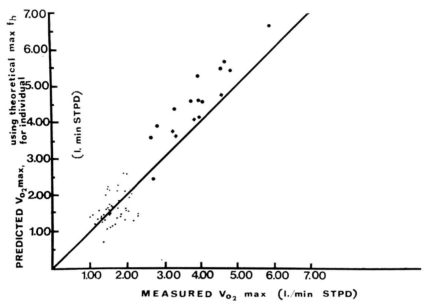

FIGURE 7-4. The relationship between the directly measured maximum oxygen intake and that predicted by use of the conductance equation. • Children aged 10-12, ● Young adults, ⋅ data of Saltin *et al.* (Courtesy of the editor and publisher, *Int Z Angew Physiol* [44].)

the line of identity but no systematic discrepancy (Fig. 7-4). In adults, on the other hand, the present author's data overestimate the directly measured maximum oxygen intake by some 16 percent (44). It is difficult to dismiss this as a technical error in the measurement of alveolar ventilation or cardiac output, since the data of other authors also yields an overestimate of the directly measured value.

Possible bases for a systematic discrepancy are discussed elsewhere (44). Contributions from a dissimilarity of oxygen and CO dead spaces and from temporal oscillations of alveolar gas composition are likely to be small. There is little information on the matching of ventilation, diffusion, and perfusion within the lung during maximum exercise; in general, a mismatching of diffusion and perfusion has the greatest effect on oxygen transport, but it would be difficult to account for more than a 5 percent loss of conductance in any reasonable nine-slice model of the lung (44). It is thus necessary to postulate a substantial mismatching of diffusion and perfusion *within* individual slices of the lung. This may arise in part from differences in length of bronchial pathways (28) and in part from differences in length of the pulmonary capillaries with corresponding variations in capillary transit time (47). However, if the difference in behavior of children and young adults is confirmed, it would seem that the deterioration of function has a pathological rather than a simple anatomical basis. It would indeed be intriguing if the cumulative insults of repeated respiratory infection, air pollutants, and tobacco are already leading to a measurable loss of oxygen conductance in young men twenty to thirty years of age.

The general validity of the oxygen conductance equation is such that it could be used for the prediction of maximum oxygen intake. However, it is unlikely to be used for this purpose, since it is necessary to determine both maximum alveolar ventilation and maximum cardiac output. It is more likely to prove of value in the converse situation, where information on the alveolar ventilation and oxygen intake are available and it is necessary to estimate cardiac output. A second possible application is an overall clinical assessment of the mismatching of ventilation, diffusion, and perfusion within the lungs (based on the discrepancy between the observed and the predicted maximum oxygen intake). Finally, equation (19) allows an appraisal of the overall functional significance of a given impairment of an individual link in the oxygen transport chain; thus, a 50 percent reduction in the maximum voluntary ventilation of a patient reduces oxygen transport by much less than 50 percent.

Maximum Oxygen Intake and the Supply of Oxygen to Active Muscles

The maximum oxygen intake as measured in the laboratory is not determined simply by the consumption of oxygen in the exercising muscles; it includes also the resting metabolism and the oxygen cost of respiratory and cardiac activity.

The turbulent component of respiratory work increases approximately as the square of respiratory minute volume. Thus, although the overall oxygen conductance is increased by an increase of ventilation ($\Delta \dot{V}_{O_2} / \Delta \dot{V}_E$), there is also an increased oxygen usage in the respiratory muscles ($\Delta \dot{V}_{O_2(R)} / \Delta \dot{V}_E$). If the respiratory minute volume is progressively increased, then ultimately the point is reached where $\Delta \dot{V}_{O_2(R)} / \Delta \dot{V}_E$ exceeds $\Delta \dot{V}_{O_2} / \Delta V_E$; any further increase of ventilation then diminishes the oxygen available to the working muscles.

Until recently there have been no figures for the oxygen cost of breathing in maximum or near maximum exercise. Recent data (34) indicate that the quotient $\Delta V_{O_2(R)} / \Delta V_E$ rises from 0.5 to 1.0 ml per liter at rest to about 4 to 5 ml per liter in maximum exercise. However, this is not the main factor limiting the useful increase of ventilation; a more serious problem is created by the decrease in $\Delta \dot{V}_{O_2} / \Delta \dot{V}_E$. This is normally 30 to 40 ml per liter during maximum exercise; however, if a subject further increases his ventilation, the quotient for the added gas exchange rapidly drops to 5 ml per liter or less. Blood leaving the lungs is normally almost completely saturated with oxygen, and little additional oxygen intake can be achieved by a further increase of ventilation (unless there is a concomitant increase of pulmonary blood flow).

In a sedentary young man the critical point where $\Delta \dot{V}_{O_2(R)} / \Delta \dot{V}_E$ exceeds $\Delta \dot{V}_{O_2} / \Delta \dot{V}_E$ is reached at a ventilation of about 130 liter per minute (25, 34). In athletes the maximum cardiac output is greater, and the dramatic fall of $\Delta \dot{V}_{O_2} / \Delta \dot{V}_E$ does not occur until a larger respiratory minute volume is reached; indeed, one of the well recognized characteristics of the athlete is a low ventilatory equivalent and thus a large quotient $\Delta \dot{V}_{O_2} / \Delta \dot{V}_E$.

It would be theoretically possible for an excessive increase of cardiac output to "waste" oxygen intake in the same manner as an excessive hyperventilation. However, in practice this does not seem a real problem. Much of the work of the resting heart is performed against the tension within its walls, and the mechanical efficiency of the cardiac muscle rises dramatically with an increase of cardiac output. Thus, although the work performed is also increased by exercise, the oxygen cost per liter of cardiac output remains at or near the resting figure of 5 ml per liter. The margin between this cost and oxygen carriage ($\Delta \dot{V}_{O_2}/\Delta \dot{Q}$, 150 ml/liter in maximum exercise) is larger than for the respiratory system, and if cardiac output is further increased, there is an almost proportionate gain in the oxygen carried in the bloodstream. The oxygen needs of the myocardium still make an appreciable charge upon the overall oxygen account, but there seems little danger of reaching a critical point where increase in the cardiac output decreases the quantity of oxygen available to the exercising muscles.

Some Applications to Abnormal Environments

How is the oxygen conductance equation modified by a change in ambient pressure? Let us consider first the situation of a man exercising at altitude.

The maximum alveolar ventilation measured at body temperature and pressure and saturated with water vapor is increased (8) because the lowered density of inspired gas diminishes the work of breathing. At moderate altitudes it may thus be possible to develop an almost unchanged STPD ventilation; however, this is poorly sustained because the initial body reserves of CO_2 are smaller, and the elimination of CO_2 proceeds more readily than at sea level. A normal ventilation is developed at the expense of an increased mechanical movement of the chest wall and diaphragm, and if the altitude is further increased, a point is reached ultimately where a further increase of BTPS ventilation cannot occur, and the STPD volume falls.

Alveolar ventilation may be improved at moderate altitudes, since a lowering of the inspired oxygen tension decreases the anatomical dead space (24) and increases pulmonary arterial pressure (thus improving ventilation/perfusion relationships in the apical part of the lung [14]).

If diffusing capacity is expressed in the traditional units of the physiologist (milliliters per minute STPD per millimeters Hg), then it is unchanged by acute exposure to altitude (48), although with prolonged residence there may be a gain of 15 to 20 percent reflecting changes in the oxygen-hemoglobin reaction rate θ, the hemoglobin level, and the pulmonary capillary blood volume.

The units of the conductance equation are milliliters per minute for a concentration gradient of 1 ml per liter (that is, liters per minute STPD), and if expressed in these terms, diffusing capacity decreases in direct proportion to the decrease of dry gas pressure.

The integral $\int_0^{\dot{D}_L} \frac{1}{\lambda}$ is also modified by the decrease of alveolar oxygen pressure (Fig. 7-3); under these conditions the blood spends a larger part of the total capillary transit time in the unsaturated state and $\int_0^{\dot{D}_L} \frac{1}{\lambda}$ is decreased, thereby exaggerating the problems created by the fall of $\alpha \dot{D}_L$ and making the second term of equation (19) an important determinant of overall conductance.

The maximum cardiac output is changed little at moderate altitudes, but above five to six thousand feet there is a decrease in maximum pulse rate (26), and at altitudes of ten to twelve thousand feet there may also be some decrease of stroke volume (15). On the other hand, subjects are restricted to the steeper part of their oxygen dissociation curve, thereby increasing the effective value of the solubility coefficient λ. With prolonged residence at altitude, λ is further increased by the rise in hemoglobin content of unit volume of blood.

Detailed calculations of the oxygen conductance equation for an altitude of 7350 feet were made at the time when the Olympic Games were held in Mexico City (42). In a typical sedentary subject, who made little attempt to increase chest movements during maximum exercise, the three terms were as follows:

$$\frac{1}{\dot{G}_{O_2}} = \frac{1}{53} + \frac{1.04}{42.7} + \frac{1}{42.7}$$

$$(\dot{V}_{O_2} \text{ max} = 2.79 \text{ liter/min STPD}) \qquad (24)$$

In an athlete who was prepared to increase his chest movements deliberately to an uncomfortable level, the corresponding terms were

$$\frac{1}{\dot{G}_{O_2}} = \frac{1}{90} + \frac{1.04}{61.2} + \frac{1}{61.2}$$

$$(V_{O_2} \text{ max} = 4.18 \text{ liters/min STPD}) \qquad (25)$$

Direct measurements of maximum oxygen intake in Mexico City have shown a slightly smaller loss (8%-10%, Reference 6) than would appear from a comparison of equations (22) and (23) with equations (24) and (25). However, when the many approximations involved in the conductance equations are considered, the agreement between theory (14% loss) and practice (8%-10% loss) is probably satisfactory.

At the altitude of Mexico City (7350 feet), the conductance of the blood transport term is effectively doubled by the increase in λ, and this almost exactly compensates for the introduction of a significant second term describing the interaction of diffusion and blood transport. However, 7350 feet is a rather critical altitude for oxygen transport; if the subject is transported to a higher altitude, no compensation is possible through the increase of $\dot{V}_A$ (BTPS) or λ, while $\alpha\dot{D}_L$ and $\dot{Q}$ continue to decrease in direct proportion to the drop in ambient pressure. The maximum oxygen intake thus shows a progressive decrease at altitudes above five to six thousand feet (26).

We may note in passing that a large pulmonary diffusing capacity is advantageous to performance only when the second term of equation (19) is imposing a significant limitation upon oxygen conductance. This situation may arise when the diffusing capacity expressed in conductance units (liters per minute STPD) is reduced by altitude and when the integral $\displaystyle\int_0^{\dot{D}_L} \frac{1}{\lambda}$ is reduced by either altitude or breath-holding. The large pulmonary diffusing capacities reported for swimmers are in part an artefact attributable to the slow rate of breathing in such subjects (1). Nevertheless, the pulmonary diffusing capacity is somewhat larger in athletes than in nonathletes, and training does give a small increase of $\alpha\dot{D}_L$ roughly proportional to the gain in maximum oxygen intake (39). Such changes are of little advantage under normal conditions, but they do facilitate oxygen transport at altitude and during breath-holding.

In a diver operating at depth, changes of the oxygen conductance equation occur in the reverse sense. The volume respired is decreased if expressed under BTPS conditions, and it may also be restricted under STPD conditions because of a gross increase in the turbulent work of breathing. On the other hand, the second term of equation (19) becomes negligible, since a) $\alpha \dot{D}_L$ (liter per minute STPD) increases in direct proportion to the increase of dry gas pressure, and b) the individual is operating on the flattest part of his oxygen dissociation curve with an increase of $\int_0^{\dot{D}_L} \dfrac{1}{\lambda}$.

No problem of oxygen conductance normally arises in the diver, but at extreme depths the reduction of alveolar ventilation may hamper carbon dioxide transport.

Application of Conductance Theory to CO_2 Transport

The oxygen conductance equation (19) can equally be applied to the transport of carbon dioxide from the working tissues to the external environment. Calculations are a little simpler than for oxygen, since the solubility coefficient λ_{co_2} is a more linear function of the CO_2 concentration in the gas phase; taking account of differences of CO_2 solubility in arterial and mixed venous blood, the physiological value of λ_{co_2} is about 5.

The pulmonary diffusing capacity for CO_2 has traditionally been regarded as large; however, this deserves closer examination. Certainly, the membrane diffusing capacity is at least twenty times that for oxygen, or about 2000 liters per minute STPD. However, it is clear from equation (20) that in calculating diffusing capacity, account must be taken not only of membrane diffusing capacity $\alpha \dot{D}_M$, but also the rate of reaction between CO_2 and the red cells. Recent estimates (12) suggest that the reaction rates for CO and CO_2 are rather similar; thus, the maximum value of θV_c for CO_2 is in the range 200 to 400 liters per minute, and $\alpha \dot{D}_{L,co_2}$ is in the range 180 to 350 liters per minute STPD. The integral $\int_0^{\dot{D}_L} \dfrac{1}{\lambda}$ is also much smaller for CO_2 than for oxygen, and the exponent $e^{-\int_{\lambda}^{\dot{D}_L}\left(\frac{\alpha \dot{D}_L}{\dot{Q}}\right)}$ cannot be neglected. The probable upper and lower limits of equation (19) are thus as follows:

$$\frac{1}{\dot{G}_{CO_2}} = \frac{1}{75} + \frac{1}{3} \quad \frac{1}{150} + \frac{1}{150} \quad (26)$$

and

$$\frac{1}{\dot{G}_{CO_2}} = \frac{1}{75} + \frac{1}{15} \quad \frac{1}{150} + \frac{1}{150} \quad (27)$$

A comparison of equations (26) and (27) with equations (22) and (23) reveals that the overall conductance is somewhat greater for CO_2 than for oxygen. This is reflected in the smaller gradient of CO_2 tension from the tissues to the atmosphere (70-80 mm Hg in maximum exercise). Furthermore, CO_2 transport is determined more by the first term (alveolar ventilation) than by the second or third. This has some relevance to the prediction of oxygen consumption during submaximal industrial work. If the experimental conditions are such that cardiac stroke volume remains constant, then the pulse rate will be a fairly accurate reflection of oxygen consumption. On the other hand, ventilation reflects CO_2 output and is only representative of oxygen consumption while the respiratory quotient remains constant. This theoretical analysis is borne out by practical experience of the two methods of estimating oxygen consumption. Pulse rate predictions have their greatest validity between 50 and 90 percent of maximum oxygen intake over a range where it is recognized that the cardiac stroke volume is relatively constant. On the other hand, ventilation-based predictions are most satisfactory at light work loads where CO_2 elimination is not distorted by lactate production (40).

Summary

A conductance equation that integrates the respective contributions of ventilation, diffusion, and blood transport to the exchange of oxygen and carbon dioxide is described. Limitations of the equation introduced by such factors as the nonlinearity of the oxygen dissociation curve and regional inequalities of ventilation, diffusion, and perfusion are discussed; in young adults such inequalities apparently restrict oxygen conductance by as much as 16 percent.

The transport of oxygen at sea level is limited primarily by the blood transport term, effectively the product of hemoglobin level and cardiac output. At altitude, blood transport is improved by restriction of the subject to the steep part of his oxygen dissociation curve, and this tends to compensate for the increased importance of the pulmonary diffusion/blood transport interaction with reduction in ambient pressures. Carbon dioxide conductance is about twice that for oxygen and is limited more by ventilation than by blood transport. Practical applications of the conductance equations are discussed briefly.

References

1. ANDERSON, T.W., and SHEPHARD, R.J.: A theoretical study of some errors in the measurement of pulmonary diffusing capacity. *Respiration, 26*:102-105, 1968.

2. ANDERSON, T.W., and SHEPHARD, R.J.: The effects of hyperventilation and exercise upon the pulmonary diffusing capacity. *Respiration, 25*:465-484, 1968.

3. BARCROFT, H.: Circulation in skeletal muscle. In Hamilton, W. F. (Ed.): *Handbook of Physiology*. Section 2: Circulation. Washington, D.C., American Physiological Society, 1963, vol. 2.

4. BAR-OR, O., SHEPHARD, R.J., and ALLEN, C.L.: Exercise cardiac output of 10-13 year old children. *Proceedings of 16th Annual Meeting, American College of Sports Medicine*. Atlanta, 1969.

5. BEECKMANS, J.M., and SHEPHARD, R.J.: A theoretical basis for the partitioning of maximal cardio-respiratory performance. *Canad J Physiol Pharmacol, 45*:185-190, 1967.

6. BUSKIRK, E.R.: Physiology and performance of track athletes at various altitudes in the United States and Peru. In *International Symposium on the Effects of Altitude on Physical Performance*. Washington, D.C., Athletic Institute, 1967.

7. CHANCE, B.: Cellular oxygen requirements. *Fed Proc, 16*:671-680, 1957.

8. COTES, J.E.: Ventilatory capacity at altitude and its relation to mask design. *Proc Roy Soc [Biol], 143*:32-39, 1954.

9. DI PRAMPERO, P.E., and PIIPER, J.: Quoted by Margaria, R., and

Cerretelli, P. In Falls, H.B. (Ed.): *Exercise Physiology.* New York & London, Academic Press, 1968.

10. DOLL, E., KEUL, J., and MAIWALD, C.: Oxygen tension and acid-base equilibria in venous blood of working muscle. *Amer J Physiol, 215*:23-29, 1968.

11. EDINGTON, D.W.: Pyridine nucleotide concentration and ratios in rat muscle, heart and liver in response to acute and chronic exercise. Ph.D. thesis, Michigan State University, East Lansing, Michigan, 1968.

12. FORSTER, R.E.: Diffusion of gases. In Fenn, W.O., and Rahn, H. (Eds.) *Handbook of Physiology.* Section 3: Respiration. Washington, D.C., American Physiological Society, 1964, Vol. I.

13. GODDARD, R.F.: *The International Symposium on the Effects of Altitude on Physical Performance.* Washington, D.C., Athletic Institute, 1967.

14. GROVER, R.F.: Effects of hypoxia on ventilation and cardiac output. *Ann NY Acad Sci, 121*:662-673, 1965.

15. GROVER, R.F., SALTIN, B., HARTLEY, L.H., and JOHNSON, R.L.: Decreased stroke volume during maximum exercise in man at high altitude. *Fed Proc, 26*:665, 1967.

16. HATCH, T.F., and COOK, K.M.: Partitional respirometry. *AMA Arch Industr Health, 11*:142-158, 1955.

17. HATCH, T.F., and SWANN, H.: Absorption and storage of vapours in relation to cardio-respiratory performance. In Davies, C.N. (Ed.): *Symposium on Inhaled Particles and Vapours.* Oxford, Pergamon Press, 1961.

18. HOLLOSZY, J.O.: Biochemical adaptations in muscle. *J Biol Chem, 242*:2278-2282, 1967.

19. JÖBSIS, F.F., and STAINSBY, W.N.: Oxidation of NADH during contractions of circulated skeletal muscle. *Resp Physiol, 4*:292-300, 1968.

20. KING, D.W., and GOLLNICK, P.D.: Immediate and chronic effects of exercise on the number and structure of skeletal muscle mitochondria. *Proceedings of 15th Annual Meeting, American College of Sports Medicine.* Pennsylvania State, Pa., 1968.

21. KROGH, A: The number and distribution of capillaries in muscles, with calculations of the oxygen pressure head necessary for supplying the tissue. *J Physiol (London), 52*:409-415, 1919.

22. LANDIS, E.M., and PAPPENHEIMER, J.R.: Exchange of substances through the capillary walls. In Hamilton, W.F. (Ed.): *Hand-*

book of Physiology, Section 2: Circulation. Washington, D.C., American Physiological Society, Vol. 2.

23. MILLIKAN, G.A.: Experiments on muscle haemoglobin *in vivo;* the instantaneous measurement of muscle metabolism. *Proc Roy Soc [Biol], 123*:218-241, 1937.

24. NADEL, J.A., and WIDDICOMBE, J.G.: Effect of change in blood gas tensions and carotid sinus pressure on tracheal volume and total lung resistance to airflow. *J Physiol, 162*:13-33, 1962.

25. OTIS, A.B.: The work of breathing. In Fenn, W.O., and Rahn, H. (Eds.): *Handbook of Physiology,* Section 3: Respiration. Washington, D.C., American Physiological Society, 1964, Vol. I.

26. PUGH, L.G.C.E.: In Dill, D.B. (Ed.): *Handbook of Physiology,* Section 4: Adaptation to the environment. Washington, D.C., American Physiological Society, 1964.

27. RIGATTO, M., JONES, N.L., and CAMPBELL, E.J.M.: Pulmonary circulation time: influence of posture and exercise. *Clin Sci, 35*:183-196, 1968.

28. ROSS, B.B.: The influence of bronchial tree structure on ventilation of the lung as inferred from measurements of a plastic cast. *U.S.A.F., W.A.D.C. Tech. Rept, 55-357*:72-98, 1955.

29. SALTIN, B., BLOMQVIST, G., MITCHELL, J.H., JOHNSON, R.L., WILDENTHAL, K., and CHAPMAN, C.B.: Response to exercise after bed rest and after training. *American Heart Association Monograph 23.*

30. SHEPHARD, R.J.: Partitional respirometry in human subjects. *J Appl Physiol, 13*:357-367, 1959.

31. SHEPHARD, R.J.: Some effects of carbon dioxide on foreign gas uptake. *J Appl Physiol, 14*:333-338, 1959.

32. SHEPHARD, R.J.: Partitional respirometry in cardio-pulmonary disease. *Thorax, 14*:153-160, 1959.

33. SHEPHARD, R.J.: Emploi de faibles concentrations d'oxyde de carbone, d'ether, et d'acetylène dans l'étude des échanges gazeux alveolo-capillaires. *Le Poumon et le Coeur, 10*:1049-1063, 1960.

34. SHEPHARD, R.J.: The oxygen cost of breathing during vigorous exercise. *Quart J Exp Physiol, 51*:336-350, 1966.

35. SHEPHARD, R.J.: The physiological determinants of cardio-respiratory fitness. *J Sport Med, 7*:111-134, 1967.

36. SHEPHARD, R.J.: The maximum sustained voluntary ventilation in exercise. *Clin Sci, 32*:167-176, 1967.

37. SHEPHARD, R.J.: Pulse rate and ventilation as indices of metabolic

load. 1. Theoretical aspects. *Arch Environ Health (Chicago)*, 15:562-567, 1967.

38. SHEPHARD, R.J.: The heart and circulation under stress of Olympic conditions. *JAMA, 205*:150-155, 1968.

39. SHEPHARD, R.J., and ANDERSON, T.W.: Training, work, and increase of pulmonary diffusing capacity. In *Muskelarbeit und muskeltraining*. Stuttgart, Gentner Verlag, 1968.

40. SHEPHARD, R.J.: Oscillations of acid-base equilibrium during maximum exercise. *Int Z Angew Physiol, 26*:258-271, 1968.

41. SHEPHARD, R.J.: An integrated approach to cardiorespiratory performance at sea level and at an altitude of 7350 ft. Proceedings of 5th Pan American Congress of Sports Sciences, To be published, 1967.

42. SHEPHARD, R.J.: A non-linear solution of the oxygen conductance equation: applications to performance at sea level and at an altitude of 7350 ft. *Int Z Angew Physiol, 27*:212-225, 1969.

43. SHEPHARD, R.J.: *Endurance Fitness.* Toronto, Ontario, University of Toronto Press, 1969.

44. SHEPHARD, R.J.: The validity of the oxygen conductance equation. *Int Z Angew Physiol, 28*:61-75, 1969.

45. STAINSBY, W.N., CAIN, S.M., and OTIS, A.B.: Oxygen use by dog skeletal muscle during progressive hypoxia. *Fed Proc, 19*:380, 1960.

46. STAINSBY, W.N.: Some critical oxygen tensions and their significance. In Hatcher, I.D., and Jennings, D.B. (Eds.): *Proceedings of International Symposium on Cardiovascular and Respiratory Effects of Hypoxia.* Basel, Karger, 1966.

47. WEIBEL, E.R.: Morphometrics of the lung. In Fenn, W.O., and Rahn, H. (Eds.): *Handbook of Physiology,* Section 3: Respiration. Washington, D.C., American Physiological Society, 1964.

48. WEST, J.B.: Diffusing capacity of the lung for carbon monoxide at high altitude. *J Appl Physiol, 17*:421-426, 1962.

49. WHALEN, W.J., and NAIR, P.: Intracellular Po_2 and its regulation in resting skeletal muscle of the guinea pig. *Circ Res, 21*:251-261, 1967.

Chapter 8

ANAEROBIC CAPACITY AND POWER

P. E. DI PRAMPERO

Acording to present knowledge the reaction primarily involved in muscular contraction is the splitting of ATP to ADP and inorganic phosphate (P_i):

$$ATP \rightleftharpoons ADP + P_i$$

$$(1)$$

The amount of free energy (ΔF) liberated by reaction 1 is generally estimated at -7.0 kcal per mole (21, 23, 35) under standard conditions. The concentration of ATP in muscle is very limited, of the order of 5.0μmoles per kilogram (36). If muscular activity is to be carried on for some time, ATP must therefore be continuously resynthesized from its end products. The energy for this process is furnished by the splitting of creatinephosphate (CP) splitting, whose ΔF is of the order of -9.0 kcal per mole (23) under standard conditions:

$$CP \rightleftharpoons C + P_i \qquad (2)$$

These two reactions are generally considered in series, and by calling *phosphagen* the sum of ATP + CP = GP (17, 18, 28), the overall reaction can be written

$$GP \underset{b}{\overset{a}{\rightleftharpoons}} G + P_i + En \qquad (3)$$

where En indicates the amount of energy set free by the reaction and disposable for the performance of mechanical work.

Since the CP concentration in muscle is also limited, about 15μmoles per kilogram (36), in order for the muscle to carry on work for long periods of time, phosphagen must be continuously resynthesized. The energy for both ATP and CP resynthesis is generally provided by the oxidation of foodstuff (carbohydrates and lipids):

$$\text{Food} + O_2 \xrightarrow{c} CO_2 + H_2O + \text{En} \qquad (4)$$

When the energy required for GP resynthesis is not fully met by oxidation, an additional exergonic mechanism, anaerobic glycolysis, sets in:

$$\text{Glycogen} \underset{e}{\overset{d}{\rightleftharpoons}} \text{lactic acid} + \text{En} \qquad (5)$$

It appears therefore that a true steady state, that is, a condition in which the rate of GP splitting (reaction a) is equal to the rate of GP resynthesis (reaction b), can be reached only when reaction c, or reactions c and d, liberate the energy necessary to resynthesize the GP split to perform mechanical work.

Anaerobic work can be performed by muscle at the expenses of two different sources of energy: a) the GP splitting mechanism alone and b) lactic acid (L.A.) formation from glycogen. The latter enters into the picture only when oxidative processes are insufficient to account for all the energy necessary for GP resynthesis.

For a full understanding of the anaerobic sources of energy, the following characteristics should be known: a) the rate of energy output (power), b) the total energy available (capacity), and c) the efficiency of each of the processes described above.

The Lactacid Mechanism

Power

When performing an exercise which requires a maximal oxygen consumption, power does not increase further with an increase in the total energy requirement. Under these conditions the extra energy necessary for work cannot be provided by the GP splitting mechanism unless the exercise is of very short duration because the GP system has a very low capacity. Disregarding the beginning of exercise, any increase of work intensity above the maximal aerobic power is thus sustained only by the glycolytic process.

The lactic acid production in supramaximal exercise has been studied by Margaria *et al.* (31); his subject ran on a treadmill at 12 km per hour at inclines varying from +2 to +14 percent. The energy cost of exercise was known from previous experiments (30) and was such as to lead to exhaustion in two to ten minutes.

The L.A. concentration in venous blood under these experimental conditions increased linearly with time (Fig. 8-1), that is, with the total amount of work performed by the subject. Moreover, the slope of the line (which is the increase of blood L.A. concentration per unit time) increased with the intensity of exercise, thus emphasizing the relation between work intensity and lactic acid production from glycogen.

The amount of L.A. produced by an exercising man can be calculated from its concentration in the blood if the assumption is made that L.A. is uniformly distributed in the water phase of the body. The rate of L.A. production also appears to be a linear function of the intensity of exercise (Fig. 8-2). The line cuts the abscissa at a value of energy requirement below which no L.A. is produced. This value corresponds to the maximum oxygen consumption of the subject, thus emphasizing the fact that until

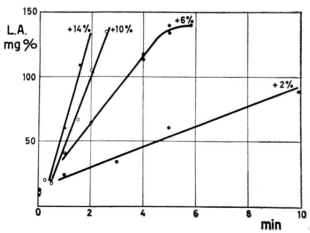

FIGURE 8-1. Lactic acid (L.A.) concentration in blood (milligram %) as a function of time from the beginning of exercise (minutes) in a subject running on a treadmill at a speed of 12 kilometers per hour and at inclines of 2, 6, 10, and 14 percent (from Reference 31).

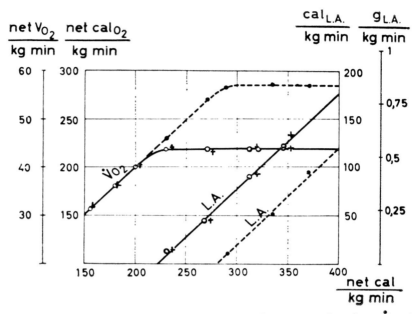

FIGURE 8-2. Oxygen consumption in excess of resting value (net $\overset{\bullet}{V}o_2$ in milliliters per kilogram minute) and lactic acid (L.A.) production (grams per kilogram minute) as a function of the energy requirement of the exercise (net calories per kilogram minute). Data for two nonathletic subjects ($\circ$; $+$) and one athlete ($\bullet$). The intercepts of the L.A. lines on the abscissa indicate the work intensity which can be sustained without L.A. production. This appears to be higher in the athlete; the maximal O_2 uptake, indicated by flattening of the $\overset{\bullet}{V}o_2$ lines is also higher in this subject. The slope of the L.A. line is the same in nonathletic and athletic subjects; its reciprocal represents the caloric equivalent of L.A. and amounts to 222 calories per gram. On the basis of this value the L.A. production can be transformed to calories (calories$_{L.A.}$ per kilogram minute), and if the same is done for $\overset{\bullet}{V}o_2$ (1 ml = 5 cal), the sum of the two processes gives a straight line at 45 degrees which accounts for the whole energy expenditure (from Reference 31).

O_2 can no longer be provided to the tissues in sufficient amounts to meet the energy requirement, no L.A. formation takes place: glycolysis is, in effect, an emergency mechanism that enters into play when the oxidative mechanism is inadequate (31).

The reciprocal of the slope of the L.A. line of Figure 8-2, that is, $\dfrac{d \text{ cal,}}{d \text{ L.A.}}$ is the energy equivalent of L.A. as released in the body from glycogen (31): this appears to amount to 220 cal per gram independently of the physiological condition of the subjects (being unaffected by such variables as athletic capacity and anoxia). A similar value has been obtained in dogs running on a treadmill (12).

As shown in Figures 8-1 and 8-2, the rate of L.A. production increases with the intensity of exercise. The upper limit of L.A. production has not been reached in the experiments of Figure 8-1. In another series of experiments where the subjects performed more strenuous exercise, it was shown that this limit was reached when the intensity of the exercise was such as to lead to exhaustion in less than forty seconds (32). In this range of work loads $\dfrac{d.\ L.A}{dt}$ is constant, as shown in Figure 8-3. The maximal possible rate of L.A. production thus appears to be 1.6 gram L.A. per kilogram minute, or 350 cal per kilogram minute, and this is therefore the *maximal power of the lactacid mechanism*.

Capacity

As the maximal possible concentration of L.A. in blood is of the order of 150 mg%, or 1.1 gram per kilogram body weight, *the maximal capacity of the lactacid mechanism* amounts to about 250 cal per kilogram. This value, however, is not strictly constant, as it depends on the glycogen content of the muscle, which varies with many factors including training, diet and nutritional state (4, 5, 13).

From these data it can be calculated that when L.A. is produced at a maximal rate (350 cal/kg min), the lactacid mechanism is exhausted in about forty to forty-five seconds (Table 8-I).

The capacity of the glycolytic mechanism is also affected by age, as it increases during the first two decades, reaches its highest value (about 1.1 gm/kg) at twenty to twenty-five years, and decreases slowly thereafter, being reduced to about 0.3 per gm per kilogram at the age of seventy (2, 9, 37).

Chronic hypoxia, by decreasing the alkali reserve of the body,

TABLE 8-I

CAPACITY AND POWER OF EXERGONIC MECHANISM
IN MUSCULAR CONTRACTION

	Power cal/kg min	Capacity cal/kg	Maximal Value ml O_2/kg	O_2 Debt Time for Full Development of Debt at Maximum Speed of Running (sec)	Speed of Repayment ½ Time
Alactic mechanism (GP splitting)	750	100	22	8	22 sec
Lactacid mechanism	350	250	45	43	15 min
Oxidative mechanism	220	∞	—	—	—

affects the maximal amount of L.A. that can be accomodated in the body fluids, thus decreasing the maximal lactacid capacity (8, 20).

Efficiency

Lactic acid formation is an emergency mechanism to provide energy for the resynthesis of GP from its end products. From *in vitro* studies on tissue homogenates or slices, it has been shown that the production of 1 mole of L.A. from glycogen or from glucose yields, respectively, 1.5 and 1.0 moles of ATP.

Recent experiments on isolated frog gastrocnemius have confirmed that these values can be applied to intact muscle (1).

We have already seen that the energy equivalent of L.A. is 220 cal per gram. Thus the production of 1 mole of L.A. is equivalent to 90 x 220 = 19,800 cal; since this leads to the performance of about 5.0 kcal of mechanical work, 1 mole of GP is equivalent to 5.0/1.5 = 3.33 kcal of mechanical work.

In an isolated dog gastrocnemius preparation, when no other energy sources are available, Cerretelli *et al.* (11) have shown that the mechanical work performed at the expenses of L.A. production is the same as in man: 5.0 kcal per mole.

It has been shown by Margaria *et al.* (33) that the removal of L.A. from the body fluids in man follows an exponential course with a half-time of about fifteen minutes. The energy necessary for this process is furnished by the oxidation of about one-tenth

of the L.A. formed, while the remaining nine-tenths are recon-
verted to glycogen (33). The removal of 1 mole of L.A. therefore
requires $\dfrac{22.4 \times 3}{10}$ = 6.73 liters of oxygen, or 0.075 liters equivalent to 375 cal* per gram L.A.: the conversion of nine-tenths of
a gram of L.A. to glycogen requires $\dfrac{9 \times 220}{10}$ = 198 cal, since
the production of 1 gram of L.A. corresponds to 220 cal of
oxidative energy. The efficiency of the resynthesis of glycogen
from L.A. at the expenses of oxidation thus appears to be
198/375 = 0.53. As the mechanical efficiency with which glycogen is transformed to L.A. or is oxidized is 0.25, the overall
efficiency including the process of resynthesis of glycogen from
lactic acid amounts to 0.25 x 0.53 = 0.13 or about half the
efficiency of ordinary aerobic work without the intervention of
the lactate mechanism.

The Alactic Mechanism

Power

In the first few seconds of muscular activity, energy is drawn
only from phosphagen, and even during very strenuous effort no
L.A. is formed (32) Fig. 8-3): the L.A. mechanism seems to
initiate only when the amount of phosphagen split reaches a
critical value (32). By plotting the intensity of the exercise as a
function of the duration of work without the intervention of
L.A. (Fig. 8-4, line "Alact."), a line is obtained which, when
extrapolated back to zero time, gives an indication of the maximal power which can be sustained for a very short time. This
power is of the order of 45 kcal per kilogram hour or 750 cal
per kilogram minute in normal subjects, and it corresponds to
the *maximal anaerobic alactic power.* A similar value is obtained
by extrapolating to zero time the line describing the intensity
of work as a function of the total time of performance (Fig. 8-4,
line "Tot.").

---

*The energy liberated by oxidation of lactic acid is approximately 5 kcal per
liter of oxygen used.

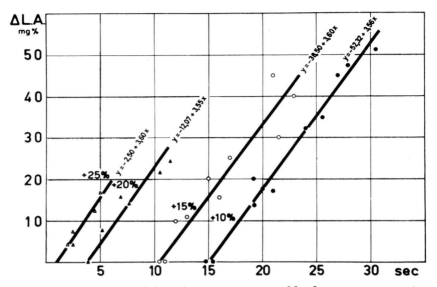

FIGURE 8-3. Lactic acid (L.A.) concentration in blood, excess over resting value (ΔL.A., mg %), as a function of the duration of the exercise. Data on four nonathletic subjects running on the treadmill at 18 km per hour and inclines of 10, 15, 20, and 25 percent. The slope of the lines (increase of blood L.A. concentration per unit time) is independent of the intensity of the exercise, thus suggesting that a maximal rate of L.A. production has been attained. The time during which the exercise can be sustained at the expenses of the alactic mechanism alone is indicated for each of the four work loads by the intercept on the abscissa of the corresponding ΔL.A. line (from Reference 32).

Capacity

The "Alact." line of Figure 8-4 can be corrected for the small amount of O_2 consumed during the first phase of work, when no L.A. is produced (32, 34), to obtain the line "Alact. corr.". This indicates the time for which an exercise of the intensity given on the ordinate can be carried on at the expense of the GP splitting mechanism alone.

The capacity of the alactic mechanism can be obtained by extrapolating the "Alact. corr." line of Figures 8-4 back to zero time and calculating the integral of this function, that is, the area between the line and the coordinates. This amounts to 196 cal

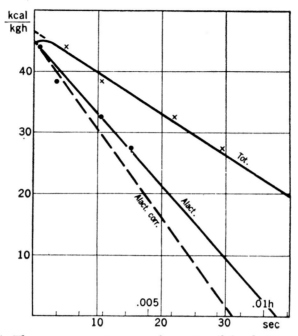

FIGURE 8-4. The energy requirement of exercise (kilocalories per kilogram hour) as a function of the total performance time in seconds (line "Tot."). Data from the experiments of Figure 8-3. The time for which the exercise can be sustained without L.A. production is also indicated (line "Alact."); this is further corrected for the small amount of "stored" O_2 consumed during this time (line "Alact. corr.") (from Reference 32).

per kilogram or 39.6 ml O_2 per kilogram. Since 1 mole of O_2 used in oxidation yields the energy for the resynthesis of 6.5 moles of GP (see 23, 27), 39.6 ml O_2 are equivalent to 11.5μmoles of GP. As the fraction of muscles in the body is about 0.4, the content of GP in muscle can be calculated as $11.5/0.4 = 29$μmoles per kilogram, a value in fairly good agreement with the figure of 25μmoles per kilogram obtained from direct chemical analysis of human muscles (3,22).

The maximal functional capacity of the alactic mechanism, however, amounts to much less; only half the phosphagen in muscle seems to be utilizable when a man performs maximal work (32). The amount of energy liberated by this process is

given by the product of work intensity (ordinate) and the corresponding maximal duration of performance at the expense of
the alactic mechanism alone (abscissa); it reaches a maximum
of 100 cal per kilogram, as compared with 196 cal per kilogram
when the duration of the alactic phase of the exercise is about
fifteen seconds (32).

Velocity Constant of Phosphagen Splitting

In Figure 8-5 the energy requirement of work in calories per
kilogram minute has been plotted as a function of the total
amount of energy spent in the first (alactic) phase for the same
experiments as described in Figure 8-4. The power developed in
these conditions appears inversely related to the total amount of
energy drawn from alactic sources. Since under these experimental conditions the whole energy requirement is met from
anaerobic alactic sources (splitting of GP), the GP concentration
in muscle must decrease with an increase in the amount of energy
spent. Consequently the maximal rate of GP splitting appears
linearly related to the GP concentration in muscle.

For a further analysis of the energetics of muscular contraction under these conditions, the two energy-yielding mechanisms
of ATP and CP splitting should be considered separately, since
the splitting of ATP is a faster process than the splitting of CP,
and under the experimental conditions of anaerobic work, a steady
state is not reached. ATP and ADP concentrations in muscle
can be considered constant during the first phase of exercise
before L.A. production sets in as ATP is rapidly resynthesized
by CP splitting while CP is still present in an elevated concentration. The energy output (ordinate of Fig. 8-5) is therefore an
index of the rate of CP splitting, a reaction coupled with ATP
resynthesis, according to Lohman:

$$CP + ADP \underset{k''}{\overset{k'}{\rightleftharpoons}} ATP + C \qquad (6)$$

where k' and k'' indicate the velocity constants of the forward
and backward reactions. The rate of CP splitting should then be

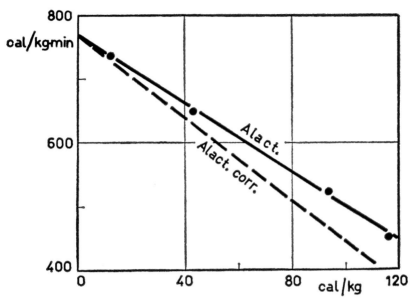

FIGURE 8-5. The energy requirement of exercise (calories per kilogram minute) as a function of the amount of energy spent (calories per kilogram) during the first phase of work, before L.A. production commences. Data from the experiments described in Figures 8-3 and 8-4 (line "Alact."). By taking into account the small amount of O_2 consumed during this phase, the line "Alact. corr." is obtained. This may be described by the equation y = 770 — 3.25 x. (From the data of Margaria *et al.*, 32.)

$$\frac{\overrightarrow{dCP}}{dt} = k' \,(CP)\,(ADP) \qquad\qquad (7)$$

The values on the ordinate of Figure 8-5 may be identified with $\frac{\overrightarrow{dCP}}{dt}$ and the values on the abscissa with the amount of CP split, or C. Since it can be assumed that C + CP = constant, equation (7) may be written

$$\frac{\overrightarrow{dCP}}{dt} = k' \,(ADP)\,(constant - C) \qquad\qquad (8)$$

This is the equation of the "Alact. corr." line of Figure 8-5.

If ADP is constant, as postulated above, the function describes a straight line; this appears to be the case in reality (Fig. 8-5), thus supporting the validity of the assumption. The slope of this line is k' (ADP), with a value of 3.25 minute^{-1}.

In previous papers (17, 28 it has been shown that during steady state submaximal work the ratio O_2 consumption/O_2 debt is indicative of the velocity constant of GP resynthesis, a process which appears to be exponential (see Reference 28). A value of 2.4 minute^{-1} has recently been obtained for the velocity constant of GP resynthesis in man, using this approach (19). Under these conditions the resynthesis of GP is coupled with oxidation reactions or, in other words, with $\dot{V}_{O_2}$, and the latter can be identified with the process of CP resynthesis according to the equation

$$\frac{dGP}{dt} = \frac{dCP}{dt} = a\ \dot{V}_{O_2} \tag{9}$$

Since from reaction (6)

$$\frac{dCP}{dt} = k''\ (ATP)\ (C) \tag{10}$$

it follows that:

$$a\ \dot{V}_{O_2} = k''\ (ATP)\ (C) \tag{11}$$

Further, since from (9) $a = CP/\dot{V}_{O_2}$, it is the oxygen equivalent of CP (or C) in O_2 and the ratio C/a has the significance of the "net" alactic O_2 debt $V_{O_2}{}^{al}$. Substituting in equation (11), we find

$$\frac{\dot{V}_{O_2}}{V_{O_2}{}^{al}} = k''\ (ATP) = 2.4\ minute^{-1} \tag{12}$$

The linear relationship between O_2 consumption and alactic O_2 debt in the steady state (33) is in agreement with the finding that the ATP concentration under these conditions is practically constant (3, 22, 36).

ATP and ADP concentrations in human muscle have been found to be fairly constant in active muscle except near exhaustion, amounting to 6.9μmoles per kilogram for ATP (3, 22) and to 0.7μmoles per kilogram for ADP (36). Assuming again that muscle accounts for 0.40 of the body weight, the ATP and ADP concentrations amount respectively to 2.76μmoles per kilogram and 0.28μmoles per kilogram of body weight or 19.3 and 1.96 cal per kilogram. The values of k' and k'' can now be calculated from equations (8) and (12), respectively $k' = \dfrac{3.25}{1.96} = 1.66$ minute^{-1} and $k'' = \dfrac{2.4}{19.3} = 0.123$ minute^{-1}.

The equilibrium constant of reaction (6) can now be derived: $K = k'/k'' = 1.66/0.123 = 13.5$. This is not too different from the value of 19 ± 3 obtained by Carlson and Siger on frog muscles (7) and by Kuber *et al.* during *in vitro* studies (24). If $K = 13.5$ the free energy change of reaction (6) can be estimated as $\Delta F^{\circ} = - RT \ln K = - 1.60$ kcal per mole, in agreement with the ordinary concept that Lohman's reaction is almost thermoneutral under standard conditions.

Measurements of Maximal Power in Man

Recently Margaria and co-workers (29) have developed a convenient and easy method to measure maximal anaerobic power. This is based on the observation that oxidative reactions and lactic acid formation from glycogen are delayed processes which do not contribute appreciably to energy liberation in the first four to five seconds of muscular activity. In this short period of time the power developed by maximal voluntary effort appears constant; it does not increase if the duration of maximal exercise is reduced further, but it tends to decrease if the exercise lasts for longer than five seconds.

The maximal power developed in a very short period of exercise may thus be considered indicative of the phosphagen splitting mechanism alone. The exercise used in this test consists of running up a staircase at maximal speed. The mechanical power output per kilogram of body weight (in kilograms per kilogram second) may be identified with the vertical component of the speed in meters per second, measured with a very sensitive electronic timing device. Observations are made over a very brief interval when the speed has reached a constant value, that is, about two seconds after starting the exercise. At this stage almost all of the energy is employed to lift the body, the amount necessary to overcome speed changes at each step being inappreciable. The efficiency approaches 0.25 for this type of

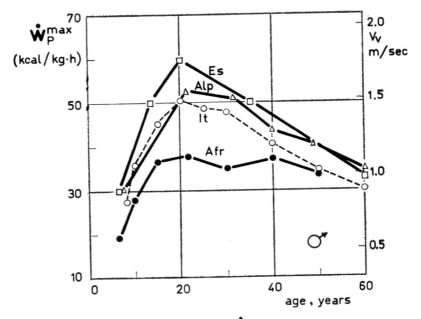

FIGURE 8-6. Maximal anaerobic power ($\dot{W}_p^{max}$), expressed as the equivalent energy expenditure (kilocalories per kilogram hour). Data for male subjects of different ethnic groups at various ages. On the right-hand ordinate the maximal vertical velocity (meters per second) is also indicated: this identifies the mechanical power output from which the energy expenditure was calculated, assuming a mechanical efficiency of 0.25. Es: Eskimo, Alp: Alpine population, It: Italian city dwellers (from Reference 29), and Afr: Africans (from Reference 15).

exercise (26, 30), and the corresponding energy expenditure can be calculated from this figure.

Results obtained with this method on subjects from various ethnic groups are plotted as a function of age (Fig. 8-6). In all groups the maximal anaerobic power increases to the twentieth year of age and decreases slowly thereafter. No significant ethnic differences are seen except that values for the Africans are sensibly lower, particularly in the age range of fifteen to forty; this difference is probably due to the poor nutritional states of these subjects (10) and/or the unusual geometry of their lower limbs (15). The normal maximal value, as attained at twenty to twenty-five years of age, is of the order of 50 kcal per kilogram hour or 165 ml O_2 per kilogram minute in all groups except the Africans. However, in athletic subjects the maximal anaerobic power is sensibly larger. The highest values recorded on athletes competing at the Olympic games in Mexico were of the order of 215 ml O_2 per kilogram minute (16).

Efficiency

The overall efficiency of muscular contraction when work is performed under aerobic conditions amounts to 0.25 (26, 30). This value is the product of the efficiency of two distinct processes which, in the steady state, proceed at the same rate: a) the splitting of GP to perform mechanical work and b) the resynthesis of GP at the expenses of oxidations:

$$\frac{W}{O_2} = \frac{W}{\text{mole GP}} \times \frac{\text{mole GP}}{O_2} = 0.25 \quad (13)$$

The value of ΔH (enthalpy change*) for CP splitting has been measured in frog muscle and found to be of the order of $- 11$ kcal per mole (6, 25, 39). The oxidation of glycogen yields, per mole of hexose, energy for the resynthesis of 39 moles ATP (see 23, 27) and liberates 672 kcal. As 39 moles ATP yield 11 x 39 = 429 kcal, the efficiency of this process is 429/672 = 0.63. From equation (13), the efficiency of the mechanical work performed at the expenses of GP splitting therefore amounts to 0.25/0.63 = 0.40. The splitting of 1 mole of GP should thus yield 11 x 0.40 = 4.4 kcal of mechanical work. Experiments on the dog gastrocnemius under anaerobic conditions (11) have given a value of 5.2, while in frog muscles poisoned with fluorodinitrobenzene a value of 5.5 has been obtained (14).

It must be pointed out that in the calculation of efficiency the enthalpy change* (ΔH) has been used and not the free energy change (ΔF), which only represents the energy available to perform work (38).

Conclusions

The power and capacity of the two anaerobic exergonic

---

*For further discusion of enthalpy, see Chapter 1.

processes that may be involved in muscular activity are summarized in Table 8-I. Data are for normal subjects and are expressed in terms of the oxidative energy required. Analogous data for the oxidative mechanism are also shown, together with the speed of payment of the oxygen debt, both alactic and lactacid.

From the point of view of performance predictions, the most indicative data are a) the power of the oxidative mechanism and b) the power of the alactic mechanism. These are as much as 50 percent greater in athletes, long distance runners, and sprinters, respectively. On the contrary, the speed of payment of the oxygen debt is presumed to be similar for all subjects, as it depends mainly on the biochemical characteristics of muscle.

References

1. AMBROSOLI, G., DI PRAMPERO, P.E., and CERRETELLI, P.: L' influenza del contenuto in fosfageno (PC + ATP) sul rendimento meccanico del muscolo. *Boll Soc Ital Biol Sper,* In Press, 1969.

2. ASTRAND, I.: Aerobic work capacity in men and women with special reference to age. *Acta Physiol Scand, 49 (Suppl.)*:169, 1960.

3. BERGSTRÖM, J.: Local changes of ATP and phosphorylcreatine in human muscle tissue in connection with exercise. *Circ Res, (Suppl. to Vol. XX and XXI) 1*:91-96, 1967.

4. BERGSTRÖM, J., HERMANSEN, L., HULTMAN, E., and SALTIN, B.: Diet, muscle glycogen and physical performance. *Acta Physiol Scand, 71*:140-150, 1967.

5. BERGSTRÖM, J., and HULTMAN, E.: Muscle glycogen synthesis after exercise: an enhancing factor localized to the muscle cells in man. *Nature (London), 210*:309-310, 1966.

6. CARLSON, F.D., HARDY, D., and WILKIE, D.R.: The relation between heat produced and phosphorylcreatine split during isometric contraction of frog's muscle. *J Physiol, 189*:209-235, 1967.

7. CARLSON, F.D., and SIGER, A.: The creatine phosphoryltransfer reaction in iodoacetate-poisoned muscle. *J Gen Physiol, 43*:301-313, 1960.

8. CERRETELLI, P.: Lactacid O_2 debt in acute and chronic hypoxia.

In Margaria, R. (Ed.): *Exercise at Altitude.* Excerpta Medica Foundation, 1967.

9. CERRETELLI, P., AGHEMO, P., and ROVELLI, E.: Aspetti fisiologici dell' adolescente in relazione alla pratica dello asercizio fisico. *Med Dello Sport, 21*:400-406, 1968.

10. CERRETELLI, P., DI PRAMPERO, P.E., and CANTONE, A.: Rilievi sullo stato di nutrizione di uomini della tribù Turkana del Kenia. *Boll Soc Ital Biol Sper, 43*:259, 1967.

11. CERRETELLI, P., DI PRAMPERO, P.E., and PIIPER, J.: Energy balance of anaerobic work in the dog gastrocnemius muscle. *Amer J Physiol,* In Press, 1969.

12. CERRETELLI, P., PIIPER, J., MANGILI, F., and RICCI, B.: Aerobic and anaerobic metabolism in exercising dogs. *J Appl Physiol, 19*:29-32, 1964.

13. CHRISTENSEN, E.H., and HANSEN, O.: Arbeitfähigkeit und Ernähr-ung. *Skand Arch Physiol, 81*:160-171, 1939.

14. DAVIES, R.E., KUSHMERICK, M.J., and LARSON, L.E.: ATP activa-tion and the heat of shortening of muscle. *Nature (London), 214*:148-151, 1967.

15. DI PRAMPERO, P.E., and CERRETELLI, P.: Maximal muscular power (aerobic and anaerobic) in African natives. *Ergonomics, 12*:51-59, 1969.

16. DI PRAMPERO, P.E., PINERA-LIMAS, F., and SASSI, G.: Maximal muscular power (aerobic and anaerobic) in 116 athletes per-forming at the XIX Olympic Games in Mexico. *Ergonomics,* In Press, 1969.

17. DI PRAMPERO, P.E., and MARGARIA, R.: Relationship between O_2 consumption, high energy phosphates and the kinetics of the O_2 debt in exercise. *Pflüeger Arch Ges Physiol, 304*:11-19, 1968.

18. DI PRAMPERO, P.E., and MARGARIA, R.: Mechanical efficiency of phosphagen (ATP + CP) splitting and its speed of resynthesis. *Pflüeger Arch Ges Physiol, 308*:197-202, 1969.

19. DI PRAMPERO, P.E., and MARGARIA, R.: Différentes composantes de la contraction de la dette d'oxygène. *J Physiol (Paris),* In Press, 1969.

20. EDWARDS, H.T.: Lactic acid in rest and work at high altitude. *Amer J Physiol, 116*:367-375, 1936.

21. GEORGE, P., and RUTMAN, R.J.: The "high energy phosphate bond" concept. *Progr Biophys, 10*:2-53, 1960.

22. HULTMAN, E., BERGSTRÖM, J., and McLENNAN ANDERSON, N.: Break-down and resynthesis of phosphorylcreatine and adenosine-triphosphate in connection with muscular work in man. *Scand J Lab Invest, 19*:56-66, 1967.

23. KARLSON, P.: In: *Kurzes Lehrbuch der Biochemie für Mediziner und Naturwissenschaftler.* Stuttgart, Georg Thieme Verlag, 1966.

24. KUBY, S.A., NODA, L., and LARDY, H.A.: Adenosinetriphosphate-creatine transphosphorylase. *J Biol Chem, 210*:65-82, 1954.

25. MARÉCHAL, G.: *Le métabolisme de la phosphorylcréatine et de l'adénosine triphosphate durant la contraction musculaire.* Ed. Arscia. Paris, Bruxelles—Libraire Maloine, 1964.

26. MARGARIA, R.: Sulla fisiologia e specialmente sul consumo energetico della marcia e della corsa a varie velocità ed inclinazioni del terreno. *Atti Acad Naz Lincei, Classe Sci Fis Mat, Serie VI,* 7, 1938.

27. MARGARIA, R.: *Principi di chimica e fisico-chimica fisiologica.* Casa Editrice Ambrosiana Milano, 1958.

28. MARGARIA, R.: Aerobic and anaerobic energy sources in muscular exercise. In Margaria, R. (Ed.): *Exercise at Altitude.* Excerpta Medica Foundation, 1967.

29. MARGARIA, R., AGHEMO, P., and ROVELLI, E.: Measurement of muscular power (anaerobic) in man. *J Appl Physiol, 21*:1662-1664, 1966.

30. MARGARIA, R., CERRETELLI, P., AGHEMO, P., and SASSI, G.: Energy cost of running. *J Appl Physiol, 18*:367-370, 1963.

31. MARGARIA, R., CERRETELLI, P., DI PRAMPERO, P.E., MASSARI, C., and TORELLI, G.: Kinetics and mechanism of oxygen debt contraction in man. *J Appl Physiol, 18*:371-377, 1963.

32. MARGARIA, R., CERRETELLI, P., and MANGILI, F.: Balance and kinetics of anaerobic energy release during strenuous exercise in man. *J Appl Physiol, 19*:623-628, 1964.

33. MARGARIA, R., EDWARDS, H.T., and DILL, D.B.: The possible mechanism of contracting and paying the oxygen debt and the role of lactic acid in muscular contraction. *Amer J Physiol, 106*:689-715, 1933.

34. MARGARIA, R., MANGILI, F., CUTTICA, F., and CERRETELLI, P.: The kinetics of the oxygen consumption at the onset of muscular exercise in man. *Ergonomics, 8*:49-54, 1965.

35. MORALES, M.F., BOTTS, J., BLUM, J., and HILL, T.L.: Elementary process in muscle action: an examination of current concepts. *Physiol Rev, 35*:475-505, 1955.

36. PIIPER, J., DI PRAMPERO, P.E., and CERRETELLI, P.: Oxygen debt and high energy phosphates in gastrocnemius muscle of the dog. *Amer J Physiol, 215*:523-531, 1968.

37. ROBINSON, S.: Experimental studies of physical fitness in relation to age. *Arbeitsphysiol, 10*:251-323, 1938.

38. WILKIE, D.R.: Thermodynamics and the interpretation of biological heat measurements. *Progr Biophys, 10*:260-298, 1960.

39. WILKIE, D.R.: Heat work and phosphorylcreatine breakdown in muscle. *J Physiol, 195*:157-183, 1968.

Chapter 9

PRESENT CONCEPTS OF THE RELATIONSHIP BETWEEN LACTATE AND OXYGEN DEBT

A. De Coster

THE CONCEPT of the relationship between O_2 debt and lactate metabolism has been the subject of critical analysis during recent years. However, in reviewing this topic it first seems necessary to recall the classical concepts elaborated more than thirty years ago by Hill and colleagues (27) and some years later by Dill (18) and Margaria (39, 40).

The Classical Concepts

O_2 Consumption ($\dot{V}o_2$) Before, During, and After Physical Work

Continuous measurement of $\dot{V}o_2$ during exertion on a bicycle ergometer or a treadmill reveals the following: The first observation is of an exponential $\dot{V}o_2$ increase on initiation of exercise. At this time the O_2 consumption is less than the O_2 requirement; the latter is a function of the load and the type of exercise. The deficient oxygen intake forces the organism to contract an *oxygen debt,* which is the difference between the O_2 actually consumed and the metabolically required oxygen.

Anaerobic metabolism occurs in the muscles because of the O_2 lack. The severity of the oxygen debt is a function of the load, the physical fitness of the exerciser, and the speed and efficiency of the cardiorespiratory adjustments to exercise. At moderate work load the $\dot{V}o_2$ remains constant after a few (2 to 4 or 5) minutes, as a steady state is reached. At this point the O_2 uptake is equal to the O_2 requirement, and there is no anaerobic metabolism. After work the $\dot{V}o_2$ returns to the basal level, the pattern of this return being exponential. Mathematical

174

analysis of the recovery curve shows two components with very different time constants, a slow one and a rapid one which will be dealt with later. The excess of O_2 consumed over the basal level during the recovery period corresponds to the repayment of the debt, and in consequence, that portion of excess O_2 consumption is often incorrectly designated the "oxygen debt." The excess O_2 consumption of the repayment period is used to oxidize part of the accumulated lactate, thereby providing the necessary energy to resynthesis the remaining lactate to glycogen.

At work loads exceeding the aerobic power of the subject, the amount of O_2 transported by the blood (equal to the arterio-venous difference multiplied by the cardiac output) is insufficient to meet metabolic demands, and anaerobic metabolism occurs throughout the period of work. Sometimes $\dot{V}_{O_2}$ may *appear* constant, but in fact this constancy reflects the inability of the organism to further increase its $\dot{V}_{O_2}$. The steady state is only apparent, and the $\dot{V}_{O_2}$ corresponds in fact to the individual's maximal O_2 intake. In such circumstances the oxygen debt persists throughout the exercise, the O_2 requirement remaining higher than the O_2 consumption. The measurement of the oxygen debt and its repayment may then be very difficult, if not impossible. Obviously, this type of work can only be sustained for a relatively short period of time.

Lactate (L) and Pyruvate (P) During Physical Work

Metabolism of L and of P is a function of the oxidation of $DPNH_2$. If metabolism is sustained by anoxic energy, the metabolic fate is altered; P is converted to L while DPNH is transformed to DPN, according to the equation

$$\overset{P}{DPNH + CH_3COCOOH + H^+} \overset{LDH}{\rightleftharpoons}$$
$$\underset{}{\overset{L}{CH_3CHOHCOOH + DPN}}$$

In the case of O_2 lack the transformation of DPNH to DPN and of P to L allows glycolysis to proceed without regeneration of DPNH by O_2. Therefore, the increase of L is a sign of O_2 lack in the cell. According to the classical concepts of Margaria and colleagues (41), L increases only at a $\dot{V}o_2$ greater than 2,500 ml per minute. During work of high intensity and constant rate, the increase of L is linear with time, and the slope of this relationship reflects the rate of production of lactate. The rate of production is also a function of the severity of the physical work. The maximal blood level of L does not exceed 150 mg per 100 ml. Assuming a homogenous distribution of L in total body water, the total quantity of L can be measured and correlated with O_2 consumption or corresponding energy values. The course of the P concentration curve is quite different. P increases at the beginning of work but to a lesser extent than L, so that the ratio L/P increases. Later, P approaches a steady value.

After work L returns gradually to normal; this decrease is exponential and is relatively slow, having a long time constant. A formula based on these findings was proposed to calculate L at any time (39). In some cases L does not return to its basal value, even after forty-five minutes. The recovery phase corresponds to the resynthesis of glycogen from L, a phenomenon that can only occur at the expense of the oxidation of a determined fraction of L. The excess O_2 consumption or the "repayment" is used in part for that oxidation; the fraction of O_2 consumed in this way corresponds to the lactacid O_2 debt. But, as stated above, the decrease of excess O_2 consumption after work shows two components. One is a slow phase with a long time constant, and this corresponds to the lactacid O_2 debt. The second component corresponds to a very rapid process, with a half-time constant of less than one minute. This component always occurs, even if the load is light and no L appears in the blood. The corresponding debt, which is always less than 3 liters, is contracted at the onset of the work. It is due to an anaerobic but alactic process, the degradation of ATP and creatine phosphate, both compounds with a high energetic potential but only available in sufficient quantity to sustain metabolism for a short time. This kind of debt is repaid in the first minutes after ceasing work and is a linear function of the intensity of the exercise.

Because the mechanism has nothing to do with L, it has been called the alactic O_2 debt.

Correlation Between L and O₂ Payment

As was stated previously, a part of the excess O_2 consumption is used to oxidize a fraction of the L produced. Now, the question arises, what part of L is oxidized and what part is transformed back to glycogen? According to Hill (27) and Meyerhof (44), the excess $\overset{\bullet}{V}_{O2}$ consumption is directly responsible for the L oxidation. Based on frog muscle experiments and thermodynamic considerations, they concluded that about 20 percent of L was oxidized, the remainder being converted into glycogen. Accordingly, O_2 debt should equal O_2 payment. Later, Dill (18) and Margaria (39) studied the correlations between total body L and excess O_2 consumption, and they concluded that at most, 10 percent of L was burnt, the remaining L being converted to glycogen, mostly by the liver. To a lesser extent brain, heart, and kidney are able to transform L into glycogen.

The Concept of Excess Lactate

In 1958 Huckabee stated that a simple measurement of plasma L was insufficient to give a good idea of the oxidation-reduction status of the cells. He showed that an increase of L may be correlated not only with cellular anoxia but also with other clinical conditions, such as infusion of glucose or pyruvate, injection of epinephrine, hyperventilation, or metabolic alkalosis (28-32). Such features could explain the lack of correlation that some authors have found between L removal and excess O_2 consumption. He also claimed that the most important fact to be considered was not the simple measure of L, but the excess lacate as calculated from the formula

$$XL = (L_n - L_o) - (P_n - P_o) \cdot L_o/P_o$$

where L = lactic acid

P = pyruvic acid

n = value of the sample at time n

o = value of the sample at time o

He regarded XL as positive only in cellular hypoxia, and the correlation between XL and the excess O_2 consumption after work was thus ideal. The concept has subsequently been applied to different clinical and pathological conditions by many authors.

Critical Analysis of the Classical Concepts

O_2 Debt and O_2 Payment

THE MEASUREMENT OF THE O_2 PAYMENT. There are different ways of expressing the repayment of the O_2 debt. Some authors (47, 51) have calculated the O_2 payment as a percentage of the increase over resting values. Others—De Mitcheli (17)—have expressed the O_2 pament as a function of the time needed for a 50% decrease of excess O_2 consumption. Yet other methods have been proposed—(Donald and colleagues (19a). It is therefore difficult to compare the results obtained. We are of the opinion that the ideal way to measure the O_2 payment is to collect the total ventilation after work, to measure the total O_2 consumption, and to subtract the resting O_2 consumption from this value. However, this apparently "simple" technique can be very difficult. After heavy work the O_2 consumption may remain (36) elevated for a long time. With a load of 1,100 kg per minute, the O_2 debt is only repaid after forty minutes. Sometimes, the basal $\dot{V}o_2$ after work is less than the basal $\dot{V}o_2$ before work. What should we then subtract—the greatest value, the lowest value, or the average value? All of these difficulties were underlined by Hill as long ago as 1924. So, it is not surprising that great discrepancies can be seen between the measurements reported by different authors. In 1963 Wasserman and colleagues reported that the O_2 debt of trained subjects performing the same level of work ranged between 540 and 2,060 ml! So, as stated by Denolin in 1952, the O_2 payment may vary largely, even in normal subjects. Yet, as we shall see, this is not one of the major difficulties of the problem.

THE RELATION BETWEEN O_2 PAYMENT AND O_2 DEBT. Different authors have obtained different results for this relation. Hill (25) and Royce (50) found the O_2 payment was the exact mirror of the O_2 debt with respect to oxygen consumption. On the other hand, Lukin and colleagues (37) found that the payment was always greater than the O_2 debt. We found the same results and when normal subjects sustained a load of 600 kg per minute for fifteen minutes, the ratio of payment to debt had an average value of 1.3. In fact, a ratio of unity is unlikely because after work the excess O_2 consumption has many different functions, including transformation of L into P; resynthesis of ATP; oxidation of different enzymes; resaturation of myoglobin; increase in ventilatory and cardiac work relative to resting levels; compensation of the O_2 deficit in the working legs and resaturation of the venous blood, which may sometimes reach a very low saturation during work; and increase of basal metabolism related to the higher temperature of the body (in heavy work). Of course, none of these factors are operative at the beginning of the work.

The Mechanism of the Oxygen Debt

Most investigators have stated that the origin of the oxygen debt and consequently the reason for cellular hypoxia is an insufficient or delayed increase of the cardiac output (CO). This was first suggested by Meakins and colleagues (43) and by Harrison and colleagues (24), and it was confirmed again by Huckabee in 1958. According to this last author a normal subject is able to supply 95 percent of the body O_2 requirements, while patients with mitral stenosis or heart failure are able to supply only 50 to 80 percent. However, Huckabee also said that although cardiac output is less in cardiac patients, the mean increase does not differ significantly from normal subjects, and there is a large scatter of the experimental points. The importance of a reduced cardiac output and its relation to O_2 debt was investigated experimentally by Alpert (4). He was unable to find any correlation between the reduction of CO caused by cardiac tamponade, the $\dot{V}o_2$ "missed" during exercise, and the recovery O_2 consumption.

In our view there is not an exact relationship between the rate of increase of the cardiac output, the oxygen debt, and the level of L. We have measured the cardiac output at repeated intervals at the beginning of physical work and compared these results with the level of L, both in normal patients and in cases of mitral stenosis. Although the validity of the Stewart Hamilton

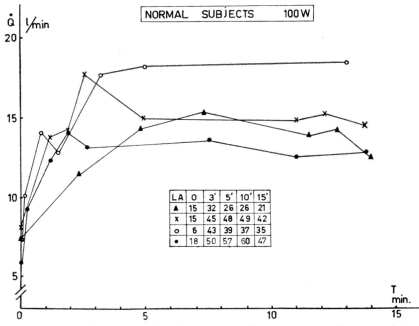

FIGURE 9-1. The relationship between cardiac output and accumulation of arterial lactate during exercise. Data on four normal subjects.

technique may be open to some criticism on account of the absence of a true steady state (but when does a true steady state begin and end?), we think that our results may be taken into account on the basis of both the validity and reproducibility of the curves obtained and the results themselves (Figs. 9-1 and 9-2).

In normal subjects the resting CO is about 6 to 8 liters per minute. One normal subject has a slow increase of CO, and we observe the lowest levels of L in his case. In the three other subjects the increase of CO is of uniform magnitude and occurs with uniform delay. Steady state CO values of about 13 liters per minute are obtained for each of these three subjects, but the levels of L measured at the third, fifth, tenth, and thirteenth minute are quite different from one subject to another.

In patients with mitral stenosis the resting CO is lower than in normal subjects, but the increase of CO is rapid and the

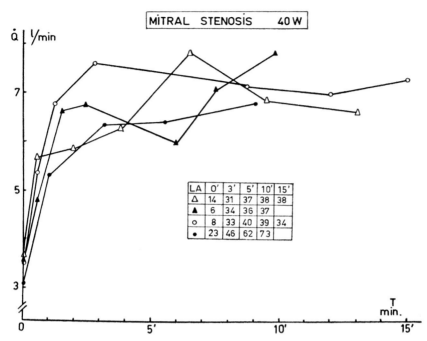

LA	0'	3'	5'	10'	15'
Δ	14	31	37	38	38
▲	6	34	36	37	
o	8	33	40	39	34
●	23	46	62	73	

FIGURE 9-2. The relationship between cardiac output and accumulation of arterial lactate during exercise. Data on patients with mitral stenosis.

changes of flow with time are quite different from one subject to another. Here too, the discrepancy between the levels of L may sometimes be very important (compare case ▲ and case Δ), and there seems a lack of correlation between the evolution of cardiac output at the beginning of work and the level of L.

Thus, the relationships between O_2 debt, the rate of increase of CO, and the level of L is probably much more complicated than was appreciated previously. One other factor that may also be important is the amount of flow to the working legs. It is well known that in the exercising limb, the blood flow may increase to more than fifteen times the resting value, and in severe exercise the blood flow to the legs may represent 70 to 80 percent of the total blood flow (56). The saturation of venous blood may then be very low, and values of 5 percent have been reported. The techniques used by Wade and colleagues give only approximate results; nevertheless, they have made the very important observation that during physical activity there is a major redistribution of blood flow, leading to a decrease in perfusion of the resting legs and the splanchnic area (19a) (21). The decrease occurs in a resting leg even if the other leg is working (9). The saturation of venous blood (Sv,o_2) in the working leg thus gives a good indication of the blood flow: the lowest Sv,o_2 corresponds to the highest extraction of oxygen with little need for anaerobic processes (9). On the contrary, when the Sv,o_2 is relatively high with a high pulse rate and thus a high cardiac output, a relatively small proportion of the total CO is directed to the working legs, while a greater amount of blood flows through inactive tissues. This is characteristic of vasoregulatory asthenia, a condition where there may be a very high level of L even if CO is normal or elevated because, for the same increase in heart rate, 50 percent of the increased CO is directed to the working legs compared with 75 percent or more in trained subjects (10). This implies that the measurement of the partial pressure of P,o_2 is insufficient and certainly does not mirror the state of hypoxia of the cell. If the flow to the working muscle is adequate, O_2 extraction is high, L level is low, and Sv,o_2 is low. If the flow to the working muscle is inadequate, the O_2 extraction is lower, and Sv,o_2 and L are higher. The relative independence of the pO_2 of mixed venous blood, the level of L, and the amount of O_2 debt has been underlined in the experience of Alpert (4).

So, the important question for our study of the O_2 debt is not what occurs in the steady state period but what is the rate of increase of blood flow during the first seconds or minutes of physical work. And, in fact, what is vital is not the flow to the working limb but the flow to the active muscles. These must receive, at the beginning of work, the greatest amount of O_2 in the shortest time possible. Unfortunately, it is very difficult, if not impossible, to measure the slope of the increase of the circulation to working muscles in man. But, in our view the adaptation of this local circulation will probably provide the key to a true understanding of the O_2 debt.

Remarks Concerning the Measurement of L and P

Many discrepancies exist in the literature about the relationship of L and P levels to O_2 consumption. Technical factors may influence the concentrations of metabolites that are found; we instance measurement in plasma or total blood and use of arterial or venous samples (the sample should always be taken from an artery or from "arterialized" blood); the moment of sampling may also be important and the level of P or L may be influenced by the type of work. All these factors have been emphasized in detail elsewhere (15).

On the basis of our experience in more than fifteen hundred tests with multiple measurements of L carried out under different conditions on normal and pathological subjects, the following features deserve emphasis:

1. We have *always* observed an increase of L with exercise, provided the measurements are made several times during work. With loads of 40W, an increase of L may be observed in untrained subjects, but this increase is temporary and of a lesser magnitude.

2. In certain cases when work is not too heavy and can be sustained for a long time (60 minutes or more), L disappears progressively during work. Our observations here are in agreement with those of others (5, 6, 23, 38). In fact, during physical work which does not exceed fifteen minutes, a progressive decrease of L often occurs, the levels being highest at the fifth minute (15). It is only during sustained work that L progressively increases, as was demonstrated by Margaria (39, 41). The significance of the progressive decrease of L during work is not clear. It is not related to an increase of the extracellular space; measurement by the thiocyanate technique shows that this does not increase (13). The most probable explanation is that if L is not present in too great a quantity, it may be metabolized during work, so that a fraction of the O_2 debt is repaid during exercise. The quantity of O_2 necessary to oxidize the small amount of L involved is not detectable by our methods of measuring O_2 consumption.

3. The *curves* for L disappearance that we have measured *after work* differ one from another (15) but we have been unable

to determine any possible mathematical basis for their analysis. In fact, the curve of blood L after work is bound to be very complicated because it is the resultant of two groups of factors, one of which is adding L to plasma and the other which is responsible for its disappearance.

The sources of L are the following: The limb muscles represent an important proportion of the body cells. At the end of exhausting work they may contain large amounts of L, which are discharged into the bloodstream and are responsible for the peak concentration of L that is sometimes observed just after work ends. L may eventually be produced by sustained hyperventilation, particularly if a high pH or a low Pa,co_2 is developed (20, 29, 52). However, in our experience we have never found high levels L in patients ventilated by a respirator, despite mild respiratory alkalosis (pH 7.5 and Pa,co_2 30). L that is produced at the beginning of physical work diffuses into the cells; after work ceases, this L leaves the cells and appears again in the plasma.

The reasons for the disappearance of L are oxidation of L to CO_2 and H_2O; synthesis of L to glycogen by the liver, using energy furnished by the oxidation of L; and loss of L in urine and sweat; this last route of loss is sometimes important when physical work is performed at high environmental temperatures.

The course of L disappearance is thus the resultant of many different factors, some acting in opposite ways and directions, and it is not surprising that the curve does not conform to any convenient mathematical formula.

Remarks Concerning the Equivalence Between the O_2 Excess, O_2 Consumption, and the Oxidation of L

In order to carry out this type of calculation, it is necessary to assume that L is evenly distributed in the water phase of the body when exercise stops. If this is so and assuming that we know the water fraction of blood and tissues, the total L of the body may be calculated. Unfortunately, although L is very diffusible within the organism, a number of facts and experiments make it obvious that L is not distributed equally throughout the body water:

1. We have calculated the level of L in red cells and in plasma; corrections were made for the protein content of these two media. Even with these corrections there is an important gradient of L between plasma and red cells. Similar observations have been made for P. For L the regression equation can be expressed as follows:

$$Y_{plas.} = -10.8 + 2.2\, x_{cells}$$

For P the regression equation can be expressed by

$$Y_{plas.} = 0.64 + 1.42\, x_{cells} \quad (15)$$

It can be seen that the difference in concentration of P between plasma and red cells is more marked than for L. It is highly probable that similar gradients of L and P concentrations exist between other cells in the organism. Differences of L level between red cells, plasma, muscles, and testicles have been demonstrated by Gesell and colleagues (22). These differences are much more marked for high than for low levels of L.

2. When a subject is exercising on a bicycle and when blood samples are taken from the brachial artery and the brachial vein, there is always an important difference of L and P level between the two sampling sites, particularly if L exceeds 30 mg%. When the L level is higher (for example, more than 75 mg%), the arteriovenous difference remains throughout work and for as long as fifteen minutes afterwards. These observations prove that the saturation of the tissues with L is incomplete and that the diffusion of L into the tissues is slower than was thought previously. The disappearance of L is not due to some metabolic effect, since it is known that isolated muscle does not transform L into glycogen except in small amounts. An "uptake" of L by resting tissues was observed by De Coster (15), Carlson and colleagues (10), Freyschuss (21), and many others.

3. After strenuous work there is a discrepancy between the course of L disappearance and the decrease of $\dot{V}O_2$, the latter being normal while L has not yet returned to the basal level. This observation was made by Margaria in 1963.

4. To reproduce the disappearance of L, experiments have been conducted where L or P has been injected into dogs (1967). In such experiments L disappears slowly, while P disappears

more rapidly, showing two phases of clearance—a rapid and a slow one. This does not agree with what is observed after physical work, where both the form of the curves and the rate of disappearance of L and P are quite different. On the other hand, in the injection experiments the increase of $\dot{V}o_2$ is small and does not correspond to the amount of L that would theoretically be burnt.

5. The low diffusion rate of L has been demonstrated by Alpert and Root (2), who injected L in eviscerated and hepatectomized animals. With large injections of L, even after forty mintues the volume of diffusion represented only 70 percent of the total body water. The same investigators (2) have proved that following hypoxia, where another form of O_2 debt has been created, there is no relationship between the excess O_2 consumption and the L removed. Kayne and colleagues (35) have demonstrated that during exercise under different experimental conditions (hepatectomy; hepatectomy + evisceration; hepatectomy, evisceration, and insulin injection) there is no statistical relationship between the O_2 excess and the L removed.

So, if it is impossible to know on the one hand the quantity of L present in the total body water and on the other hand, it is difficult to calculate the oxygen debt accurately, we can conclude with Alpert that excess O_2 consumption and removal of L are coincidentally but not causally related.

Remarks Concerning the Concept of XL

The notion of XL has been very popular during the last few years, and it has been used by many investigators who have studied different conditions, including shock (8, 49), where hypoxia may be very severe. However, Olson (48) and Hughes and colleagues (34) have criticized the concept of Huckabee from both theoretical and chemical points of view. They have pointed out that the rates of variances in competing reactions are more important than equilibrium constants, that there are at least two pools of DPNH/DPN in the cells and that the behavior of these two systems may be different, that there are many chemical processes taking place within the cells, and that XL may increase without anoxia. These various factors may explain some of the amazing results that we have observed, like a progressive decrease of XL or even a negative value if exercise is slight. Similar observations have been made by Thomas and colleagues (53), Wasserman and colleagues (55), and P. Harris and colleagues (23). We did not find the ideal correlation between XL and O_2 debt described by Huckabee, nor did we find high levels of L in cases of hyperventilation with respiratory alkalosis. We are of the opinion that the concept of Huckabee needs further confirmation, and we are in complete agreement with Hughes and colleagues (34), Kayne and Alpert (35), and Olsen (48), who demonstrated that measurement of XL during exercise adds little to the measurement of blood lactate alone.

References

1. ALPERT, N.R.: Effect of acute cardiac tamponade upon respiratory metabolism of the dog. *Amer J Physiol, 168*:565, 1952.

2. ALPERT, N.R., and ROOT, W.S.: Relationship between excess respiratory metabolism and utilization of intravenously infused sodium racemic lactate and sodium L (-) lactate. *Amer J Physiol, 177*:455, 1954.

3. ALPERT, N.R., KAYNE, H., and HASLETT, W.: Relationship among recovery oxygen, oxygen missed, lactate production and lactate removal during and following severe hypoxia in the unanesthetized dog. *Amer J Physiol, 192*:585, 1958.

4. ALPERT, N.R.: Lactate production and removal and the regulation of metabolism. *Ann NY Acad Sci, 119*:995, 1965.

5. ASTRAND, P.O., HÄLLBACK, I., HEDMAN, R., and SALTIN, B.: Blood lactates after prolonged severe exercise. *J Appl Physiol, 18*:619, 1963.

6. BANG, O.: The lactate content of the blood during and after muscular exercise in man. *Skand Arch Physiol, 74* (Suppl. 10), 1936.

7. BERTRAM, F.W., WASSERMAN, K., and VAN KESSEL, A.L.: Gas exchange following lactate and pyruvate injections. *J Appl Physiol, 23*:190, 1967.

8. BRODER, G., and WEIL, M.N.: Excess lactate: an index of reversibility of shock in human patients. *Science, 143*:1458, 1964.

9. CARLSON, L.A., and PERNOW, B.: Studies on the peripheral circu-

lation and metabolism in man. (I) O_2 utilization and lactate pyruvate formation in the legs at rest and during exercise in healthy subjects. *Acta Physiol Scand,* 52:328, 1961.

10. CARLSON, L.A., PERNOW, B., and ZETTERQUIST, S.: Studies on the peripheral circulation and metabolism in man. III) O_2 utilization and lactate pyruvate formation in the legs at rest and during exercise in subjects with hyperkinetic circulation and low physical capacity (vasoregulatory asthenia) and in healthy females. *Acta Med Scand,* 172:389, 1962.

11. DE COSTER, A., and MESSIN, R.: Evolution des acides lactiques artériel et veineux au cours des épreuves d'effort. *Arch Int Physiol,* 72:567, 1964.

12. DE COSTER, A., MESSIN, R., and FRANCKSON, J.R.M.: Répartition de l'acide lactique entre plasma et globules rouges chez l'homme. comparaison des résultats fournis par différentes méthodes de dosage. *Arch Int Physiol,* 74:251, 1966.

13. DE COSTER, A.: Les éspaces extracellulaires au cours de l'effort physique. Fonds de la Recherche Scientifique Médicale, 1966, p. 136.

14. DE COSTER, A., MESSIN, R., and DEGRÉ, S.: Etude critique de la notion d'excess lactate. *Fonds de la Recherche Scientifique Médicale,* 1966, p.129.

15. DE COSTER, A., DENOLIN, H., MESSIN, R., and VANDERMOTEN, P.: Role of the metabolites in the acid-base balance during exercise. *Medicine and Sport,* 3:15, 1969.

16. DENOLIN, H.: Exploration de la fonction cardiopulmonaire au cours de l'effort. *Acta Clin Belg,* 7:229, 1952.

17. DE MICHELI, A.: Contribution à l'étude de la fonction cardio-respiratoire au cours de l'exercice musculaire et de la phase de récupération chez les sujets normaux. *Rev Franç Etud Clin Biol,* 2:251, 1957.

18. DILL, D.B.: The economy of muscular exercise. *Physiol Rev,* 16:273, 1936.

19. DILL, D.B., EDWARDS, H.T., NEWMAN, E.V., and MARGARIA, R.: Analysis of recovery from anaerobic work. *Arbeitsphysiol,* 9:299, 1936.

19a. DONALD, K.W., BISHOP, J.M., CUMMING, G., and WADE, O.L.: The effect of exercise on the cardiac output and circulatory dynamics of normal subjects. *Clin Sci,* 14:37-73, 1955.

20. EICHENHOLZ, A.: Respiratory alkalosis. *Arch Int Med, 116*:699, 1965.
21. FREYSCHUSS, U., and STRANDELL, T.: Limb circulation during arm and leg exercise in supine position. *J Appl Physiol, 23*:163, 1967.
22. GESELL, R., KRUEGER, K., NICHOLSON, H., BRASSFIELD, C., and PELECOVICH, M.: A comparison of the response of the anesthetized dog to lowered alveolar O_2 during uniform alveolar ventilation and during normally controlled respiration. *Amer J Physiol, 100*:202, 1932.
23. HARRIS, P., BATEMAN, M., BAYLEY, T.J., GLOSTER, J., and WHITEHEAD, J.: Observation on the course of the metabolic events accompanying mild exercise. *Quart J Exp Physiol, 53*:43, 1968.
24. HARRISON, T.R., and PILCHER, C.: Studies in congestive heart failure. II. The respiratory exchange during and after exercise *J Clin Invest, 8*:291, 1930.
25. HILL, A.V., LONG, C.N.H., and LUPTON, H.: Muscular exercise, lactic acid and the supply and utilisation of oxygen. I. *Proc Roy Soc, [Biol] 96*:438, 1924.
26. HILL, A.V., LONG, C.N., and LUPTON, H.: Muscular exercise, lactic acid, and the supply and utilisation of oxygen. II. *Proc Roy Soc [Biol], 97*:84, 1924.
27. HILL, A.V., LONG, C.N., and LUPTON, H.: Muscular exercise, lactic acid and the supply and utilisation of oxygen. III. *Proc Roy Soc [Biol], 97*:155, 1925.
28. HUCKABEE, W.E.: Relationships of pyruvate and lactate during anaerobic metabolism. 1) Effects of infusion of pyruvate or glucose and of hyperventilation. *J Clin Invest, 37*:244, 1958.
29. HUCKABEE, W.E.: Relationships of pyruvate and lactate during anaerobic metabolism. II) Exercise and formation of O_2 debt. *J Clin Invest, 37*:255, 1958.
30. HUCKABEE, W.E.: Relationships of pyruvate and lactate during anaerobic metabolism. III) Effect of breathing low oxygen gases. *J Clin Invest, 37*:264, 1958.
31. HUCKABEE, W.E., and JUDSON, W.E.: The role of anaerobic metabolism in the performance of mild muscular work. I) Relationship to oxygen consumption and cardiac output and the effect of congestive heart failure. *J Clin Invest, 37*:1577, 1958.
32. HUCKABEE, W.E.: The role of anaerobic metabolism in the per-

formance of mild muscular work. II. The effect of asymptomatic heart disease. *J Clin Invest,* 37:1593, 1958.

33. HUCKABEE, W.E.: Relationship of pyruvate and lactate during anaerobic metabolism. IV. Tissue components of total O_2 debt. *Amer J Physiol,* 196:253, 1959.

34. HUGHES, R.L., CLODE, M., EDWARDS, R.H.T., GOODWIN, T.J., and JONES, N.L.: Effect of inspired O_2 on cardiopulmonary and metabolic responses to exercise in man. *J Appl Physiol,* 24:336, 1968.

35. KAYNE, H.L., and ALPERT, N.R.: Oxygen consumption following exercise in the anesthetized dog. *Amer J Physiol,* 206:51, 1964.

36. KNUTTGEN, H.G.: Oxygen debt, lactate, pyruvate and excess lactate after muscular work. *J Appl Physiol,* 17:639, 1962.

37. LUKIN, L., and RALSTON, H.J.: Oxygen deficit and repayment in exercise. *Int Z Angew Physiol,* 19:183, 1962.

38. LUNDIN, G., and STRÖM, G.: The concentration of blood lactic acid in man during muscular work in relation to the partial pressure of oxygen of the inspired air. *Acta Physiol Scand,* 13:253, 1947.

39. MARGARIA, R., EDWARDS, H.T., and DILL, D.B.: The possible mechanisms of contracting and paying the oxygen debt and the role of lactic acid in muscular contraction. *Amer J Physiol,* 106:689, 1933.

40. MARGARIA, R., and EDWARDS, H.T.: The removal of lactic acid from the body during recovery from muscular exercise. *Amer J Physiol,* 107:681, 1934.

41. MARGARIA, R.: Biochemistry of muscular contraction and recovery. *J Sport Med,* 3:145, 1963.

42. MARGARIA, R., CERRETELLI, P., DI PRAMPERO, P.E., MASSARI, C., and TERELLI, G.: Kinetics and mechanism of oxygen debt contraction in man. *J Appl Physiol,* 18:371, 1963.

43. MEAKINS, J., and LONG, C.N.H.: Oxygen consumption, oxygen debt and lactic acid in circulatory failure. *J Clin Invest,* 4:273, 1927.

44. MEYERHOF, O.: Die Energieumwandlungen im Muskel. I. Ueber die Beziehungen der Milchsaure zur Warmebildung und Arbeitleistung des Muskels in der Anaerobiose. *Arch Ges Physiol,* 182:232, 1920.

45. MEYERHOF, O.: Die Energieumwandlungen im Muskel. II. Das Schicksal der Milchsaure in der Erholungsperiode des Muskels. *Arch Ges Physiol,* 182:284, 1920.

46. MEYERHOF, O.: Die Energieumwandlungen im Muskel. III. Kohlenhydrat und Milchsaureumsatz im Froschmuskel. *Arch Ges Physiol, 185*:11, 1920.

47. NYLIN, G.: The practical applicability of the cardiopulmonary function test. *Acta Med Scand (Suppl.), 93*:7, 1938.

48. OLSON, R.E.: Excess lactate and anaerobiosis. *Ann Int Med, 59*:960, 1963.

49. PERRET, CL.: L'acidose métabolique au cours du choc. *Journées de réanimation neuro-respiratoire, Hôpital Claude-Bernard,* 1966, p. 129.

50. ROYCE, J.: Oxygen consumption during submaximal exercises of equal intensity and different duration. *Int Z Angew Physiol, 19*:218, 1962.

51. SUTTON, F.C., BRITTON, J.A., and CARA, J.G.: Estimation of cardiopulmonary functional capacity by means of oxygen debt studies. *Amer Heart J, 20*:423, 1940.

52. TAKANO, N.: Blood lactate accumulation and its causation: factors during passive hyperventilation in dogs. *Jap J Physiol, 16*:481, 1966.

53. THOMAS, H.D., BOSHELL, B., GAOS, C., and REEVES, J.J.: Cardiac output during exercise and anaerobic metabolism in man. *J Appl Physiol, 19*:839, 1964.

54. THOMAS, H.D., GAOS, G., and JAUGHMAN, C.W.: Respiratory O_2 debt and excess lactate in man. *J Appl Physiol, 20*:898, 1965.

55. WASSERMAN, K., BURTON, G.G., and VAN KESSEL, A.L.: Excess lactate concept and 0_2 debt of exercise. *J Appl Physiol, 20*:1299, 1965.

56. WADE, O.L., and BISHOP, J.M.: Cardiac Output and Regional Blood Flow. Oxford, Blackwell Scientific Publications, 1962.

Chapter 10

CURRENT CONCEPTS OF WALKING AND RUNNING

RODOLFO MARGARIA

The Components of Mechanical Work During Locomotion

T HE TOTAL mechanical work done by the muscles during loco-motion may be considered as having two component fractions, external and internal. The *external work* is the component that leads to displacement of the center of gravity of the body. The *internal work* is the remaining fraction, and this is spent a) in isometric contractions that confer rigidity on the limbs and fix the joints, b) in equal and opposite movements of body parts with no displacement of the center of gravity of the body, and c) in overcoming muscle viscosity. As the mechanical work can be measured only when the acceleration of the center of gravity of the body or the force that is applied to it is known, the direct measurement of the internal work accomplished is not possible. The external work, on the contrary, may be calculated from the displacement of the center of gravity of the body if this can be measured.

Measurement of External Work

Photography

There are three methods to measure displacements of the center of gravity of the body. The first method is to take either static pictures of the moving body at intervals (9, 10) or high speed motion pictures (6, 7, 8). The center of the body is not fixed; in the erect position it is situated in the trunk some-what in front of the lumbar vertebrae, but it is displaced with the movements of the limbs relative to the trunk; in consequence, displacements of the trunk are not representative of the displacement of the center of gravity of the body. A correction must be made for displacements of the center of gravity within the trunk: this is possible if the position of the limbs relative to the trunk is known and if the limbs are considered as separate systems with known mass and position of their center of gravity; the method has been illustrated in detail by Fisher (10) and Fenn (8).

Accelerometry

Cavagna, Saibene, and Margaria (2) measured external work from displacements of the trunk as recorded by applying to the lumbosacral segment of the vertebral column a small three-directional accelerometer sensitive to vertical, forward, and lateral components of motion: by a double graphic integration of three records, the displacements of the trunk in the three directions could be calculated. To measure displacement of the center of gravity within the trunk, the displacements of the limbs relative to the trunk were measured at the same time with the aid of a cine-camera, following Fisher's method. However, the triple accelerometer does not have a very wide range of application because a change in inclination of the trunk and consequently of the accelerometer, changes the action of the earth's gravitational field upon the three elements of the accelerometer. This effect is particularly great in running, thus rendering the method unapplicable under these conditions.

The most direct and convenient method to measure the forces applied to the body in walking or running is to step on a platform sensitive to the vertical and to the forward components of the force exerted by the foot on the ground: the lateral component is small (less than 1%) and can therefore be neglected. From these indications the extent and the direction of the force acting on the center of gravity of the body (acceleration) can be recorded, and by successive integration, velocity changes and displacement of the center of gravity can be calculated.

Calculation of External Work

When the vertical displacement S_v of the center of gravity of the body is known, the work performed in lifting the body is easily calculated if the weight of the body P is also known. The *potential energy* change (W_v) is given by $W_v = P S_v$. The work (W_F) that is met in overcoming the cyclic speed changes that take place at every step (the *kinetic energy* change) can also be calculated from the equation

$$W_F = \tfrac{1}{2} m \left(V^2_{max} - V^2_{min} \right)$$

where V_{max} and V_{min} are, respectively, the known frontal maximum and minimum speeds and m is the body mass. The total mechanical energy E_{TOT} may then be considered as the sum of potential and kinetic components; the assumption is made provisionally that no other kind of mechanical energy is produced, as, for example, the energy involved in stretching an elastic body such as contracted muscle.

Walking

It has been shown that in walking the cyclic changes of potential energy are substantially opposite in phase to the changes of kinetic energy; consequently, the resultant total energy change E_{TOT} shows a smaller cyclic variation than that of the two components (see Fig. 10-1).

The implication of this appears to be that in walking the potential energy is transformed into kinetic and vice versa: the speed increases when the center of gravity of the body is lowered, and deceleration in the direction of progression takes place when the body is rising.

Running

When running at a constant speed, on the contrary, the kinetic and potential energy changes are substantially in phase, and the total energy change turns out to be approximately the sum of the two components (Fig 10-2). In running the transformation of energy from kinetic into potential and vice versa cannot take place, as both increase or decrease simultaneously.

A Comparison of Walking and Running

If the transformation of one form of energy into the other were complete in walking, the total external work performed

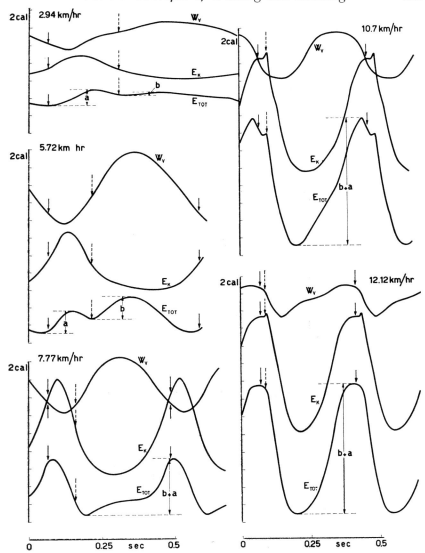

FIGURE 10-1. Work against gravity (W_v), kinetic energy of the body (E_k), and total energy change ($E_{tot} = W_v + E_k$). On the ordinate, 2 cal between marks; on the abscissa, time in seconds. The different groups of curves refer to different walking speeds as indicated. The full arrow indicates the moment at which the heel contacts the ground; the broken arrow, the moment at which the other foot leaves the ground. The increments a and b of the curve E_{tot} indicate the positive external work performed at each step. (From Cavagna and Margaria, 1966.)

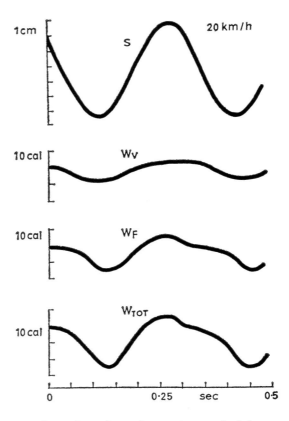

FIGURE 10-2. Work resulting from changes in speed of the center of gravity of the body in forward direction (W_F) and from vertical displacements (W_V) during level running at 20 km per hour; W_{TOT} is the sum of the two. Displacements of the center of gravity of the body in a vertical direction are indicated by S. The scale for W is 10 cal between marks and for S is 1 cm between marks. (From Cavagna *et al.*, 1964.)

would be nil, and no work would be required to maintain a constant speed. As a matter of fact, transformation is never complete, and some external work must be performed at each step to maintain a constant speed of progression. However, a large percentage is transformed, and this is probably the reason why walking is so much more economical than running; at the most economical speed, it requires half the energy needed for running the same distance. From the determinations of Margaria (12) and Margaria and others (17), the cost of covering 1 meter is 0.5 cal per kilogram when walking, while it amounts to 1.0 cal per kilogram when running.

The Mechanical Efficiency of Walking

The curve of the total energy level of the body during walking (W_{TOT}) indicates that there are two phases of increasing energy *a* and *b*, which are separated by two interposed phases in which the energy level decreases (Fig. 10-1). An increase of energy level requires external *positive work*, which must be performed by the muscles: a decrease of the energy level, on the contrary, implies either the performance of *negative work* by the muscles (the contracted muscle being stretched instead of being allowed to shorten) or other forms of energy dissipation such as friction. Assuming that the work resulting from friction is negligible while walking on the level at a constant moderate speed, then the negative work performed by the muscles is exactly equal to the positive work performed at other points in the stepping cycle.

The performance of both positive and negative work requires energy, which is supplied by the contracting muscles. The efficiency of both processes is well known; from measurements of the energy cost of exercise implying only positive or negative work: it was found to be 0.25 for the positive and −1.2 for the negative (11, 14, 15). Assuming that no work is lost in friction and that the decrease of the overall energy level (E_{TOT}) is due only to the negative work performed, the efficiency of walking on the level is easily calculated as 0.207.

The Analogy of a Rolling Egg

The opposition of phase between the kinetic and potential energy curves, then, leads to a rather flat curve of W_{TOT}, indicative of transformation of one form of energy into the other; it reminds one of the condition of an egg rolling end over end on a horizontal surface. The vertical trajectory of the egg's center of gravity will be similar to the curve S_v, and the potential and the kinetic energy levels will follow paths similar to the curves

W_v and W_F. However, the sum of the two curves (W_{TOT}) would simply be a horizontal line in the idealized case in which the egg neither performed work on the environment nor gathered energy from it.

Strictly speaking, the egg loses some energy in friction, and the conversion of potential into kinetic energy and vice versa is not complete: some extra energy must therefore be supplied to the egg if its speed is to be maintained constant.

In this respect the rolling egg is a very good model of human walking: in the human case extra energy is supplied by the push of the foot on the ground, a force that is directed substantially upward toward the center of gravity of the body. Practically vertical at low speed, the push of the foot is displaced a little forward as one walks faster; however, even at maximum walking speed the line of the body is not greatly displaced from the vertical. The force supplied by muscular activity therefore has a very small component in the direction of progression. It is utilized mainly in lifting the body, thereby increasing its potential energy; the latter in turn is transformed into kinetic energy, which is responsible for the horizontal displacement of the body.

The Analogy of a Bouncing Ball

The situation in running is quite different. Running differs from walking mainly in that the push of the foot at each step is directed both upward and frontward, increasing the potential and the kinetic energy of the body at the same time. While the upward component of the push reaches a constant value, that is, about the same magnitude as the body weight and independent of speed (Fig. 10-3) (16), the forward component increases as the speed increases, so that the direction of push must be inclined in a more forward direction. The contemporary increase of the kinetic and potential energy components leaves no possibility that one kind of energy is transformed into the other.

The rolling egg is no longer a good model; running can better be compared to a bouncing ball: in this the energy of the bounce comes from elastic energy stored as an effect of the deformation that takes place when the ball strikes the ground.

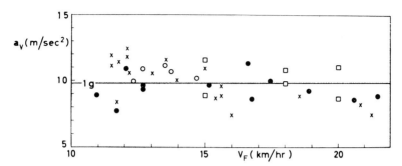

FIGURE 10-3. Mean values for the vertical acceleration of the center of gravity of the body at each step (a_v) as a function of running speed (v_F). A line has been drawn at the 1 g value. (From Margaria and Cavagna, 1964.)

The Frictional Speed Limit

As the speed reached in running is due to the horizontal component of the push and the vertical push is constant and independent of speed, the running speed is therefore directly related to the angle that the direction of the push makes with the horizontal. This reaches a minimum value of about 45 degrees on hard ground. A smaller angle would imply that the horizontal component of the force was greater than the weight of the runner; on any conceivable surface the runner's feet would then slip. This is why sprinters wear shoes that nail themselves to the ground. If a man is running on ice or on sandy ground where the coefficient of friction is less than for ordinary soil, the push must necessarily be more nearly vertical, decreasing the possible forward component and therefore the speed of progression.

The Importance of Body Weight and
Gravitational Acceleration

As the maximal speed of progression is limited by the angle that the direction of the push makes with the horizontal and as the vertical component of the push is constant and equal to the body weight, it follows that by increasing the body weight, the horizontal component of the push and therefore the speed of progression can be increased correspondingly, provided, of course that the muscles can meet the increased energy requirement. Conversely, people with a low body weight are limited in their maximal speed of progression.

On the moon, where the *gravitational force* is about a sixth of that on earth; the weight of the body and therefore the vertical force exerted by the foot on the ground when running will be reduced by the same factor; the energy cost of this work component will also be correspondingly reduced. As the angle of the push cannot be reduced below 45 degrees, the horizontal component of the maximal push, that is, the propelling force in the direction of progression, will also be reduced to a sixth. Although the length of step will be about the same as on earth, the time taken per step will be much greater, and the step frequency will thus be lower. The time required for the center of gravity to shift from its highest to its lowest position (time of fall) will also be increased under conditions of lunar gravity by

about $\sqrt{\dfrac{1}{6}} = \dfrac{1}{2.5}$. For all these reasons the speed of walking

on the moon will be no greater than 2 to 2.5 km per hour, and the speed of running no more than 6 to 12 km per hour, depending on the coefficient of friction between the feet and the surface of the ground (16, 13).

To reach a higher speed of progression on the moon, a third mechanism must be tried, namely *jumping*. This will be very easy because the muscular power per kilogram of body weight is increased sixfold on the moon: this would give us a favorable condition comparable to that met by kangaroos or grasshoppers on earth. A jump will take longer, however, thus limiting the frequency of jumping, particularly for powerful jumps; on the other hand, the greater the push, the greater will be the horizontal component of it and the consequent speed of progression. A speed as high as that attained when running on the earth will probably be possible, even where the frictional coefficient between the foot and the soil is very low. However, astronauts on the moon will not enjoy the same freedom that athletes have on earth because their space suits may limit movements considerably.

The Influence of Slope on Mechanical Efficiency

If the mechanical work is measured when walking or running on the level as described above, the efficiency of this exercise can be calculated, since the energy costs of walking and running are both well known (11, 17). The energy expenditure of walking at different speeds on different inclines is summarized in Figure 10-4. For running the energy cost per kilometer covered appears to be constant and independent of speed; it can therefore be plotted simply as a function of the incline of the ground (Fig 10-5). By assuming that the components of work required to sustain the vertical oscillations of the body and its speed changes at every step are negligible and considering only the changes of potential energy level, the slope of the ground can be related to the mechanical work performed per meter covered and per kilogram of body weight: isoefficiency lines can then be drawn. It appears that when walking up increasing inclines, the efficiency tends to 0.25, a value which is maintained constant for inclines from 0.20 to 0.40; walking downhill a tendency to an efficiency of about −1.2 is evident; this reaches a constant value for inclines greater than about 0.15. Whether walking uphill or downhill, at high incline values the center of gravity no longer oscillates vertically but moves in one direction only; also, when walking uphill at a necessarily slow speed, the work resulting from speed changes at every step is negligible. The assumptions made above are therefore valid at high incline values. However, when walking on the level, these assumptions are no longer correct, and the mechanical work must be measured more precisely, using the methods indicated early in this chapter.

Efficiency During Running

While walking at the most economical speed, the mechanical work performed, as measured from the vertical oscillations of the body and from the speed changes, is just about a quarter of the energy expenditure, thus supporting an efficiency of 0.25. In running the mechanical work appears to be half the energy expenditure or a little less, corresponding to an efficiency, as calculated conventionally, of about 40 to 45 percent. This "im-

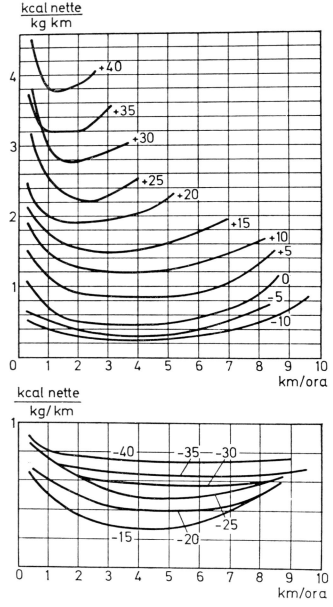

FIGURE 10-4. The energy expenditure of a man walking on a treadmill has been measured and the basal value subtracted to obtain the net cost of walking: by dividing this value by the speed, the energy expenditure per

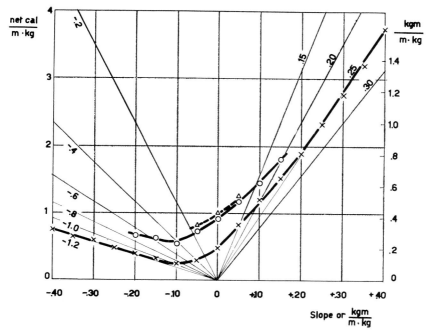

FIGURE 10-5. Energy expenditures per kilogram of body weight and per meter, walking at the most economical speed (x) and running as a function of the incline of the ground: the data for running are valid for all speed values. (○) athletes, (Δ) nonathletes. Isoefficiency lines are also indicated. (From Margaria *et al.*, 1963.)

possible" efficiency led to the discovery that a very substantial fraction of energy is absorbed by contracted muscle during the falling phase of each step at the impact of the foot on the ground; this energy is given back as positive work immediately afterwards, during the shortening phase of muscular action (3). The energy, in great part at least, is stored in the elastic form through stretching of the series elastic elements of the muscle.

◄

kilometer is obtained: this, related to 1 kg of body weight (ordinate) is plotted as a function of the speed in kilometers per hour (abscissa) at different inclines in uphill (+) and downhill (−) walking as indicated. (From Margaria, 1938.)

Thus, during running the negative work performed by the muscles as they are stretched by the body weight and by inertial forces at the end of each step is not all wasted; a considerable fraction of it can be utilized and given back as positive work immediately afterwards. Walking downhill, on the contrary, the negative work performed by the muscles is not utilized; at the end of the phase of stretching the muscles rest, and the elastic energy accumulated during the stretch is dissipated.

The positive work done in running, as measured by Cavagna *et al.* (3), is therefore not all due to chemical transformations that take place in the actively shortening muscles but is to a considerable extent contaminated by the elastic recoil of the previously stretched contracted muscles.

On account of this "error," the calculated efficiency appears to be paradoxically higher in running than in walking uphill at a necessarily slow pace. Running involves fast movements and a high speed of contraction and possibly accessory movements; however, in walking uphill no appreciable negative work is performed during any phase of the step, and therefore, no accumulation of elastic energy takes place.

Usage of Energy in Walking and Running

The problem arises how the energy is spent when walking or running. The energy spent in locomotion may ultimately be transformed a) into internal work, as defined above; b) into various forms of frictional work, such as wind resistance (which is nil while walking on a treadmill), the friction of the foot on the soil, and friction within the joints and muscles; and c) into changing the energy level of the body, namely in performing positive and/or negative work.

We have seen that the energy expenditure data for walking, plotted as a function of the incline of the ground (Fig. 10-5), is a straight line for a wide range of steep inclines. The relationship can be extrapolated back to zero slope, and since the change in energy level of the body is related to slope, this indicates, in my opinion, that all the energy expended in level walking at the most economical speed is due to changes in the energy level of the body, and no appreciable amount is spent in performing internal work or overcoming friction. If there were any form of frictional resistance to progression, this would be largely affected by speed, but in fact, speed seems to have very little influence on the cost of walking over a wide range of speeds around the optimal (Fig. 10-4), and in running (where a considerably higher speed is attained), it apparently has no influence at all.

The conclusion can thus be reached that the energy spent in locomotion over the speed range considered here is employed substantially to perform mechanical positive or negative work. When walking on the level at a constant speed, the change of overall energy level is nil, but changes that take place within the step must be considered: the positive work performed at a certain step phase is obviously equal to the negative work performed at a different phase of the step. By calling this mechanical work, W, the total energy expenditure can then be calculated, since the efficiency values for positive and negative work are known:

$$\text{Energy expended} = \frac{+W}{0.25} + \frac{-W}{-1.2} = \frac{W}{0.207}$$

All the energy spent walking on the level may be considered wasted, as it does not lead to any energy gain or loss by the body. In general, we may consider as wasted that amount of work, positive or negative, which is balanced by a corresponding amount of work of the opposite sign. As the efficiency in performance of the wasted work, W_w, is 0.207, the general formula for energy expenditure can be given as

$$\text{Energy expended} = En_g + \frac{1}{0.207} \cdot W_w$$

where En_g, the expenditure for energy gain, or loss, may be defined by

$$En_g = \frac{+W}{0.25}$$

for positive work and by

$$En_g = \frac{-W}{-1.2}$$

for negative work. The energy expenditure for the wasted work can be visualized in Figure 10-5 as the vertical distance between the experimental curve and the lines marked 0.25 or −1.2; it tends to zero for steep slopes, whether positive or negative (Fig. 10-6).

When walking or running on the level at conventional speeds, energy is spent only in restoring to a constant value the energy level that tends to fall in a certain phase of the step because of the peculiar characteristics of human lococotion. The same pattern of positive (or negative) work performance to compensate for negative (or positive) work performed previously is seen when a man climbs a staircase and then comes back to the starting point; however, in this case the alternation of positive and negative work is much better visualized, as it does not take place repetitively within each step cycle.

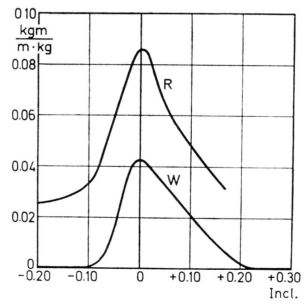

FIGURE 10-6. The amount of work wasted through performance of equal amounts of positive and negative work (ordinates); subjects walking (W) at the optimal speed and running (R) uphill (+) and downhill (−) (abscissa). (From Margaria, 1968.)

The Horizontal Component of Force

The energy expenditures shown on the ordinates of Figure 10-5 are expressed in kilograms per meter kilogram. If these data are multiplied by the efficiency, a figure is obtained for the mechanical work performed in covering unit distance; in other words, the constant pull in kilogram per kilogram of body weight required to keep the body in motion and meet the resistance to progression.

A constant pull of the amount thus indicated would successfully replace the pull developed by the muscles if it were employed to meet a) a frictional resistance or b) a gravitational resistance, such as is met in cycling, skating, swimming, skiing, (skilifting), and so forth, where only positive work is performed and no negative work takes place in any phase of exercise. However, this is not the case for walking or running; when walking downhill on a 4.4 percent incline, a constant pull of 44 gm per kilogram of body weight is acting in the direction of movement, the same as that involved in walking on the level; the energy expenditure in this condition should thus be nil. Nevertheless, it is reduced to only 60 percent of the value found when walking on the level, and even on steeper inclines the cost of walking is never reduced to less than 50 percent of the level value.

The fact that a constant external pull cannot completely take over the pull developed by the muscles is further evidence that the energy expended in level walking is employed not to meet resistance to progression but to perform positive and negative work within the step. The external pull can replace the work performed by the muscles during the positive phase of the stepping cycle, but it leads to an increase of the work that the muscles are bound to perform during the negative phase of the cycle, adding to the work load imposed by inertial forces. To avoid muscular action during the phase of negative work, the pull should be altered to a corresponding intensity in the reverse direction. However, the replacement of the pull of the muscles by an external force which changes direction and intensity within the step cycle appears a very difficult task.

We may conclude that, in both walking and running at ordinary speeds, the energy expenditure which does not appear as a change in the energy level of the body is employed in the performance of alternating positive and negative work within the step cycle; no appreciable amounts of energy are spent to overcome viscosity within the muscles or joints or to overcome the friction of the foot with the soil.

References

1. CAVAGNA, G.A., and MARGARIA, R.: Mechanics of walking. *J Appl Physiol, 21*:271-278, 1966.

2. CAVAGNA, G.A., SAIBENE, P., and MARGARIA, R.: External work in walking. *J Appl Physiol, 18*:1-9, 1963.

3. CAVAGNA, G.A., SAIBENE, P., and MARGARIA, R.: Mechanical work in running. *J Appl Physiol, 19*:249-256, 1964.

4. ELFTMANN, H.: Force exerted by ground in walking. *Arbeitsphysiol, 10*:485-491, 1939.

5. ELFTMANN, H.: Force and energy changes in the leg during walking. *Amer J Physiol, 125*:339-356, 1939.

6. FENN, W.O.: Mechanical energy expenditure in sprint running as measured by moving pictures. *Amer J Physiol, 90*:343-344, 1939.

7. FENN, W.O.: Frictional and kinetic factors in the work of sprint running. *Amer J Physiol, 92*:583-611, 1930.

8. FENN, W.O.: Work against gravity and work due to velocity changes in running. *Amer J Physiol, 93*:433-462, 1930.

9. FISCHER, O.: Der gangdes menschen. II Teil: Die Bewegung des gesamtschwerpunktes und die äusseren kräfte—Leipzig-Abh, 1899.

10. FISCHER, O.: Methodik der spesillen Bewegung slehere. *Tigerstedt's Handbook der Physiol, Meth II, 1*:188-208, 1911.

11. MARGARIA, R.: Sulla fisiologia e specialmente sul consumo energetico della marcia e della corsa a varie velocità ed inclinazioni del terreno. *Reale Acc Naz Linceri, Serie VI, Vol. III, fasc. V.* 297-299, 368, 1938.

12. MARGARIA, R.:Energy cost of walking, and running at different speeds and inclines of the ground. *Médicine, Éducation Physique et Sport,* numéro spéciale, Août 1963.

13. MARGARIA, R.: Walking, running and jumping on the moon. *New Scientist,* pp. 226-227, 1965.

14. MARGARIA, R.: Positive and negative work performances and their efficiencies in human locomotion. *Int Z Angew Physiol,* 25:339-351, 1968.

15. MARGARIA, R.: Capacity and power of the energy processes in muscle activity: their practical relevance in athletics. *Int Z Angew Physiol,* 25:352-369, 1968.

16. MARGARIA, R., and CAVAGNA, G.A.: Human locomotion in subgravity. *Aerospace Med,* 35:1140-1146, 1964.

17. MARGARIA, R., CERRETELLI, P., AGHEMO, P., and SASSI, G.: Energy cost of running. *J Appl Physiol,* 18:367-370, 1963.

Chapter 11

VISCERAL BLOOD FLOW AND METABOLISM DURING EXERCISE

Loring B. Rowell

Introduction

In resting man, the hepatic-splanchnic region receives a greater percentage of the total cardiac output than any other region— about 25 percent. Since, at resting blood flow, the splanchnic tissues extract only 10 to 25 percent of the available oxygen, a considerable reduction of flow could be tolerated before oxygen demand exceeded the supply. Thus, flow could be diverted from the region to supply increased flow elsewhere without compromising splanchnic function. This mechanism would also contribute to the maintenance of relatively constant total peripheral resistance. Flow to other organs could increase without increase in cardiac output.

In 1912 Krogh (22) postulated the necessity for a large venous reservoir capable of quickly delivering an autotransfusion of blood into the right heart during exercise—particularly in upright man. From Krogh's point of view the liver, by expelling a considerable volume of blood at the onset of exercise, could reduce any lag in venous return resulting from a sudden surge of blood from dilated resistance vessels of the muscle into compliant venous beds. In this way any residual imbalance between left and right ventricular output could be corrected rapidly. However, there is no evidence that rapid volume changes occur in the splanchnic vascular bed of man under these conditions. Rather,

Note: Studies from the author's laboratory were supported by National Heart Institute Grant-in-Aid HE-09773 and by the Clinical Research Center facility of the University of Washington, supported by the National Institutes of Health (Grant FR-37) and the Washington State Heart Association.
The author is an established investigator of the American Heart Association.

210

the work of Bevegård and Shepherd (5, 6) strongly suggests that reflex changes in peripheral venomotor tone at the onset of exercise serve the function of "autotransfusion" postulated for the liver by Krogh.

After Krogh, Bock *et al.* (10) postulated a conceptually different role for the hepatic-splanchnic circulation in muscular exercise. These latter inevstigators reasoned that increased blood flow to muscle and maintenance of arterial blood pressure during "steady state" exercise must be effected in part by decreased splanchnic blood flow.

There is conflicting evidence whether demands for increased muscle blood flow during moderate to heavy exercise must be met in part by redistribution of blood flow from nonexercising regions to working skeletal muscle. In the dog most studies indicate that such a reaction is absent (36). Although most authors have utilized exercise which is relatively very mild for a dog, VanCitters and Franklin (41) recently found no reduction in the visceral blood flow of sled dogs who were severely stressed.

In man there are conflicting results because of differences in posture, severity of work, and the methods used to measure blood flow. There has long been evidence that renal blood flow is reduced in response to exercise (1, 15, 45). Furthermore, this reduction is proportional to the severity of upright exercise (14, 17). In 1948 Bradley (11), utilizing the Bromsulphthalein® (BSP) extraction method, demonstrated a significant decrease in splanchnic blood flow in a single subject during mild supine exertion. Bishop *et al.* (7) added further evidence when they found a marked widening of hepatic arteriovenous oxygen difference with increasing severity of exercise in normal supine men. Patients with a limited cardiac output response to exercise show very marked widening of their hepatic arteriovenous oxygen difference during very mild supine exercise (18). These studies assumed that no increase in hepatic oxygen uptake occurred during exercise, and therefore, percentage decrements in splanchnic blood flow could be estimated directly from percentage increments in splanchnic arteriovenous oxygen difference. These assumptions were supported later by the work of Wade and colleagues (43), who estimated the hepatic blood flow of their subjects by the BSP extraction method during mild supine exercise. All of these human studies were carried out in recumbency, using mild to moderate exercise; however, cardiovascular responses during exercise in this posture are fundamentally different from those in an upright subject (4, 27).

In 1964 we undertook a series of experiments which raised the following questions about visceral blood flow and metabolism during moderate to maximal *upright* exercise in normal man and cardiac patients.

1. Is hepatic-splanchnic blood flow reduced as a function of the severity of upright exercise—that is, does splanchnic vascular resistance increase in proportion to metabolic rate?

2. Is splanchnic blood flow reduced even further when additional vascular beds are dilated during exercise; for example, when the cutaneous vascular bed dilates during superimposed heat stress?

3. Is splanchnic blood flow reduced during prolonged exercise? If so, of what significance is this reduction to such important metabolic roles of the liver as conversion of lactic acid to glucose and supply of substrate to the energy pool? Do local splanchnic hypoxia, hyperthermia, and/or diminished production of metabolic substrate contribute to ultimate failure in capacity to work?

Methodology

Briefly, we have applied two methods to the study of hepatic-splanchnic blood flow during upright exercise. The technique of single rapid injections allowed the measurement of responses at multiple levels of oxygen uptake. Only a short time (10-15 minutes) at each oxygen uptake was required; thus, measurements could be made even at levels of work requiring close to maximal oxygen uptake. This method is illustrated in Figure 11-1. The dye used is indocyanine green (ICG); unlike BSP it has the advantage of being cleared from the circulation exclusively by the liver (13, 21). Since the hepatic extraction efficiency for this dye always increased by 5 to 10 percent with the reduced

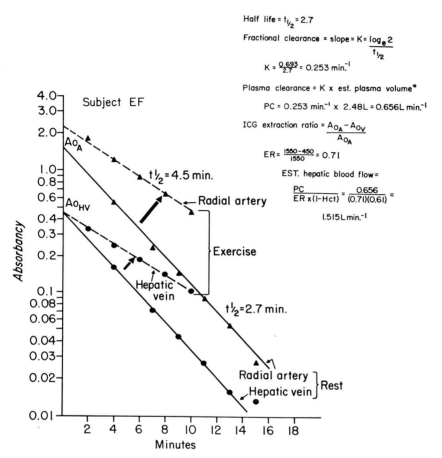

FIGURE 11-1. Peripheral arterial and hepatic venous plasma clearance of indocyanine green dye (ICG). The clearance (change in plasma absorbancy of ICG) is shown for a representative subject while at rest (continuous lines) and during exercise requiring an oxygen consumption of 28.5 ml per kilogram minute (broken lines). The method of calculating hepatic blood flow is shown. During exercise hepatic blood flow fell from 1515 ml per minute to 765 ml per minute, while extraction efficiency rose from 71 to 77 percent. Note that the percentage reduction in fractional clearance rate was 40 percent (the half clearance time, t½, increased from 2.7 to 4.5 minutes), while blood flow actually fell 49.5 percent—that is, the percentage changes in fractional ICG clearance rate underestimated the changes in blood flow. (Reproduced by permission of the *Journal of Clinical Investigation* [Reference 28].)

liver blood flow of exercise, the changes in its peripheral clearance conservatively reflect changes in hepatic-splanchnic blood flow (28).

The second method is the traditional one used since Bradley and colleagues (12) introduced the BSP constant infusion technique. This method has the advantage of eliminating the need for independent measurement or estimation of plasma volume and can be applied over prolonged periods. Its disadvantage is that approximately twenty minutes are required before the removal rate of indicator equilibrates with the infusion rate to yield a stable concentration of indicator in the blood. We have applied the first technique to study control of the splanchnic circulation during graded levels of exercise and the second to study splanchnic blood flow and metabolism during prolonged work.

The major disadvantage of any current technique for measuring hepatic-splanchnic blood flow is the lack of a suitable sampling site to obtain pooled venous blood from various regions of the liver. Available evidence suggests that regional differences for BSP (12) or ICG extraction are relatively small (46). Collection of blood specimens from the largest of the five hepatic veins appears to provide a good estimate of hepatic blood flow and to minimize catheter induced sampling errors (16, 20, 31, 46).

FIGURE 11-2. The top panel shows the correlation between fractional clearance rate of ICG, expressed as a percentage of the resting value and oxygen uptake, expressed in milliliters per kilogram minute. The broken lines about the least square regression line indicate the 95 percent confidence limits for the true value of y (ICG clearance) in an individual having a given value of x (oxygen uptake); the regression equation is also shown. The bottom panel shows the correlation between the fractional clearance of ICG (percentage of resting value) and oxygen uptake, expressed as a *percentage of maximal oxygen uptake* (relative oxygen uptake). About the least square regression line are shown the 95 percent confidence limits (shaded area) for the true *mean* value of y at a given value of x. The wider confidence limits are for a given *individual* value of y. Note the reduction in scatter and increased correlation coefficient (r) when data are expressed as a percentage of maximal oxygen uptake. (Reproduced with permission of the *Journal of Clinical Investigation* [Reference 28].)

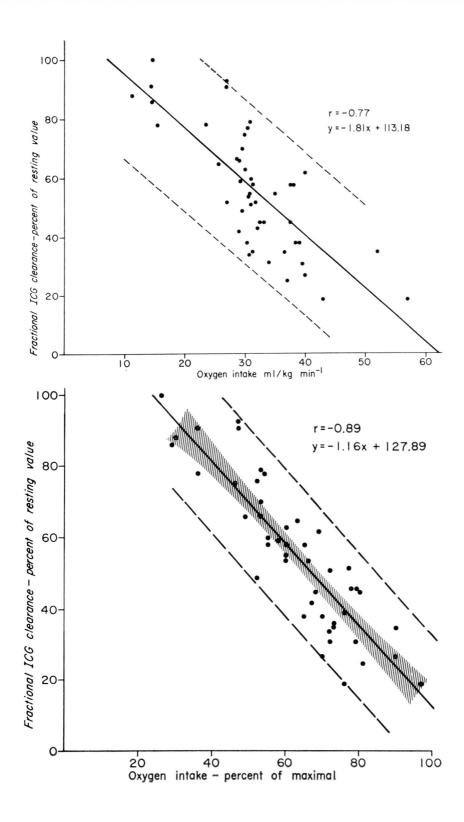

Visceral Blood Flow at Various Levels of Oxygen Uptake

In a group of seventeen young men with fairly wide differences in maximal oxygen uptake—a measure of the functional capacity of their cardiovascular systems (9, 24)—there was a negative correlation of −0.77 between the oxygen consumption per kilogram of body weight and the splanchnic blood flow, expressed as a percentage of the resting value (Fig. 11-2) (28). The scatter was quite wide, but this would be expected, since the cardiovascular and metabolic capacities of the subjects differed. In order to reduce the influence of interindividual differences in aerobic power, we may express these data on a relative scale; that is, as a percentage of the individual's maximal metabolic rate or maximal blood flow. In this way responses are related to the "full scale" response of the organism. If this is done, the correlation between hepatic blood flow and *relative* metabolic demand is increased to −0.89 (Fig. 11-2), showing the close inverse proportionality between the perfusion of splanchnic tissues and the percentage of maximal oxygen uptake and/or maximal cardiac output required during work. More recently Grimby (17) has found a similar relationship for renal blood flow. It is possible the relationship may extend to most tissues not directly challenged by the exercise (42).

To test further the hypothesis of proportional control of splanchnic blood flow, the response was determined in seven patients with pure mitral stenosis (9). These patients had no other valvular lesions and no myocardial failure; clinical pulmonary and systemic venous congestion were absent, and liver size and function were normal at rest. All had normal resting cardiac outputs. These patients constituted a group having a low maximal cardiac output and oxygen consumption solely as a result of their low stroke volume. Their maximal heart rate and maximal total arteriovenous oxygen differences were normal. Their maximal oxygen consumptions were established objectively according to the criteria of Taylor *et al.* (40) by demonstrating a plateau of oxygen uptake as work was increased to maximal tolerable levels. The maximal oxygen consumption of these patients averaged only 1.3 liters per minute (23.3 ml per kilogram minute).

As predicted, the reduction of splanchnic blood flow in these patients was much greater at any given absolute level of oxygen consumption (Fig. 11-3). But, the reduction followed an essentially normal course when related to the percentage of maximal oxygen consumption.

If we compare splanchnic blood flow during exercise in three groups of people who show very high, normal, and very low maximal oxygen consumptions (endurance athletes, sedentary men, and patients with mitral stenosis), the relative nature of these changes is illustrated further. Those with the lowest metabolic and cardiovascular capacity require the greatest reduction in splanchnic blood flow at a given absolute level of oxygen consumption. Those with the greatest capacity require the least reduction. Yet all show essentially the same reduction at a

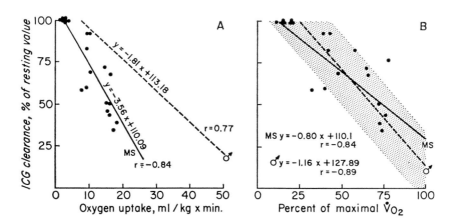

FIGURE 11-3. Correlation between fractional clearance rate of ICG (expressed as a percentage of the resting value) and (A) absolute or (B) relative metabolic rates. Regression lines with appropriate regression equations and correlation coefficients (r) are shown for seven patients with pure mitral stenosis (solid lines, labeled MS) and from normal young men (broken lines). Normal data from Rowell, Blackmon and Bruce (28). Note that in graph B all but three points from the patients fall within the 95 percent confidence limits for normal subjects. (Reproduced from Physiological Significance of Maximal Oxygen Intake in "Pure" Mitral Stenosis by Blackmon, Rowell, Kennedy, Twiss, and Conn [*Circulation*, 34:497-510, 1967] by permission of the American Heart Association, Inc.)

given percentage of maximal oxygen uptake. One might say that in those with the lowest maximal cardiac output, the heart required proportionally more assistance via redistribution of left ventricular output in meeting the metabolic demand of skeletal muscle. Redistribution of blood flow normally directed to the splanchnic region can supply working muscle with up to 400 ml of oxygen per minute without any additional increase in cardiac output (28).

The importance of this adjustment to total oxygen transport becomes more obvious as the capacity of the heart to pump blood is reduced; for example, in the mitral stenosis patients cited above. In the functional class III or IV cardiac patient with a limited or fixed cardiac response to work, almost 100 percent of any increase in the oxygen supply to muscle must come about by redistributing blood flow away from nonworking to working tissues (42). This contribution could supply only 20 percent of the normal maximum oxygen demand in a sedentary man and only 10 percent of that in the endurance athlete.

A second important function is served by the adjustment in blood flow to nonexercising regions during upright exercise. Peripheral vascular resistance is greatly reduced by vasodilatation of working skeletal muscle. This vasodilatation, which is proportional to the severity of exercise, is partially counterbalanced by visceral vasoconstriction, so that mean arterial pressure is maintained almost constant (30).

Visceral Blood Flow During Competitive Metabolic and Thermal Demands

When heat stress is superimposed on exercise or metabolic stress, the cardiovascular system must meet two competitive demands—oxygen transport and heat transport. A certain quantity of blood flow is required to conduct heat from the deep tissues to the body surface. Since this additional blood flow is unavailable for oxygen transport, the added demand must be met by either increased total blood flow, by a redistribution of blood flow from other regions to the skin, or by a combination of both mechanisms.

Nine subjects were studied at graded levels of exercise requiring 26 to 95 percent of maximal oxygen uptake at ambient temperatures of 25.6 and 43.3 C (29). At 43.3 C the reduction in splanchnic blood flow was 20 percent greater than at the corresponding absolute or relative level of oxygen uptake at 25.6 C (Figure 11-4). Cardiac outputs at 25.6 and 43.3 C were similar. This similarity persisted over a range of oxygen consumptions requiring 45 to 60 percent of the maximal value (35). Thus, under these particular conditions (short periods [15 minute] of moderate to severe exertion), any vasodilatation in the skin was compensated for by further vasoconstriction of the splanchnic vascular bed.

Renal blood flow was also reduced even further by exercise in hot environment (26). By this redistribution additional blood flow can be made available for perfusion of skin without increasing total blood flow. The arterial blood pressure was adequately maintained in the phase of combined skin and muscle vasodilatation by an increase in visceral vascular resistance (23).

Metabolic Consequences of Reduced Splanchnic Blood Flow—Normal Temperatures

The essential metabolic functions of the liver at rest are well known. At first glance basic homeostatic principles appear to be defied by the drastic reductions in liver blood flow at very high metabolic rates. Is the reduction in hepatic-splanchnic blood flow maintained only for brief periods, or does the blood flow remain very low during prolonged severe exercise? Under the conditions of our experiments we found large reductions in splanchnic blood flow; values ranged from 850 down to 426 ml per minute compared with the normal resting value of 1400 to 1500 ml per minute (11-13, 28, 42, 43). Furthermore, these reductions were sustained over one hour of continuous heavy exertion.

What are the metabolic consequences of this reduction in splanchnic blood flow? It is important to note that the liver is in series with (and follows) the rest of the splanchnic circulation. However, tissues preceding the liver make little contribution to extraction from (or addition to) blood of the substances we have

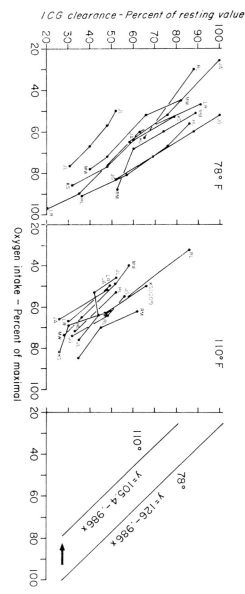

FIGURE 11-4. Percentage decrements in ICG clearance at different work loads, oxygen uptake being expressed as a percentage of maximal oxygen uptake. Data from nine subjects at 78 F (25.6 C) and at 110 F (43.3

measured in fasting man (19, 25, 38). We have concerned our-
selves only with substances of consequence to the total energy
substrate pool.

Despite low splanchnic blood flow the oxygen consumption
of these tissues increased from 68 to 90 ml per minute; this was
due to increased oxygen extraction (32). Fifty percent of the
lactate produced early in exercise was removed by the liver,
probably being converted to glucose. Hepatic carbon dioxide
production was much too small to account for oxidation of this
lactic acid. Hepatic respiratory quotient (RQ) was very low
(around 0.4) (32). This reduction in blood lactate levels had no
effect on the total oxygen debt measured in these subjects at
different times during additional experiments. No significant net
splanchnic production or uptake of phospholipid or triglyceride
was found (Fig. 11-5). Free fatty acid (FFA) uptake averaged
60μmoles to 70μmoles per minute, and 20 mg per minute of
ketone bodies were released to the circulation. The latter would
account for less than 1 percent of the total metabolic rate. Finally,
the glucose concentration in hepatic venous blood rose rapidly, so
that its net production exceeded resting output (90 mg per
minute) by a factor of 5 to 7 (34). This added production of glucose could account for 20 percent of the total energy substrate if it
were oxidized. Later studies by Bergström and Hultman (2) support our findings. Therefore, glucose is the only significant contribution that the liver makes to the total energy substrate pool
during exercise. Neither this particular metabolic function of the
liver nor the others cited appear to be compromised by a prolonged reduction in blood flow.

These findings raise the question whether exhaustion of
hepatic glucose stores might be a factor in the etiology of fatigue
or exhaustion during prolonged, severe exercise. Failure in normal regulation of cardiac output and arterial blood pressure has

◄
C) is shown in the left and center panels, with least squares regression lines
and equations for both temperatures on the right. In the experiments at
110 F, splanchnic blood flow was 20 percent lower at all levels of oxygen
uptake. (Reproduced with permission of the *Journal of Applied Physiology*
[29].)

Frontiers of Fitness

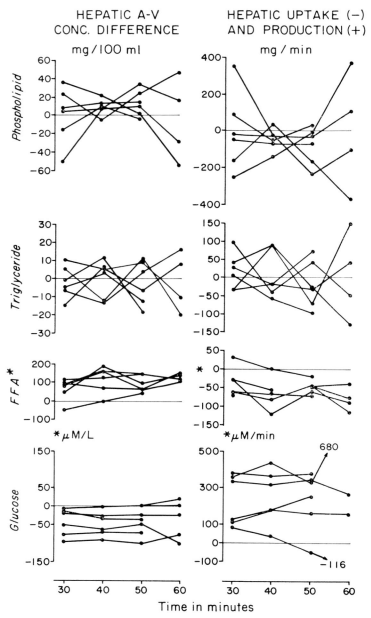

FIGURE 11-5. The left-hand panel shows hepatic arteriovenous (A-V) concentration differences for phospholipids, triglycerides, free fatty acids

not been observed even during very prolonged work to exhaustion in either hot (33) or cool environments (37). Accordingly, any hemodynamic malfunction which may occur is more subtle than the sudden crisis associated with a fall in cardiac output and blood pressure. Rather, we wondered whether accumulated body heat might eventually require further redistribution of blood flow away from hepatic-splanchnic organs to meet needs for increased skin blood flow; in this case any hemodynamic malfunction might manifest itself as a reduced flow to splanchnic tissues. This could lead to serious local and general metabolic disturbances. Such changes might explain the symptoms of gastrointestinal distress which frequently attend exhaustive work. Also, the central-lobular necrosis which develops in patients with restricted cardiac output may result from frequent repetition of similar changes.

A study of hepatic-splanchnic metabolism was undertaken at the highest metabolic rate which a man could endure for approximately one hour in a 48.9 C environment. This should produce the greatest possible reduction in hepatic-splanchnic blood flow for the longest possible period of time, with a high rate of heat accumulation. Also, exhaustion occurs rapidly under these conditions (31).

Under these extremely severe conditions, hepatic blood flow was very low, but it did not decrease further as the stress was maintained (31). Furthermore, hepatic-splanchnic oxygen consumption increased from 80 to 115 ml per minute during forty to sixty minutes of work to exhaustion (Fig. 11-6). This rise in oxygen consumption closely followed the rise which would be predicted from the rise in tissue temperature, using the Arrhenius equation. Hepatic temperature approached 42 C at exhaustion (31).

Although the lactate removal rate was normal, blood lactate

◄
(FFA), and glucose during exercise at oxygen uptakes of 29.2 to 30.0 ml per kilogram minute. The right-hand panel shows the product of these arteriovenous differences and hepatic blood flow, expressed as either production (+) or uptake (−). Only glucose production made a significant contribution to total energy substrate. (Reproduced by permission of the *Journal of Applied Physiology* [34].)

SPLANCHNIC PRODUCTION (+) AND UPTAKE (−)

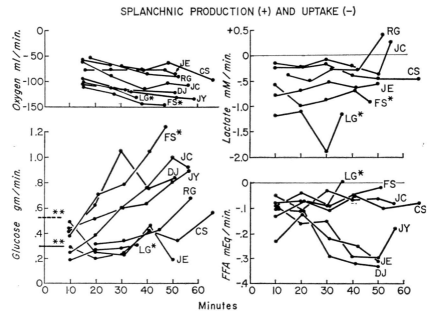

Minutes

FIGURE 11-6. Splanchnic production and uptake of oxygen, glucose, lactate, and FFA during work requiring 42 to 56 percent of maximal oxygen uptake. Studies were conducted at an enviromental temperature of 48.9 C and ended in exhaustion of subjects. Uptakes are indicated by negative values (oxygen, lactate, and FFA) and production by positive values. Interrupted lines and (**) on the ordinate represent glucose production at similar levels of oxygen uptake at 25.6 C (34). Note that five subjects show an extreme outpouring of hepatic glucose in the heat. (Reproduced by permission of the *Journal of Applied Physiology* [31].)

levels were elevated and hepatic lactate extraction efficiency was subnormal. Two men showed a net splanchnic production of lactate at exhaustion. Free fatty acid removal was normal. However, glucose production rose to an extremely high level, exceeding resting values fourteenfold. If oxidized, this could account for 50 percent of the 1.8 to 2.6 liters of oxygen consumed each minute.

Two findings suggest that the liver became progressively hypoxic as exhaustion was approached. Hepatic venous oxygen content approached zero at exhaustion in five men, the oxygen content of this blood falling to 0:5 ml per 100 ml. Also, hepatic glycogenolysis always seems to be associated with liver hypoxia (3). Liver glycogen stores after a twelve-hour fast are sufficient to account for the total glucose release in these studies (18). However, gluconeogenesis cannot be discounted. The elevated lactate and FFA levels would certainly stimulate gluconeogenesis if the oxygen supply were adequate (38, 44). It is not known whether gluconeogenesis could proceed at a rate sufficient to produce this much glucose. However, changes in two major factors affecting gluconeogenesis (glucagon and insulin) were apparently not involved, as the blood levels of these hormones remained constant from rest to exhaustion in the two men in whom measurements were made.

The high glucose production might be viewed as an emergency measure, guarding the glucose supply to the brain and possibly to the working muscle as well. Clearly, exhaustion under these conditions could not be due to glucose depletion—unless the glucose released by the liver was unavailable for oxidation within the muscle cell.

In conclusion: a) There are well-defined inverse relationships between hepatic-splanchnic and renal blood flow and *relative* oxygen consumption. These relationships indicate a uniform degree of redistribution of blood flow in cardiac patients, sedentary men, and endurance athletes at a given percentage of their respective maximum cardiac outputs and/or maximal metabolic rates. b) The redistribution may provide 500 or 600 ml of oxygen per minute to working muscle without any increase in total blood flow; redistribution is the major means of increasing total oxygen consumption in patients with restricted cardiac output. c) Redistribution of blood flow away from visceral organs also provides a compensatory increase in peripheral vascular resistance as muscle vasodilates during exercise (this helps to maintain mean arterial blood pressure) and additional blood flow for cutaneous perfusion when thermal stress is added to metabolic stress (the visceral vasoconstriction is even greater under these conditions, thus helping to compensate for the additional decrease in peripheral vascular resistance. Blood pressure is still maintained).

d) Despite very large reductions in hepatic blood flow, the liver increases its oxygen consumption during prolonged work; it continues to metabolize lactate and FFA and eventually releases glucose at rates sufficient to supply 20 to 50 percent of the total energy demand. The extremely low hepatic oxygen tension, coupled with the outpouring of glucose (and occasionally lactate), plus high local splanchnic temperatures may herald impending failure of this organ system.

References

1. BARCLAY, J.A., COOKE, W.T., KENNEY, R.A., and NUTT, M.C.: The effects of water diuresis and exercise on the volume and composition of the urine. *Amer J Physiol, 148*:327-337, 1947.

2. BERGSTRÖM, J., and HULTMAN, E.: A study of the glycogen metabolism during exercise in man. *Scand J Clin Lab Invest, 19*:218-228, 1967.

3. BERNELLI-ZASSERA, A., and GAJA, G.: Some aspects of glycogen metabolism following reversible and irreversible liver ischemia. *Exp Molec Pathol, 3*:351-368, 1964.

4. BEVEGÅRD, S., HOLMGREN, A., and JONSSON, B.: The effect of body position on the circulation at rest and during exercise with special reference to the influence on the stroke volume. *Acta Physiol Scand, 49*:279-398, 1960.

5. BEVEGÅRD, B.S., and SHEPHERD, J.T.: Changes in tone of limb veins during supine exercise. *J Appl Physiol, 20*:1-8, 1965.

6. BEVEGÅRD, B.S., and SHEPHERD, J.T.: Reaction in man of resistance and capacity vessels in forearm and hand to leg exercise. *J Appl Physiol, 21*:123-132, 1966.

7. BISHOP, J.M., DONALD, K.W., TAYLOR, S.H., and WORMALD, P.N.: Changes in arterial-hepatic venous oxygen content difference during and after supine leg exercise. *J Physiol (London), 137*: 309-317, 1957.

8. BISHOP, J.M., DONALD, K.W., and WADE, O.L.: Changes in the oxygen content of hepatic venous blood during exercise in patients with rheumatic heart disease. *J Clin Invest, 34*:1114-1125, 1955.

9. BLACKMON, J.R., ROWELL, L.B., KENNEDY, J.W., TWISS, R.D., and CONN, R.D.: Physiological significance of maximal oxygen intake in pure mitral stenosis. *Circulation, 36*:497-510, 1967.

10. Bock, A.V., Vancaulaert, C., Dill, D.B., Fölling, A., and Hurxthal, L.M.: Studies in muscular activity. III. Dynamical changes occurring in man at work. *J Physiol (London)*, 65:136-161, 1928.

11. Bradley, S.E.: Hepatic blood flow. Effect of posture and exercise upon blood flow through the liver. In *Transactions of the Seventh Conference on Liver Injury.* New York, Josiah Macy, Jr., Foundation, 1948, p.53-56.

12. Bradley, S.E., Ingelfinger, F.J., Bradley, G.P., and Curry, J.J.: The estimation of hepatic blood flow in man. *J Clin Invest*, 24:890-897, 1945.

13. Caesar, J., Shaldon, S., Chiandussi, L., Guevara, L., and Sherlock, S.: The use of indocyanine green in the measurement of hepatic blood flow and as a test of hepatic function. *Clin Sci*, 21:43-57, 1961.

14. Castenfors, J., and Piscator, M.: Renal haemodynamics. Urinary protein excretion during exercise in supine position at different loads. *Acta Med Scand (Suppl)*, 472:321-244, 1967.

15. Chapman, C.B., Henschel, A., Minchkler, J., Forgsgren, A., and Keys, A.: The effect of exercise on renal plasma in normal male subjects. *J Clin Invest*, 27:639-644, 1948.

16. Drapanas, R., Kluge, D.N., and Schenk, W.G.: Measurement of hepatic blood flow by bromsulphthalein and by the electromagnetic flowmeter. *Surgery*, 48:1017-1021, 1960.

17. Grimby, G.: Renal clearances during prolonged supine exercise at different loads. *J Appl Physiol*, 20:1294-1298, 1965.

18. Hildes, J.A., Sherlock, S., and Walshe, V.: Liver and muscle glycogen in normal subjects, in diabetes mellitus and in acute hepatitis. I. Under basal conditions. *Clin Sci*, 7:287-295, 1949.

19. Himwich, H.E., Koskoff, and Nahum, L.H.: Studies in carbohydrate metabolism. I. A glucose-lactic acid cycle involving muscle and liver. *J Biol Chem*, 85:571-584, 1930.

20. Hultman, E.: Blood circulation in the liver under physiological and pathological conditions. *Scand J Clin Lab Invest*, 18 (Suppl. 92):27-41, 1966.

21. Hunton, D.B., Bolman, J.L., and Hoffman, H.N.: Studies of hepatic function with indocyanine green. *Gastroenterology*, 39:713-723, 1960.

22. Krogh, A.: The regulation of the supply of blood to the right heart. *Skand Arch Physiol*, 27:227-248, 1912.

23. MARX, H.J., ROWELL, L.B., CONN, R.D., BRUCE, R.A., and KUSUMI, F.: Maintenance of aortic pressure and total peripheral resistance during exercise in heat. *J Appl Physiol,* 22:519-525, 1967.

24. MITCHELL, J.H., SPROULE, B.J., and CHAPMAN, C.B.: The physiological meaning of the maximal oxygen intake test. *J Clin Invest,* 37:538-547, 1958.

25. MYERS, J.D.: Net splanchnic glucose production in normal man and in various disease states. *J Clin Invest,* 29:1421-1428, 1950.

26. RADIGAN, L.R., and ROBINSON, S.: Effects of environmental heat stress and exercise on renal blood flow and filtration rate. *J Appl Physiol,* 2:185-191, 1949.

27. REEVES, J.T., GROVER, R.F., BLOUNT, S.G., JR., and FILLEY, G.F.: Cardiac output response to standing and treadmill walking. *J Appl Physiol,* 16:283-288, 1961.

28. ROWELL, L.B., BLACKMON, J.R., and BRUCE, R.A.: Indocyanine green clearance and estimated hepatic blood flow during mild to maximal exercise in upright man. *J Clin Invest,* 43:1677-1690, 1964.

29. ROWELL, L.B., BLACKMON, J.R., MARTIN, R.H., MAZZARELLA, J.A., and BRUCE, R.A.: Hepatic clearance of indocyanine green in man under thermal and exercise stresses. *J Appl Physiol,* 20:384-394, 1965.

30. ROWELL, L.B., BRENGELMANN, G.L., BLACKMON, J.R., BRUCE, R.A., and MURRAY, J.A.: Disparities between aortic and peripheral pulse pressures induced by upright exercise and vasomotor changes in man. *Circulation,* 37:954-964, 1968.

31. ROWELL, L.B., BRENGELMAN, G.L., BLACKMON, J.R., TWISS, R.D., and KUSUMI, F.: Splanchnic blood flow and metabolism in heat stress in man. *J Appl Physiol,* 24:475-484, 1968.

32. ROWELL, L.B., KRANING, K.K., II., EVANS, T.O., KENNEDY, J.W., BLACKMON, J.R., and KUSUMI, F.: Splanchnic removal of lactate and pyruvate during prolonged exercise in man. *J Appl Physiol,* 21:1773-1783, 1966.

33. ROWELL, L.B., KRANING, K.K., II., KENNEDY, J.W., and EVANS, T.O.: Central circulatory responses to work in dry heat before and after acclimatization. *J Appl Physiol,* 22:509-518, 1967.

34. ROWELL, L.B., MASORO, E.J., and SPENCER, M.J.: Splanchnic metabolism in exercising man. *J Appl Physiol,* 20:1032-1037, 1965.

35. ROWELL, L.B., MARX, H.J., BRUCE, R.A., CONN, R.D., and KUSUMI, F.: Reductions in cardiac output, central blood volume, and stroke volume with thermal stress in normal men during exercise. *J Clin Invest, 45*:1801-1816, 1966.

36. RUSHMER, R.F., FRANKLIN, D.L., VAN CITTERS, R.L., and SMITH, O.A.: Changes in peripheral blood flow distribution in healthy dogs. *Circ Res, 9*:675-687, 1961.

37. SALTIN, B., and STENBERG, J.: Circulatory response to prolonged severe exercise. *J Appl Physiol, 19*:833-838, 1964.

38. SHERLOCK, S., and WALSHE, V.: The use of a portal anastomotic vein for absorption studies in man. *Clin Sci, 6*:113-121, 1948.

39. STEELE, R.: The influences of insulin on the hepatic metabolism of glucose. *Ergeb Physiol, 57*:91-189, 1966.

40. TAYLOR, H.L., BUSKIRK, E., and HENSCHEL, A.: Maximal oxygen intake as an objective measure of cardio-respiratory performance. *J Appl Physiol, 8*:73-80, 1955.

41. VAN CITTERS, R.L., and FRANKLIN, D.L.: Cardiovascular performance of Alaska sled dogs during exercise. *Circ Res, 24*:33-42, 1969.

42. WADE, O.L., and BISHOP, J.M.: *Cardiac Output and Regional Blood Flow.* Oxford, Blackwell, 1962.

43. COURNAND, and BRADLEY, S.E.: The effect of exercise on the splanchnic blood flow and splanchnic blood volume in normal man. *Clin Sci, 15*:457-463, 1956.

44. WEBER, G.: Feedback inhibition of key glycolytic enzymes in liver: action of free fatty acids. *Science, 154*:1357-1360, 1966.

45. WHITE, H.L., and ROLF, R.: Effects of exercise and of some other influences on the renal circulation in man. *Amer J Physiol, 152*:505-516, 1948.

46. WINKLER, K., LARSEN, J.A., MUNKNER, T., and TYGSTRUP: Determination of hepatic blood flow in man by simultaneous use of five test substances measured in two parts of the liver. *Scand J Clin Lab Invest, 17*:423-432, 1965.

SECTION THREE
TECHNIQUES OF MEASURING HUMAN PERFORMANCE

Chapter 12

STANDARD TESTS OF AEROBIC POWER

Roy J. Shephard

Introduction

Many biological measurements are now expressed relative to internationally agreed reference standards. Thus, the hemoglobin content of the blood is estimated by a specific colorimetric procedure, the test solution being compared with internationally available reference preparations of cyanmethemoglobin (26). The quinquennium of cooperative activity engendered by the International Biological Programme has given additional impetus to the search for standards of procedure and of reference; preliminary agreement on the details of methodology is indeed vital to the I.B.P. programme if different teams of research workers are to obtain comparable data in widely separated and often remote areas of the globe.

Several recent experiments have emphasized the need for standardization in the specific context of the measurement of aerobic power. Cotes and Woolmer (12) delivered a cylinder of gas to a series of U.K. laboratories, all of which were concerned with either respiratory or exercise testing, and they noted that the reported concentrations of the cylinder mixture ranged from

Note: The opinions expressed here are the personal views of the author. However, much of the experimental work on which these opinions are based was carried out jointly with members of an International Biological Programme working party (52, 53, 54).

The work described has been supported in part by research grants from the Directorate of Fitness and Amateur Sport, the Ontario Heart Foundation, and the World Health Organization. Thanks are also due to the directors of the various laboratories concerned for release of staff to participate in the I.B.P. working party.

15.70 to 16.21 percent oxygen and from 6.01 to 6.28 percent carbon dioxide. Systematic errors of this magnitude could influence estimates of the maximum oxygen intake by as much as 25 percent, and unfortunately such gross errors are not ruled out when the results of gas analyses are highly reproducible in a given laboratory. The Haldane and Scholander techniques of gas analysis have traditionally been regarded as accurate to 0.01-0.02 percent, but in fact this is their reproducibility rather than their accuracy; some of the worst systematic errors were encountered in laboratories using these procedures. Two further experiments show that the danger of a systematic error is real rather than theoretical. Bonjer (8) arranged for a panel of subjects to be tested in three Dutch laboratories; the mean maximum oxygen intake that was reported ranged from 3.88 to 4.29 liters per minute STPD. Cumming (personal communication to author) had a similar experience when organizing tests on Canadian athletes prior to the Winnipeg Pan-American games; some laboratories reported consistently low pulse rates for a given estimated submaximum oxygen consumption and consistently low respiratory quotients during maximum exercise. When athletes were circulated between cooperating laboratories, it became evident that problems of technique—particularly of gas analysis—were involved, and the estimates of an individual's maximum oxygen intake made by the various investigators differed by as much as 25 percent.

Hopefully, systematic errors of this magnitude will be avoided in the future. Substantial progress has been made towards the standardization of exercise tests and related procedures. Conferences have been held under the auspices of the International Committee on the Standardization of Physical Fitness Tests (Tokyo, 1964 and 1965; Sandefjörd 1966; Magglingen, 1967; and Mexico City, 1968); the International Council of Sport and Physical Education (Hannover, 1966; Berlin, 1967), the International Biological Programme (Kyoto, 1965; Toronto, 1966), and the World Health Organization (Geneva, 1967). Specific international working parties have been convened (52-54), and a number of detailed handbooks of methodology are in preparation or have already appeared (46, 47, 58, 59, 63). The main objective of the present article is to formulate some general principles for the standardization of exercise tests. Those requiring detailed information on specific technical points are advised to consult the proceedings of the various conferences cited.

Exercise Versus Recovery Measurements

Traditional tests of fitness such as the Harvard step test (9) have been based on the measurement of recovery rather than exercise pulse rates. This choice has been dictated largely by practical difficulties encountered in palpating or auscultating the pulse rate during exercise. Although there is a general relationship between aerobic power and the pulse rate following recovery from standard exercise, the correlation tends to be obscured by other factors, including a) the extent of the "reflex" increase of pulse rate at the commencement of exercise, b) the extent and rate of repayment of the oxygen debt, c) terminal core and environmental temperatures and the efficiency of heat dissipation, d) changes of posture and the efficiency of circulatory adaptations thereto, and e) peripheral pooling of blood and the tone of the large veins. If pulse measurements are made during and ½ to 1½ minutes following exercise (38, 42, 43), the coefficient of correlation between the two sets of data is about 0.8, implying that some 36 percent of the information content of the recovery pulse rate is derived from factors unrelated to the pulse rate during exercise. However, these confounding influences take several seconds to develop, and if the observer is skillful enough to measure the pulse rate in the first ten seconds after ceasing exercise, the correlation with the exercise pulse rate rises to 0.98, implying that only 4 percent of the information content is "unwanted."

Immediate postexercise readings thus have some value, both in the training of athletes and as a simple mass method of monitoring the intensity of exercise during coronary rehabilitation programmes (22). The course of the pulse recovery curve may also have interest in certain situations. However, in the specific context of the assessment of aerobic power, the exercise pulse rate is to be preferred. Further, an electrocardiograph (ECG) should be used to record the pulse rate unless electrical power is not available; the ECG not only gives a more accurate pulse reading, but it also permits a continuous check upon the normality of electrical conduction in the heart muscle, thus increasing the safety of the test procedure.

Maximum or Submaximum Tests

In an athlete or a young person who is accustomed to vigorous exertion, it is relatively easy to measure the maximum oxygen intake directly; providing that the criteria of maximum effort are clearly established and standard techniques are used, the result that is obtained can be open to little question. However, it is sometimes difficult to persuade older patients to reach maximum effort, and the safety of such exertion may also be questioned.

The precise risks of strenuous exercise are still the subject of debate (27, 47, 48), and unfortunately—as with many improbable occurrences—no very sound statistics are available. The present author has had no untoward incidents while testing some one-thousand unselected men and women to 85 percent of their aerobic power. However, many large hospitals have had one or two episodes of ventricular fibrillation during tests on apparently healthy men. It is probable that during exercise the irritability of the myocardium is increased by a combination of hypoxia and circulating catecholamines. The likelihood of a major dysrhythmia thus depends in part upon the anxiety attending the test and in part upon the degree of myocardial hypoxia induced. Ventricular extrasystoles have been noted in as many as 20 percent of some series of hospital patients, whereas under less "emotionally charged" field conditions, we find an incidence of only 10 percent, confined mainly to those over the age of forty. The role of anxiety in inducing and/or worsening an arrhythmia is further supported by many specific examples such as the following: a man of fifty-one performed a maximum effort step test in a field laboratory; he showed evidence of myocardial ischemia (a depressed ST segment and occasional ventricular extrasystoles) but was free of symptoms. Three weeks later he died while running up a staircase on his way to attend to a burst watermain in the apartment where he was the janitor; apparently, the combination of anxiety and exercise was too much for the ailing myocardium.

Bruce and McDonough (personal communication to author) have set the risk of myocardial infarction and/or ventricular fibrillation at about 1 in 16000 during a submaximum laboratory test and at 1 in 3000 during a maximum test. These figures refer to the average hospital patient. In a coronary-prone individual, the risks may be somewhat greater than this; figures from a number of gymnasia in Southern Ontario suggest that following myocardial infarction as many as one episode of ventricular fibrillation per 2500 one-hour patient sessions of submaximum exercise may be anticipated. If a competent cardiac resuscitation team is at hand, such episodes are not synonymous with death. Further, it can be argued that exercise has merely localized to the gymnasium or the laboratory an impending attack of dysrhythmia and that the long-term effects of exercise on morbidity, mortality, and the "quality of life" may still be favorable. Nevertheless, such figures do imply that for both the average patient and the post-infarct case, the immediate risk of vigorous exercise can be as much as a hundred times as great as that of sitting in an armchair. It thus is clear that tests involving vigorous exercise should be carried out with discretion.

Maximum exercise tests seem unwise for the older patient on several counts. Both anxiety and myocardial ischemia increase with the intensity of exercise, thus increasing the chances of inducing an attack of ventricular fibrillation. Myocardial ischemia may also induce an attack of left ventricular failure, and the extent of any rise in systemic blood pressure is greater in maximum than in submaximum exercise. The likelihood that exercise will be carried to the point where ventricular fibrillation develops is reduced if the investigator is fully aware of these hazards and uses appropriate equipment to monitor the electrocardiogram, blood pressure, and other objective indices of patient condition. Further, the risk of a fatality is decreased if a specialist team of physicians and nurses with equipment for DC defibrillation and cardiac massage is readily available. However, maximum exercise is not justified a) in the absence of a suitably trained physician, b) in situations where resuscitation would be difficult, and c) in older patients (except where there are special indications for such a test).

Maximum Tests

Criteria of Maximum Oxygen Intake

The standard criterion of maximum oxygen intake is a failure of oxygen consumption to increase with a further increase of work load; however, individual authors have differed in their concepts of an "increase" in oxygen consumption. Taylor *et al.* (56) suggested that a plateau was reached when oxygen consumption rose by less than 150 ml per minute for a 2½ percent increase in treadmill slope, Mitchell *et al.* (33) required agreement to 54 ml per minute for the same change of slope, while Astrand (4) failed to define the limits of his plateaus.

In setting a criterion, it is important that this be realistic in terms of the technical and the physiological reproducibility of the measurement. Some authors (34, 55) have set the coefficient of variation for repetitive tests as high as 7 to 8 percent; the present author has found a coefficient of 5.3 percent even under ideal conditions (laboratory measurements on well-motivated young men). It would thus seem impractical to define the plateau more closely than 5 percent of aerobic power ($\sim$150 ml/min or 2 ml/kg min in a sedentary young man). Further, if this level of definition is to be realized, individual readings for gas concentration and the like should have an absolute accuracy of 1 percent or better; this implies measurement of oxygen to within 0.03 to 0.04 percent, a standard that is only attainable with careful control of analytical technique (41).

There are other objections to the criteria of Taylor *et al.* (56) and Mitchell *et al.* (33). The stress imposed varies with body weight and treadmill speed, and the relative clarity with which the plateau is defined varies with age, weight, and cardio-respiratory fitness. The present author has proposed a standard increment of stress (5% or 10% of the estimated maximum work load), with definition of the plateau relative to body weight (an increment in oxygen consumption of less than 2 ml/kg min). This would overcome several of the objections to earlier proposals but would still leave the plateau more clearly defined in young than in elderly subjects.

There is some evidence (4, 16) that a proportion of children fail to reach a plateau, at least during bicycle ergometer exercise. This may reflect in part the need to accept results from rather brief periods of exercise ($<$ 3 minutes), where a steady-state may not be reached. It may also be due in part to the recruitment of additional muscle groups; this problem is more serious on the bicycle ergometer than during treadmill exercise, since limitation of effort is peripheral rather than central (see below), and unless the subject's performance is rigidly controlled, there are many possibilities for varying the technique of cycling. Cumming and Friesen (16) demonstrated a plateau more readily in youths who were well trained, and they suggested that in such individuals the leg muscles were developed to the point where the circulatory system could be maximally loaded.

In view of these many difficulties in defining an oxygen plateau, a number of subsidiary criteria of maximum effort have been suggested. These include a high blood lactate level, a respiratory gas exchange ratio $\geqslant$ 1.15, and a pulse rate close to the anticipated maximum value for a given age (2). In young adults the arterial lactate two minutes after maximum exercise normally exceeds 100 mg per 100 ml (52). However, some young men fail to achieve this level despite what appears to be a true maximum effort, and in children and older adults values greater than 80 mg per 100 ml are relatively uncommon; it is unclear whether true physiological differences are involved or whether some subjects are less willing to sustain the discomforts of anaerobic work. Similar uncertainties afflict estimations of respiratory quotient and maximum pulse rate; there are wide inter-individual differences, and in the case of pulse rate even the mean maximum value is open to debate in both athletes and children.

Such difficulties of definition seem an important argument against using maximum oxygen intake as a routine measurement, particularly in children and in older adults.

Warm-Up

The I.B.P. team followed tradition in that maximum oxygen intake tests were preceded by a warm-up exercise at about 50 percent of aerobic power. However, warm-up probably contributes little to aerobic power (10) other than a more rapid approach to the maximum oxygen intake (16); the main justification for a thorough warm-up is that muscle and tendon injuries are then less likely.

Mode of Exercise

The object of the maximum oxygen intake test is to stress fully the cardiorespiratory system. Any mode of exercise that involves the main muscle masses of the body would thus seem acceptable. The I.B.P. working party (52) subjected twenty-four young men to three common forms of maximum exercise (treadmill, step test, and bicycle ergometer) according to a Latin-square experimental design (Table 12-I); the maxima were on average 3 percent less during stepping and 7 percent less during cycling than during uphill treadmill exercise. Other authors (24, 40, 61) have also found a smaller maximum oxygen intake during bicycle ergometer work than during uphill running on a treadmill. The explanation seems that during bicycle ergometer work, an undue proportion of the total effort is developed by one particular muscle group (the quadriceps). Thus, effort is terminated by complaints of local weakness and pain in the thigh muscles rather than by the pattern of symptomatology expected in central exhaustion (nausea, breathlessness, chest pain, ashen-gray cyanosis, loss of coordination, and confusion). The failure of bicycle ergometer exercise to reach a centrally determined endpoint is substantiated by physiological measurements. The maximum pulse rate and more particularly the maximum stroke volume are less than in treadmill exercise, and the terminal lactate concentration is somewhat smaller, although large amounts of lactate accumulate in submaximum exercise.

Other authors have measured maximum oxygen intake, using arm ergometers and swimming mill-races. If an arm ergometer with a short crank is used, the maximum oxygen intake is sub-

TABLE 12-I
MAXIMUM EXERCISE ON THE TREADMILL, STEP TEST,
AND BICYCLE ERGOMETER*

	Treadmill	Step Test	Bicycle Ergometer
Limiting symptom	Breathlessness Chest pain Staggering gait Ashen-gray pallor Nausea Confusion	Breathlessness and chest pain or leg pain and weakness	Leg pain Weakness of legs
Maximum oxygen intake (liters/min STPD ± S.D.)	3.81 ± 0.76	3.68 ± 0.73	3.56 ± 0.71
Maximum pulse rate (per min)	190 ± 5	188 ± 6	187 + 9
Arterial lactate 2 min after exercise (mg/100 ml)	122 ± 21	105 ± 26	112 ± 15
Arterial lactate 2 min after exercise at 80% of aerobic power (mg 100 ml)	38	25	55
Cardiac stroke volume (ml)	150 ± 21	—	137 ± 20

*Values for 24 young men tested according to a Latin-square experimental design (52).

stantially less than for any form of leg exercise (6). On the other hand, if the machine is fitted with a long crank and the subject stands so as to exercise his back muscles, the results may be comparable with those for leg work (36). During swimming the maximum oxygen intake of water polo players averages only 88 percent of the bicycle ergometer value (25); even girl swimming champions reach only 92 percent of the bicycle ergometer figure while in the pool (7).

The results obtained in athletes are to some extent conditioned by muscular development. Cyclists generally perform well on a bicycle ergometer, whereas contestants in sports that lead to specific development of the arm muscles (for instance, Kayak paddlers) perform relatively poorly on all tests involving leg exercise.

The conclusion of the I.B.P. working party (52) was that for most purposes maximum exercise is best performed on the treadmill. However, under field conditions useful results can be obtained from either a step test or a bicycle ergometer, and if an appropriate scaling factor is introduced, the data can be compared with treadmill results.

Continuous and Discontinuous Tests

The traditional procedure for the measurement of maximum oxygen intake has been to make a series of tests, each separated from the other by an interval of several days, until a plateau of oxygen consumption is defined. The choice of work load for the first "maximum" test is gauged from the individual's response to a warm-up exercise, and the work load in subsequent tests is adjusted according to the physiological reactions to this stress. Adequate definition of an oxygen consumption plateau by this approach is tedious to both the subject and the investigator; there is also a physiological problem in that the test itself improves aerobic power by about 1 percent per session (52).

Fortunately, in young adults (where the maximum oxygen intake is most commonly measured), almost identical information can be obtained from a single test in which the load is increased progressively every two minutes, starting at 90 to 100 percent of aerobic power as judged from the response to a warm-up exercise (Table 12-II).

If the same progressive test procedure is applied to children, difficulty is encountered in sustaining maximum loads for more than a few minutes (16, 54). Accordingly, it is common for chil-

TABLE 12-II

A COMPARISON OF DISCONTINUOUS AND CONTINUOUS TESTS
FOR THE ESTIMATION OF MAXIMUM OXYGEN INTAKE (52)

	Maximum Oxygen Intake (ml/min STPD)		
Type of Exercise	*Discontinuous Test*	*Continuous Test (Maximum Known)*	*Continuous Test (No Prior Information)*
Treadmill (n = 7)	3.59 ± 1.32	3.69 ± 1.14	3.70 ± 1.22
Step test (n = 9)	3.81 ± 0.60	3.97 ± 0.71	3.71 ± 0.55
Bicycle ergometer (n = 8)	3.79 ± 0.61	3.82 ± 0.77	3.55 ± 0.60

dren to "give-up" after one or two loadings have been tried. Cumming and Friesen (16) suggest as an alternative procedure extrapolation of a submaximum work/pulse-rate line to a pulse of 230 per minute and the performance of a single three-minute ride at this load.

The progressive test has not been evaluated in older subjects, but difficulties might be encountered from a) a slow adaptation to a given work-load and b) an increased incidence of ECG abnormalities with the more sustained work load.

Details of Technique

Good technique is essential if reproducible and systematically accurate figures are to be obtained for maximum oxygen intake. Appropriate procedures are best learned by a period of training in a reference laboratory.

The subjects to be tested should be well motivated and carefully prepared. Measurements should not follow a heavy meal, previous heavy exercise, or exposure to heat.

The apparatus used to collect expired gas should have a small dead space (preferably less than 50 ml) and a low resistance to gas flow (less than 5 cm H_2O at 300 liters/min flow). Gas must be collected without leakage, preferably using a mouthpiece with a large flange, and gas analysis must be performed without systematic error.

Finally, the subject must exercise long enough to reach a "steady-state" of oxygen consumption. A minimum of three minutes is desirable in discontinuous tests and a minimum of two minutes at each level in progressive tests.

Submaximum Tests

Principles of Submaximum Testing

In general, submaximum tests of aerobic power are based upon the rather consistent relationship between the exercise pulse rate and the corresponding oxygen consumption or equivalent work load. Several authors have shown (5, 30) that this relationship is essentially linear between 50 and 90 percent of an individual's aerobic power.

The method of reporting the information collected varies considerably. Some authors state the work load at a specified pulse rate (for example, the P.W.C.$_{170}$, Reference 57), the pulse rate at a specified work load or oxygen consumption (for example, the $f_{h, 1.5}$, Reference 11), or the slope of the pulse/work relationship (oxygen pulse, Leistungspulsindex, Reference 35). Those who favor this type of approach argue that the information content of the data is not increased by extrapolation to some arbitrary "maximum" pulse rate for the population under study; indeed, in making the extrapolation, possibly unwarranted assumptions are made regarding the linearity of the pulse/work relationship. The main difficulty that arises with the direct reporting of data is that performance capabilities vary markedly with age; thus, one proposed standard of oxygen consumption (1.5 liters/min) is beyond the capacity of some older patients yet imposes a negligible stress on a fit young man. This problem may be overcome in the future by the use of a series of age-related target pulse rates, each corresponding to a fixed percentage of aerobic power (Table 12-III).

If an extrapolation procedure is used to predict aerobic power, then it is important to ensure that the pulse/work rate relationship is extended to a pulse rate appropriate to the individual, the mode of exercise, and the circumstances of the test. The maximum pulse rate declines with age (2), altitude (37), and possibly with an improvement in cardiorespiratory fitness (17); however, no striking ethnic differences have yet emerged. Extrapolation may be carried out simply, using a pencil, ruler, and graph paper; a linear regression may be fitted to four or more paired observations at suitably graded work loads (30); nomograms based on one (5) or two (29) pairs of observations are available; or finally,

TABLE 12-III

TARGET PULSE RATES CORRESPONDING TO FIXED PERCENTAGES
OF AEROBIC POWER AT DIFFERENT AGES

Age (Years)	75% of Aerobic Power (49)	85% of Aerobic Power (3)
20-30	160	170
30-40	150	160
40-50	140	150
50-60	130	140

a small desk-top computer can be programmed to carry out the corresponding operations (47).

Warm-Up

Whether a continuous or a discontinuous form of test is used, it is usual to perform several intensities of exercise on the same day, commencing at a relatively low level of effort. No formal warm-up is thus required; the first load provides a warm-up for the second and so on.

Mode of Exercise

Theoretically, any device that enables a subject to perform suitably graded intensities of exercise could be used in submaximum testing. The treadmill is used in some U.S. laboratories, but in general, attention has been concentrated on step and bicycle ergometer tests. This is partly because the work performed on these two devices can be measured fairly accurately and partly because the type of exercise involved is reasonably familiar. Familiarity is an important asset. With an unfamiliar task there is a progressive reduction in pulse rate as the test is repeated because of lessening of anxiety ("habituation") and greater efficiency of effort ("learning").

In terms of physiological response (53), the I.B.P. team found few differences between step, bicycle ergometer, and treadmill exercise. At a given fraction of aerobic power, pulse rates were closely similar for the three types of test. The respiratory minute volumes were a little greater for bicycle than for stepping or treadmill exercise, reflecting the accumulation of lactate in submaximum exercise (Table 12-I); the stroke volume was also a little lower on the bicycle than on the treadmill, perhaps reflecting a less efficient venous return.

Habituation was compared at a standard oxygen consumption of 1.5 liters per minute STPD. During treadmill exercise the pulse rate decreased by an average of six beats per minute from Day 1 to Day 2 (53); during stepping there was a decrease of three beats per minute, and during bicycle ergometer exercise a statistically insignificant increase of one beat per minute. Thus, it would seem that in the young men tested under the I.B.P. programme, changes in anxiety level were least for bicycle ergometer exercise. Assuming that the treadmill readings for Day 1 were used in the prediction of aerobic power, an error of 0.5 liters per minute STPD (about 13.5%) would arise. A rather smaller systematic discrepancy is encountered if predictions are based on pulse rates in the range 150 to 170 per minute, as suggested by the present author (45).

Some learning occurred with all three types of tests. The mechanical efficiency of stepping increased from 15.7 to 16.1 percent (2.6% change) over five days of testing (53). The corresponding figures for the bicycle ergometer were 21.1 and 21.9 percent (3.7% change). The absolute efficiency of treadmill exercise was not estimated, but a 7 percent change in oxygen cost was noted over five days of testing. Interindividual differences in the efficiency of effort gave rise to a coefficient of variation of 10.1 percent for stepping (7.2% in laboratory subjects) and 4.9 percent for cycling (7.2% in laboratory subjects). The popular myth that work can be measured on the bicycle but not during stepping thus has little basis in fact.

The scatter of predictions of maximum oxygen intake about the directly measured value (Table 12-IV) was similar for all three forms of exercise (53). The treadmill predictions initially gave a systematic underestimate of the maximum oxygen intake (5%-10%, depending on the prediction procedure used); however, this became smaller as the subjects habituated to their task. The step test gave the smallest systematic discrepancy, both on Day 1 and on Day 5. The bicycle ergometer data tended to overestimate the directly measured value on both occasions, perhaps because of the difficulty encountered in reaching a centrally limited maximum oxygen intake on the bicycle ergometer.

Continuous and Discontinuous Tests

A discontinuous test where work is performed at four intensities with minimal rest periods will occupy both the subject and the investigator for more than an hour. Accordingly, interest has centered on the more rapid continuous and progressive type

TABLE 12-IV

THE PREDICTION OF AEROBIC POWER (LITERS/MIN STPD) FROM MEASUREMENTS OF PULSE RATE AND OXYGEN CONSUMPTION DURING SUBMAXIMUM EXERCISE*

Type of Exercise	Error of Prediction; Mean Discrepancy Day 1 ± SD			Error of Prediction; Mean Discrepancy Day 5 ± SD		
	Astrand Nomogram	Margaria Nomogram	Maritz Extrapolation	Astrand Nomogram	Margaria Nomogram	Maritz Extrapolation
Treadmill	− 0.27 ± 0.37	− 0.35 ± 0.67	− 0.17 ± 0.57	− 0.04 ± 0.39	− 0.39 ± 0.61	− 0.22 ± 0.44
Step test	− 0.18 ± 0.46	− 0.09 ± 0.39	− 0.03 ± 0.36	+ 0.16 ± 0.25	+ 0.12 ± 0.28	+ 0.12 ± 0.28
Bicycle ergometer	+ 0.30 ± 0.31	+ 0.18 ± 0.27	+ 0.19 ± 0.28	+ 0.33 ± 0.35	+ 0.13 ± 0.35	+ 0.18 ± 0.34

*Data for 24 healthy young men (53).

of test. If a completely continuous pattern of loading is adopted (for instance, by progressively advancing the metronome speed in stepping or by use of a special bicycle ergometer of the Müller type), the subject has no time to reach a steady state, and the pulse response to exercise is a little less than in a discontinuous test. More usually, the work load is increased every third or fourth minute, and most physiological parameters then approximate closely to the corresponding steady state values (45). There are two main reasons why the time at individual loads can be shortened: a) Since the increment in work load is small, the changes that occur in physiological parameters are also small, and b) the total duration of exercise is longer, leading to some rise of core temperature; this "thermal artefact" helps ventilation and pulse readings to reach their steady-state values.

It is now established beyond question that in young adults predictions of maximum oxygen intake based on measurements of pulse and oxygen consumption during the third minute of a progressive test differ in no way from similar predictions based on data from a discontinuous test (Table 12-V). However, if the subjects are elderly or there is reason to believe that the circulation time is increased, it may be desirable to increase the duration of each exercise load to four minutes (46); in such circumstances it is necessary to strike a balance between the objective of "steady-state" results and exhaustion of the patient.

TABLE 12-V

A COMPARISON OF DISCONTINUOUS AND CONTINUOUS TESTS
FOR THE PREDICTION OF MAXIMUM OXYGEN INTAKE*

Mode of Exercise	Mean ± SD, Predicted Maximum Oxygen Intake (Liters/min STPD)		
	Discontinuous Test	Continuous Test	Difference
Treadmill	3.83 ± 0.90	3.79 ± 0.89	− 0.04 ± 0.61
Step test	3.75 ± 0.87	3.73 ± 0.93	− 0.02 ± 0.34
Bicycle ergometer	3.57 ± 0.81	3.64 ± 0.86	+ 0.07 ± 0.29

*Results are in each case based on linear extrapolation of the data to the predicted maximum pulse rate. Data for 24 healthy young men (53).

Intensity of Loading

The choice of loads depends to some extent upon the method that is to be used in interpreting the results. If the Maritz extrapolation (30) is adopted, the aim should be to achieve four evenly-spaced loads ranging from 40 to 50 percent to 80 to 90 percent of aerobic power; in a young person the corresponding target pulse rates range from 120 to 180 per minute. If the nomogram procedures (5, 29) are used, then the most accurate predictions of aerobic power are obtained from pulse rates in the range 150 to 170 per minute (45). Since the Åstrand nomogram (5) is based on a single pair of observations, the Margaria homogram (29) uses two pairs, and the Maritz extrapolation (30) four pairs, the relative accuracy of the predictions should be Maritz > Margaria > Åstrand. In practice (Table 12-IV) the I.B.P. team found little difference in the scatter of predictions with the three procedures, although the systematic error tended to be smaller for the Martiz extrapolation than for the nomograms. One practical problem with a four-point regression line is that the slope of the line is influenced very heavily by the pulse response to the lowest work load; traditionally this is regarded as more susceptible to emotional disturbance than the response at higher work loads.

The oxygen cost of exercise should normally be measured. However, if this is not possible, the load should be kept below the level at which significant anaerobic metabolism occurs. This is about 55 percent of aerobic power on the bicycle ergometer, 65 percent of aerobic power on the treadmill, and 80 percent of aerobic power on the step test (53).

Details of Test

The general details of the test procedure are essentially as for maximum exercise. However, even more attention is necessary to the conditions in the testing room and to the preparation of the subject, since a small elevation of pulse rate resulting from a hot and humid environment, a recent meal, or anxiety regarding the conduct and results of the test can lead to large errors in the predicted aerobic power.

The effects of anxiety are greatly diminished by a simple repetition of the test procedure (an example of habituation or negative conditioning). Recent studies of habituation (19, 51) indicate that anxiety causes a rather uniform lateral displacement of the pulse rate/oxygen consumption relationship at moderate and large work loads; the traditional view that emotion has a greater effect at light work loads is not true, *unless* the increment in pulse rate is expressed as a percentage of the pulse rate after the effects of anxiety have been eliminated. If the environment is hot and the subjects are unfit, there may be a large (25%-30%) systematic discrepancy between the directly measured and the predicted maximum oxygen intake on Day 1 (39). On the other hand, if the room is held to a comfortable temperature, the exercise is familiar, and the speed of performance does not engender anxiety, the initial error is rarely more than 10 to 15 percent.

These discrepancies generally disappear if the test is repeated. However, habituation can also be lost if there is a substantial interval between two series of submaximum tests (51), and this can lead to difficulties in the evaluation of response to a training regime.

Davies (18, 19) has recently suggested that the error of submaximum predictions is such as to make them of little value. However, this is not borne out by the I.B.P. working party data (Table 12-IV). The standard deviation of the discrepancy between predicted and directly measured values was ~ 0.4 liters per minute; perhaps a quarter of this is attributable to the direct measurement with which comparison is made, leaving a coefficient of variation of 7 to 8 percent. This is greater than for a direct measurement but not alarmingly so. The other potential criticism of the prediction procedure is a systematic error. Taking the evidence of the Maritz extrapolation (Table 12-IV), the step-test data gave no systematic error on Day 1; the treadmill gave a small (4.5%) underestimate, and the bicycle ergometer a small (5.1%) overestimate of aerobic power. While these errors are undesirable, they do not seem sufficient to rule out use of predictions based on the response to submaximum exercise, especially in field studies.

Choice of Exercise Machine

A number of factors involved in the choice of exercise machine have already been discussed. Additional points are also considered in two recent works of reference (46, 47).

Step Test

The main merits of the step test are that it is simple, cheap, portable, familiar to most subjects, and requires no extensive calibration. The work performed can also be estimated fairly accurately if a) the subject is paced by either a metronome or a contact in the stair-tread (21) and b) care is taken to ensure that the steps are ascended and descended completely at each cycle. Wyndham (62) has recently suggested that the efficiency of stair climbing varies with body weight. Certainly, the efficiency is a little lower in those who are obese; however, the difference is small, and could equally reflect ageing rather than obesity (Shephard, In press).

A good quality ECG record can be obtained from standard chest leads during stepping (53), and there is no difficulty in carrying out such maneuvers as the collection of expired gas. However, ancillary measurements such as the determination of blood pressure or cardiac output are not readily performed while a subject is climbing.

Different authors have suggested a wide variety of step heights. In some instances a variation of step height (23) or rate (31) has been proposed to "adjust" the test for interindividual differences in body weight. In fact, if it is intended to perform exercise at a constant fraction of aerobic power, little adjustment is necessary for body weight (Table 12-VI), although some allowance should be made for age, sex, and estimated cardiorespiratory fitness. The height of the step and the rate of ascent are thus determined mainly by the convenience of the subject. A height of nine inches is comparable with the typical domestic staircase, thus minimizing problems of anxiety and learning. Sixty to 150 paces per minute represent a comfortable range of climbing rates; with a slower pace the patient tends to hold his limb poised, waiting for the beat of the metronome; at a pace of more than 150 per minute the gait becomes an ungainly gal-

TABLE 12-VI
NUMBER OF ASCENTS OF AN EIGHTEEN-INCH STAIRCASE
PER MINUTE CORRESPONDING TO A WORK LOAD
75 PERCENT OF AEROBIC POWER*

(a) Male Patients
Body Weight (Pounds)

Age (Years)	110	120	130	140	150	160	170	180	190	200	210	220
20-30	20	20	20	21	21	21	21	21	21	21	21	21
30-40	18	19	19	19	19	19	19	19	19	20	20	20
40-50	16	16	16	17	17	17	17	17	17	17	17	17
50-60	13	13	13	13	13	13	14	14	14	14	14	14

(b) Female Patients
Body Weight (Pounds)

Age (Years)	80	90	100	110	120	130	140	150	160	170	180	190
20-30	16	17	17	17	17	18	18	18	18	18	18	18
30-40	16	16	17	17	17	17	17	18	18	18	18	18
40-50	14	14	14	15	15	15	15	15	15	15	16	16
50-60	10	10	10	10	10	10	10	10	10	10	10	10

*Figures apply to patient of average cardiorespiratory fitness for his age (59).

lop, leading to a loss of mechanical efficiency and a danger of tripping on the staircase.

Reference to Table 12-VI shows that most subjects can perform exercise at 40 to 80 percent of aerobic power while climbing a double nine-inch step at 60 to 150 paces per minute. However, subjects with a high level of cardiorespiratory fitness may need to make thirty to thirty-five ascents per minute. This can be achieved by climbing a single eighteen-inch step, although the task is then less familiar and tends to be uncomfortable, particularly for shorter subjects.

In summary, the step test is more suited to submaximum than maximum exercise and is particularly valuable in field situations where extensive ancillary measurements are not required.

Bicycle Ergometer

The bicycle ergometer is a rather more complicated piece of apparatus than a simple staircase, and if one objective of testing is to motivate an individual to continued participation in a training programme, it may succeed in impressing some patients with the scientific nature of the rehabilitation regime. The relative immobility of the arms is also an important asset when it is intended to carry out a wide range of ancillary investigations.

On the other hand, a bicycle ergometer is expensive ($300 to $3000), and cycling is an unfamiliar form of exercise to the present generation of adults. In consequence, the stress placed on one muscle group (the quadriceps) is excessive relative to their development. Anaerobic work occurs in submaximum exercise (53), and maximum exercise is limited by peripheral rather than central factors (52). It may also be difficult for the subject to dismount in an emergency (46).

It has traditionally been asserted that the work performed on a bicycle ergometer is known with considerable accuracy and that this form of exercise is thus peculiarly suitable for use in situations where the oxygen consumption cannot be measured. The apparent mechanical effciency of effort is perhaps a little more consistent than for stepping (see section on Mode of Exercise). However, the development of torque calibrators (15) has shown that both mechanical and electrically braked bicycle ergometers are subject to alarming systematic errors. A few of the more expensive designs, such as the Fleisch "ergostat" (Jacquet Ltd., Basel, Switzerland) are initially calibrated to take account of frictional losses in the pedals and bearings; however, the widely used Von Döbeln machine commonly has a systematic error of 8 to 10 percent.

The bicycle ergometer is a popular form of test with children and would seem the procedure of choice for submaximal exercise if a wide range of physiological parameters are to be examined. However, if it is intended to monitor only oxygen consumption and the electrocardiogram, it has no real advantage over the step test; the choice will depend upon the personal preference of the investigator and the circumstances of the experiment.

Use of a supine bicycle ergometer permits a further increase in the range of investigations, including cardiac catheterization. It is thus quite a popular procedure in hospital laboratories. Good shoulder supports and toe straps are essential for cycling while supine and even with optimum positioning it is a rather unnatural form of exercise.

The arm crank ergometer has some value in the testing of subjects with leg injuries and/or unusual development of the arm and shoulder muscles. However, this form of exercise is even more prone to limitation by local muscular fatigue than is leg work on the bicycle ergometer. The pulse rate/oxygen consumption line is displaced upwards and to the left relative to leg work (1), the maximum stroke volume is limited by pooling of blood in the leg veins (Shephard and Simmons, To be published), and the maximum oxygen intake is substantially lower than any form of leg work (6). These generalizations do not apply to the large shoulder cranks used in some German laboratories (36); with such machines the subject stands and applies a force to the crank with both arm and back muscles, so that the maximum oxygen intake may equal that found in leg work. There have been proposals for the standardization of the shoulder crank test (32); however, unless the investigator has a special interest in the arm and shoulder muscles, there seem no specific advantages to be gained from using this type of ergometer.

Treadmill

Treadmills vary greatly in their power. Some models intended for clinical testing at low walking speeds are sufficiently small to store in a cupboard. However, the smaller treadmills tend to be underpowered and in consequence, fail to maintain a constant belt speed. Larger treadmills are available to the experimental physiologist; these are costly and often rather noisy but are capable of rapidly attaining speeds of 20 to 25 m.p.h. Such speeds are sometimes needed for the testing of sprint athletes, but the average young man will reach his maximum oxygen intake on a treadmill capable of a speed of 6 m.p.h. with an 18 percent grade.

Several nomograms are now available (28, 50, 60) to calculate the cost of treadmill walking and running; one that is particularly convenient for a series of submaximum tests expresses the oxygen cost of slow running as the gross cost in milliliters per minute per kilogram of body weight (Fig. 12-1). During walk-

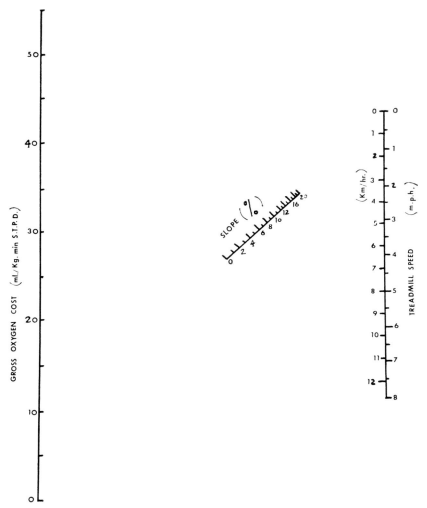

FIGURE 12-1. The gross oxygen cost of slow treadmill running (50). (Courtesy of the *Journal of Sports Medicine and Fitness.*)

ing, oxygen consumption is a curvilinear function of treadmill speed. The same might be anticipated during running; however, in practice, oxygen consumption is a linear function of speed over quite a wide range of slow and more rapid rates of running (50). The nomograms predict oxygen consumption rather less precisely than it can be estimated for bicycle or stepping exercise; however, the discrepancy between the observed and the predicted oxygen cost of running is not more than 10 percent in young and healthy men (44).

The main disadvantages of the treadmill are its cost, size, and (usually) the noise of operation. Subjects adapt relatively quickly to level walking, but uphill running is an unfamiliar task that may provoke anxiety. At high speeds there is an appreciable risk of injury from stumbling. Thus, although the treadmill is the procedure of choice for maximum testing, there is little to commend it for submaximum tests.

Simple Tests for Clinical Use

The clinician commonly requires a simple test for aerobic power and the associated ECG responses for such purposes as a) the assessment of fitness for work, sports, and other strenuous activities, including prescription of an appropriate starting point and a suitable rate of progression for patients who wish to participate in a training programme; b) an objective evaluation of overall functional status of the cardiovascular and respiratory systems, including appraisal of symptons such as dyspnoea, and signs such as cardiac enlargement; c) a prediction of the likelihood of developing specific diseases (particularly myocardial infarction) and a decision regarding prognosis where disease or injury of the heart is already present; d) the control of the intensity of exercise in specific programmes for the prevention and treatment of myocardial disease; e) an objective assessment of the response to surgery and/or drugs; and f) the continued motivation of the patient during a prolonged rehabilitation programme.

Many physicians feel intuitively that the tests used by the exercise physiologist are too complicated to administer in their practice. They would like a test that is brief and imposes a light load without appreciable risk to the patient. The single and double step tests of Master (31) have been very popular for this reason. However, there are several disadvantages to the standard Master's tests: a) The duration of exercise (1½ minutes in a single stage, 3 minutes in a double stage test) is too short. The minimum time allowance to achieve a steady state should be five minutes in a single-stage test and three minutes in a continuous progressive test; even longer may be required when dealing with clinical material. b) The relative stress that is imposed depends upon the age, weight, and cardio-respiratory fitness of the individual. c) The intensity of stress imposed is too light, particularly in younger patients.

One of the main objectives of the clinician is to evaluate the electrocardiographic response to exercise. It is thus desirable that all patients should be compared at a load that is a constant percentage of their aerobic power. The present author feels that 75 percent of aerobic power is a reasonable stress for field conditions, striking a balance between the need for a vigorous test and considerations of safety. Scandinavian workers have recently proposed 85 percent. The corresponding target pulse rates are shown in Table 12-III, while the required rates of ascent of an eighteen-inch step are shown in Table 12-VI. The speed of ascent varies little with body weight but does of course vary with cardio-respiratory fitness. If the pulse rate is ten beats per minute higher than the target for a specified rate of ascent, he is unfit, while if it is ten beats per minute lower; he has a good standard of cardiorespiratory fitness.

Table 12-VI can be used as the basis of a simple five-minute test, using a double nine-inch step and comparing the individual's final pulse rate with the target figure. However, there are several advantages to a multistage procedure, commencing with three minutes of exercise at 50 percent and with a further three minutes at 75 percent of the stepping rate shown: a) The final rate of stepping can be modified if necessary to give a pulse rate that is very close to the target value. b) The test can be halted at a lower intensity of exercise if the patient develops an unfavorable reaction. c) Some information is obtained even if the patient is unable or unwilling to complete the third period of exercise.

In the present author's experience, based mainly on the citizens of Metropolitan Toronto, almost all healthy men and women up to the age of seventy are able and willing to drive themselves to at least 75 percent of aerobic power when tested on a double nine-inch step. If a single eighteen-inch step is used, the oxygen cost of climbing is almost identical (45), but perhaps because the step height is unfamiliar, almost a quarter of the healthy but sedentary men we have examined give up before they have completed a single-stage five-minute test at 75 percent of aerobic power. If a similar 75 percent test is performed on the bicycle ergometer, young and healthy subjects find no difficulty in maintaining their effort for five minutes, but older patients sometimes stop before the end of the test, complaining of weakness in the leg musculature.

The use of Tables 12-III and 12-VI as a basis of standardized clinical tests would considerably enhance the diagnostic value of the ECG and other records. Further, if more sophisticated assessments of cardiorespiratory fitness were later desired, these could readily be derived from the measured pulse rate, stepping rate, and body weight.

Procedures for Personal and Mass Testing

Cooper (10A) has suggested that the individual can make a rough assessment of his aerobic power in milliliters per kilogram minute by testing the distance he can run in twelve minutes; Balke previously proposed a similar fifteen-minute test.

Such procedures have some attraction not only for personal use but also for the mass testing of schools, the armed services, and the like. There seems little question that the twelve-minute test is more accurate than the 300-yard run and the 600-yard walk-run included in two recent performance batteries; the latter barely stress the cardiorespiratory system, and their correlation with the maximum oxygen intake is correspondingly poor (14, 20).

Tests in boys and in servicemen have shown coefficients of correlation as high as 0.9 between the directly measured aerobic power and scores on the twelve-minute test (Cooper, Personal communication to author). However, the validity of the twelve-minute score is highly dependent upon the motivation of the subjects, and probably for this reason the correlation of results with the maximum oxygen intake drops to 0.7 or less in women. Further, it is essential that all entrants compete to the limit of their aerobic power. Twelve minutes of maximum exercise seems an undesirable stress for untrained middle-aged subjects, both from the viewpoint of causing tendon injuries and also from the risk of inducing ventricular fibrillation. In recognition of these dangers, Cooper now advocates six weeks of preliminary conditioning before participation in a twelve-minute test.

Conclusions

Standard techniques for the testing of aerobic power in the laboratory, the field, and the doctor's office have been discussed. There seems little question that the best available single index of cardiorespiratory fitness is a careful measurement of maximum oxygen intake. In laboratory tests on young adults, direct measurement during uphill treadmill running is recommended. In the field, particularly when dealing with older patients, submaximum tests on a step or a bicycle ergometer are to be preferred, while even simpler procedures may suffice for the physician's office and for personal and mass testing.

Finally, it seems important to emphasize that although objective physiological measurements have many advantages over gymnasium-type tests, aerobic power is not the sole determinant of physical performance. Brief events are greatly influenced by strength, explosive power of the muscles, reaction time, skill, agility, and tolerance of oxygen debt. Prolonged exercise depends upon maintenance of heat and water balance and the extent and mobility of food reserves in the muscle and liver. And even in exercise of moderate duration, traditionally the realm of oxygen transport, performance may be influenced by many other factors, including efficiency of effort, motivation, and the strength of individual muscle groups. If fitness for an athletic contest is to be evaluated, a consideration of these other factors is an important part of the total assessment of the individual.

References

1. Asmussen, E., and Hemmingsen, I.: Determination of maximum working capacity at different ages in work with the legs or with the arms. *Scand J Clin Lab Invest*, 10:67-71, 1958.

2. Asmussen, E., and Molbech, S.V.: Methods and standards for evaluation of the physiological working capacity of patients. *Comm Testing and Obs Inst*, Hellerup, Denmark 4, 1959.

3. Astrand, I.: Chairwoman of Committee of Scandinavian investigators meeting in Stockholm.

4. Åstrand, P-O: *Experimental Studies of Physical Working Capacity in Relation to Sex and Age*. Copenhagen, Munksgaard, 1952.

5. Åstrand, P-O., and Ryhming, I.: A nomogram for calculation of aerobic capacity (physical fitness) from pulse rate during submaximal work. *J Appl Physiol*, 7:218-221, 1954.

6. Åstrand, P-O., and Saltin, B.: Maximal oxygen uptake and heart rate in various types of muscular activity. *J Appl Physiol*, 16:977-981, 1961.

7. Åstrand, P-O., Engstrom, L., Eriksson, B., Karlberg, P., Nylander, I., Saltin, B., and Thoren, C.: Girl swimmers. With special reference to respiratory and circulatory adaptation, and gynaecological and psychiatric aspects. *Acta Paediat Scand (Suppl.)*, 147:1, 1963.

8. Bonjer, F.H.: Measurement of working capacity by assessment of the aerobic capacity in a single session. *Fed Proc*, 25:1363-1365, 1966.

9. Brouha, L.: The step test: a simple method of measuring physical fitness for muscular work in young men. *Res Quart*, 14:31-36, 1943.

10. Clasing, D., and Durussy, F.P.: Der Einfluss des Warmlaufens auf submaximale Fahrradergometerarbeit. *Sportarzt und Sportmedizin, 4*.

10A. Cooper, K.H.: *Aerobics*. New York, Evans, 1968.

11. Cotes, J.E.: Tests for lung function. In *Respiratory Function Tests in Pneumoconiosis*. Geneva. Int. Labour Office. Occ. Safety & Health, publication No. 6.

12. Cotes, J.E., and Woolmer, R.F.: A comparison between twenty-seven laboratories of the results of analysis of an expired gas sample. *J Physiol (London)*, 163:36P-37P, 1962.

13. Cotton, F.S., and Dill, D.B.: On the relationship between the

heart rate during exercise and that of the immediate post-exercise period. *Amer J Physiol, 111*:554-556, 1935.

14. CUMMING, G.R., and KEYNES, R.: A fitness performance test for schoolchildren and its correlation with physical working capacity and maximal oxygen uptake. *Canad Med Assoc J, 96*:1262-1269, 1967.

15. CUMMING, G.R., and ALEXANDER, W.D.: The calibration of bicycle ergometers. *Canad J Physiol Pharmacol, 46*:917-919, 1968.

16. CUMMING, G.R., and FRIESEN, W.: Bicycle ergometer measurements of maximal oxygen uptake in children. *Canad J Physiol Pharmacol, 45*:937-946, 1967.

17. DAVIES, C.T.M.: In Proceedings of International Symposium on Physical Activity and Cardiovascular Health. *Canad Med Assoc J, 96*:743-744, 1967.

18. DAVIES, C.T.M.: Limitations to the prediction of maximum oxygen intake from cardiac frequency measurements. *J Appl Physiol, 24*:700-706.

19. DAVIES, C.T.M., TUXWORTH, W.T., and YOUNG, J.M.: Habituation to standardized exercise on a bicycle ergometer. *J Physiol (London), 197*:26, 1968.

20. DRAKE, V., JONES, G., BROWN, J.R., and SHEPHARD, R.J.: Fitness performance tests and their relationship to maximum oxygen intake. *Canad Med Assoc J, 99*:844-848, 1968.

21. DUGGER, B.C., and SWENGROS, G.V.: The design of physical activity programs for industry. Ergonomics-Medical Session. Amer. Industr. Hyg. Conference, St. Louis, Missouri, 1968.

22. DUNCAN, W.R., ROSS, W.D., and BANISTER, E.W.: Heart rate monitoring as a guide to the intensity of an exercise program. *Brit Col Med J, 10*:8, 1968.

23. GILSON, J.C., and HUGH-JONES, P.: Lung function in coalworkers' pneumoconiosis. *M.R.C. Special Report Series, 290*:1-266, H.M. Stationary Office, U.K., 1955.

24. GLASSFORD, R.C., BAYCROFT, G.H.Y., SEDGWICK, A.W., and MAC-NAB, R.B.J.: Comparison of maximal oxygen uptake values determined by predicted and actual methods. *J Appl Physiol, 20*:509-513, 1965.

25. GOODWIN, A.B., and CUMMING, G.R.: Radiotelemetry of the electrocardiogram, fitness tests, and oxygen uptake of water-polo players. *Canad Med Assoc J, 95*:402-406, 1966.

26. International Committee for Standardization in Haematology. *Brit Med J, (i)*:645, 1965.
27. JOKL, E.: *The Clinical Physiology of Physical Fitness and Rehabilitation.* Springfield, Charles C Thomas, 1958.
28. MARGARIA, R. CERRETELLI, P., AGHEMO, P., and SOSSI, G.: Energy cost of running. *J Appl Physiol, 18*:367-370, 1963.
29. MARGARIA, R., AGHEMO, P., and ROVELLI, E.: Indirect determination of maximal O_2 consumption in man. *J Appl Physiol, 20*: 1070-1073, 1965.
30. MARITZ, J.S., MORRISON, J.F., PETER, J., STRYDOM, N.B., and WYNDHAM, C. H.: A practical method of estimating an individual's maximum oxygen intake. *Ergonomics, 4*:97-122, 1961.
31. MASTER, A.M., and ROSENFELD, I.: *Mod Conc Cardiov Dis, 36*:19, 1967.
32. MELLEROWICZ, H.: Standardisierung ergometrischer Leistungsmethoden. XVI. *Weltkongress für Sportmedizin, Hannover,* Germany, 1966.
33. MITCHELL, J.H., SPROULE, B.J., and CHAPMAN, C.B.: The physiological meaning of the maximum oxygen intake test. *J Clin Invest, 37*:538-547, 1958.
34. MONCRIEFF, J.: Individual differences, reliabilities, and intercorrelations of oxygen intake measures. *J Sports Med, 8*:153-157, 1968.
35. MÜLLER, E.A.: Ein Leistrungs-Pulsindex als Mass der Leistungsfahigkeit. *Arbeitsphysiol, 14*:27, 1950.
36. NOWACKI, and MELLEROWICZ, H.: In Hansen, G. (Ed.): *Internationales Seminar für Ergometrie.* Berlin, Germany, 1966.
37. PUGH, L.G.C.E.: Physiological and medical aspects of the Himalayan Scientific and Mountaineering Expedition 1960-61. *Brit Med J (ii)*:621-633, 1962.
38. RYHMING, I.: A modified Harvard step test for the evaluation of physical fitness. *Arbeitsphysiol, 15*:235-250, 1954.
39. ROWELL, L.B., TAYLOR, H. L., and WANG, Y.: Limitations to predictions of maximum oxygen intake. *J Appl Physiol, 19*:919-927, 1964.
40. SALTIN, B., and ÅSTRAND, P-O.: Maximal oxygen uptake in athletes. *J Appl Physiol, 23*:353-358.
41. SHEPHARD, R.J.: A comparison of paramagnetic and chemical methods for the determination of oxygen. *Int Z Angew Physiol, 22*:279-284, 1966.

42. SHEPHARD, R.J.: On the timing of post-exercise pulse readings. *J Sports Med, 6*:23-27, 1966.

43. SHEPHARD, R.J.: The prediction of maximum oxygen intake from post-exercise pulse readings. *Int Z Angew Physiol, 24*:31-38, 1967.

44. SHEPHARD, R.J.: The relative merits of the step test, bicycle ergometer, and treadmill in the assessment of cardiorespiratory fitness. *Int Z Angew Physiol, 23*:219-230, 1966.

45. SHEPHARD, R.J.: The prediction of "maximal" oxygen consumption using a new progressive step test. *Ergonomics, 10*:1-15, 1967.

46. SHEPHARD, R.J.: Rapporteur: Exercise tests in relation to cardiovascular function. *W.H.O. Tech Rept, 388*, 1968.

47. SHEPHARD, R.J.: *Endurance Fitness.* Toronto, University of Toronto Press, 1969.

48. SHEPHARD, R.J.: In Larson, E. (Ed.): *Encyclopaedia of Sports Medicine.* New York, MacMillan, 1969.

49. SHEPHARD, R.J.: Communication to workshop on "Exercise in the prevention, in the evaluation, and in the treatment of heart disease," Myrtle Beach, S.C., 1969.

50. SHEPHARD, J.R.: A nomogram to calculate the oxygen cost of running at slow speeds. *J Sports Med, 9*:10-16.

51. SHEPHARD, R.J.: Learning, habituation and training. *Int Z Angew Physiol, 28*:38-48.

52. SHEPHARD, R.J., ALLEN, C., BENADE, A.J.S., DAVIES, C.T.M., DI PRAMPERO, P.E., HEDMAN, R., MERRIMAN, J.E., MYHRE, K., and SIMMONS, R.: The maximum oxygen intake. An international reference standard of cardio-respiratory fitness *Bull WHO, 38*:757-764, 1968.

53. SHEPHARD, R.J. ALLEN, C., BENADE, A.J.S., DAVIES, C.T.M., DI PRAMPERO, P.E., HEDMAN, R., MERRIMAN, J.E., MYHRE, K., and SIMMONS, R.: Standardization of submaximal exercise tests. *Bull WHO, 38*:765-775, 1968.

54. SHEPHARD, R.J.: ALLEN, C., BAR-OR, O., DAVIES, C.T.M., DEGRÉ, S., HEDMAN, R., ISHII, K., KANEKO, M., LACOUR, J.R., DI PRAMPERO, P.E., and SELIGER, V.: The working capacity of Toronto School-children. *Canad Med Assoc J, 100*:560-566, 705-714, 1969.

55. TAYLOR, C.: Some properties of maximal and submaximal exercise with reference to physiological variation and the measurement of exercise tolerance. *Amer J Physiol, 142*:200-212, 1944.

56. TAYLOR, H.L., BUSKIRK, E., and HENSCHEL, A.: Maximal oxygen

intake, as an objective measure of cardio-respiratory performance. *J. Appl Physiol,* 8:73, 1955.

57. WAHLUND, H.G.: Determination of the physical working capacity: A physiological and clinical study with special reference to standardization of cardio-pulmonary functional tests, 1948.

58. WEINER, J.S.: Handbook of agreed methodology for Human Adaptability Project, International Biological Programme. In preparation.

59. WORLD HEALTH ORGANIZATION: Handbook of methodology for exercise tests. In preparation, 1969.

60. WORKMAN, J.M., and ARMSTRONG, B.W.: Oxygen cost of treadmill walking. *J Appl Physiol,* 18:798-803, 1963.

61. WYNDHAM, C.H., STRYDOM, N.B., LEARY, W.P., and WILLIAMS, C.G.: A comparison of methods of assessing the maximum oxygen intake. *Int Z Angew Physiol,* 22:285, 1966.

62. WYNDHAM, C.H., and SLUIS-CREMER, G.: The capacity for physical work of white miners in South Africa. *S Afr Med J,* 42:841-844, 1968.

63. YOSHIMURA, H., and WEINER, J.S.: *Human Adaptability and Its Methodology.* Tokyo, Japan Society for the promotion of sciences, 1966.

Chapter 13

CORRELATION OF PHYSICAL PERFORMANCE WITH LABORATORY MEASURES OF FITNESS

G. R. CUMMING

T HE PURPOSES of correlation studies in exercise physiology are a) to predict from field tests values for time-consuming detailed tests that are either best done in the laboratory or can only be administered to a small segment of the population; b) to define the confidence limits of any predictions; and c) to investigate the factors that contribute to a given performance or physiologic function, to find the order of importance of these factors, and to eliminate factors that are unimportant.

With correlation analyses it must always be kept in mind that a high correlation fails to prove cause and effect; it may indicate rather a coincidental association or the relationship of two or more variables to other obscure factors. In this study we have relied on linear multiple regression studies between laboratory measures of fitness and physical performances. Mellits (29) has pointed out the advantages of constructing intersecting straight lines to analyze some data, particularly in studies of children where the slope of change may alter abruptly at some time such as puberty. We have not utilized this technique or other more complex multivariate procedures (12) in our studies.

Fitness tests can be broken down into laboratory measures of specific functions such as lung function tests, strength tests, and cardiopulmonary capacity tests and into performance tests which are dependent on many additional factors including speed, agility, skills both inborn and learned, and complex physiological and psychological attributes.

Note: Work was supported by The Fitness and Amateur Sports Directorate, Ottawa.

Lung Function and Performance

The functional capacity of the lungs to move air in and out of the body and to exchange gases can be measured accurately. Åstrand (7) has reported a close correlation between vital capacity and maximum oxygen uptake, and it is commonly held by some athletes and coaches that a good lung capacity is equivalent to a good wind and a high level of endurance. In a recent study from this laboratory (16), the capacity of the chest to move air was assessed in 103 teenage boys and girls; a computerized wedge spirometer was used to measure vital capacity (VC), mean expiratory flow rate (MMEF), and maximum voluntary ventilation (MVV). The boys were tested at a summer track camp; they were highly motivated, and they received training in track and field events to produce some equalization of skill factors. At the end of the camp session, performance in ten track and field events was measured under competitive conditions. When body size was taken into consideration, there was no significant correlation between athletic performance and VC or MMEF. Significant correlations were found between MVV and the performances of the boys in the 100-yard dash, the 120-yard hurdles, and the shot put. Because only one or two breaths are required for the sprints and the breath is held for the shot put, a large MVV is neither needed nor used in these events. For these reasons it is likely that the observed correlation between MVV and performance in these events was due to coincidental factors of motivation, coordination, and muscular speed and strength. There were no significant correlations between athletic performance and lung function in girls when body size was taken into consideration.

The pulmonary function tests showed correlation coefficients as high as 0.85 with body size, while the highest correlation coefficient between athletic performance and pulmonary function was 0.54. Surprisingly, no positive correlation was found for either sex between lung function and performance in the 880-yard and cross-country runs, events where aerobic power and the exchange of a large volume of air are required. It is likely that the capacity of the normal lungs to exchange air has such a large reserve that this seldom becomes a limiting factor in athletic performance (32); hence, the lack of correlation.

In normal exercising subjects diffusion of oxygen from the lungs into the blood is more vital than the exchange of air between the atmosphere and the lung surface. The maximum diffusing capacity during exercise might thus be expected to show a higher correlation with endurance running times than function tests simply measuring the movement of air from the lungs to the atmosphere. However, the diffusing capacity during exercise is closely correlated with both maximum oxygen uptake and maximum cardiac output, which in turn are also closely correlated with performance in endurance events. While studies correlating lung function and performance are not available for all sports, it is possible that large lung volumes are important in swimmers. The training of swimmers is associated with an increase in vital capacity and functional residual volume (8). On the other hand, the vital capacity and MVV of runners, including both sprinters and distance men, do not improve with training (1), and static lung volumes are no higher in marathon runners than in the general population (25).

Physical Performance Tests and Laboratory Measures of Endurance Fitness

The assessment of the fitness of school children and the effectiveness of their physical education programs is facilitated by performance tests that have been developed by the American and Canadian associations, AAHPER and CAHPER (3,11). The individual items in these tests are somewhat similar. However, both associations must have had a very low opinion of either the endurance capacity of the youth or their willingness to take part in an endurance run because the longest item in the American test battery was a 600-yard walk-run, while the Canadian test shortened this to a 300-yard run. As we have found no difficulty in having eight-year-old children run one to two miles in twelve minutes, it is thus difficult to understand the lack of a distance test in the AAHPER and CAHPER batteries. The argument that the test needs to be administered rapidly in areas lacking any facilities is not valid, and these performance tests should be revised to include a true test of endurance fitness.

Cumming and Keynes (20) correlated maximum oxygen uptake ($\dot{V}o_2$ max) and physical working capacity (PWC_{170}) with scores for the CAHPER test. Young people six to eighteen years of age were tested, and their mean performances in the CAHPER test were slightly above the published national averages (11) The predominant factor governing the physical performance of this group was body size. Without considering size, correlation coefficients as high as 0.76 were found between performance and $\dot{V}o_2$ max. However, when body size was included with the performance items in a multiple regression analysis, the only significant factor relating performance to aerobic power was the duration of the arm hang. The standard error of prediction of $\dot{V}o_2$ max and PWC_{170} was not reduced below that obtained with body surface area alone by adding all of the performance results to the multiple regression analysis. It was concluded that the CAHPER test did not measure any factor related to endurance fitness. Such performance tests are highly dependent on speed, balance, agility, and skills, as well as motivational factors; on the other hand, motivational factors are eliminated in ideal measurements of PWC_{170} and maximum oxygen uptake.

It is quite likely that a group of highly trained and athletically inclined children would score higher in these performance tests than a group of sedentary and poorly coordinated children. It is also understandable that the athletic children would have above average $\dot{V}o_2$ max values. However, the performance tests as they now stand would not appear to be of any value in the assessment of cardiorespiratory fitness in average children.

In seventy-six boys seventeen and eighteen years of age, Orlee *et al.* (30) found that the 600-yard run of the AAHPER test explained less than 30 percent of the variability in $\dot{V}o_2$ max results, thus confirming the results of Cumming and Keynes in a large number of subjects of the same age and approximately the same size.

The range of fitness of adults is much greater than in children, and one might expect a better correlation between performance tests and cardiorespiratory fitness measured by maximum oxygen uptake and strength measured with strain gauge systems. However, Drake *et al.* (22) found that measurements of height, weight, and skin fold thickness in adults gave as good a prediction of maximum oxygen uptake and strength as did a battery of six performance tests patterned after the AAHPER program. In contradistinction to this Falls *et al.* (24) found a correlation of .760 between $\dot{V}o_2$ max and the AAHPER test battery. The standard error of the prediction of maximum oxygen uptake was 12 percent in this study by Falls; however, the initial coefficient of variation in the maximum oxygen uptake of this group was only 19 percent, so that the performance test equation improved the prediction only slightly over that obtained by the use of body weight alone. Measurement of body fat might have resulted in the anthropometric measurements being just as good as the performance test battery in predicting aerobic power.

Prediction of Aerobic Power from Anthropometric Data

In normal children who play together and do not take part in special athletic programs, $\dot{V}o_2$ max values show little variation when body size is taken into consideration. Table 13-I shows the correlation between $\dot{V}o_2$ max and anthropometric data in an unpublished study (18) undertaken to measure the relationship between body potassium and fitness. This study was done in a small, isolated community where the children were closely associated with one another. All correlation coefficients between body size and $\dot{V}o_2$ max were above 0.88. The standard error of predicting $\dot{V}o_2$ max in girls was only 10 percent when height and weight or body potassium was considered, and only 9 percent when body weight and skin folds were considered. For the girls the standard error of the prediction of $\dot{V}o_2$ max was not improved when performance on a submaximal bicycle test was included. The standard error in predicting $\dot{V}o_2$ max in boys was 14 to 16 percent, using anthropometric data, and fell to 9 percent when PWC_{170} was included. In both sexes multiple correlation analyses were also obtained, using all of the anthropometric factors

TABLE 13-I

STRENGTH SCORES AND ATHLETIC RESULTS IN
TRACK AND FIELD CAMP

	Boys	*Girls*
Age—yr	15.1 ± 1.3	14.6 ± 1.4
Height—cm	170.9 ± 6.4	162.2 ± 5.7
Weight—kg	59.5 ± 10.4	52.8 ± 5.4
Hand grip—kg	46.2 ± 10.8	31.9 ± 6.7
Front flexion—kg	41.1 ± 12.5	27.8 ± 8.8
Back extension—kg	71.5 ± 15.7	48.4 ± 11.0
Hip flexion—kg	50.7 ± 14.8	38.6 ± 11.1
Push-up—kg	25.6 ± 7.0	15.3 ± 3.6
Pull down—kg	54.7 ± 11.6	33.9 ± 7.1
Knee extension—kg	28.8 ± 10.7	16.3 ± 6.1
Knee extension—kg cm	1017 ± 316	549 ± 199
Decathlon score	4419 ± 1119	3571 ± 1362
100 yards—sec	12.6 ± 1.2	13.6 ± 0.9
440 yards—sec	71.6 ± 7.6	76.6 ± 5.4
Discus—feet	71.9 ± 12.9	54.1 ± 12.4
Javelin—feet	83.5 ± 17.2	46.3 ± 11.1
Hurdles—sec	20.1 ± 2.4	15.6 ± 1.4
Long jump—feet	13.7 ± 1.8	11.6 ± 1.3
880 yards—sec	172 ± 23	197 ± 21
High jump—feet	4.2 ± 0.4	3.6 ± 0.4
Shot put—feet	31.8 ± 4.1	23.0 ± 3.5
Cross-country run—yards/sec	5.5 ± 0.5	4.8 ± 0.4

plus PWC_{170}; when calculations were made in this way, only the PWC_{170} regression coefficient was significant.

When height, weight, and skin folds allow the prediction of $\dot{V}o_2$ max or PWC_{170} with a standard error of ± 10 to 15 percent, it is difficult to judge the value of any performance test that cannot produce a better statistical prediction. These comments are in no way intended to belittle the value of performance tests. It is perhaps more important for a boy to be able to run fast and throw a ball far than to take in a lot of oxygen out of the atmosphere and put back a lot of carbon dioxide. The factor common to all fitness tests is that they are task-specific. Even the submaximal tests, such as the Åstrand bicycle ergometer test, are only able to predict $\dot{V}o_2$ max with a ±12 percent standard error (6). The average youth has an aerobic power within a relatively narrow range, and the prediction of $\dot{V}o_2$ max from work tests may thus be little better than the prediction from anthropometric data. In middle-aged adults, where the range of fitness is much

TABLE 13-II

STRENGTH SCORES VERSUS ATHLETIC RESULTS
SIGNIFICANT FACTORS IN MULTIPLE REGRESSION ANALYSIS—BOYS

Event	r	f°	Significant† t Ratios for Individual Regression Coefficients
Decathlon score	.60	1.69	Nil
100 yards	.47	0.92	Nil
Discus	.76	4.44	Back extension
Javelin	.73	0.93	Nil
Hurdles	.60	1.73	Nil
Long jump	.57	1.44	Push up
880 yards	.49	0.93	Nil
High jump	.59	1.80	Nil
Shot put	.23	3.80	Back extension
Cross-country run	.56	1.60	Nil

°5% level f $= 2.54$
†p $< .05$

wider, the submaximal work tests are of more value in estimating fitness. It should not be forgotten that under the best of circumstances, the coefficient of variation of repeat maximum oxygen uptake estimations in the same subject is 4 to 5 percent (19).

Correlation Between Twelve-Minute Run and Aerobic Power

One easily administered test is the distance that can be run in a given time; this was introduced by Balke (10) and recently modified and popularized by Cooper (13, 14). Cooper (13) reported a high correlation between the distance run in twelve minutes and $\dot{V}_{O_2}$ max. We have followed the results of over one thousand children performing the twelve-minute test run, and in several of these subjects we were able to compare the results of the twelve-minute run with the $\dot{V}_{O_2}$ max and/or the PWC_{170}. In our studies (17) the results for the twelve-minute run were quite reproducible in boys with a test-retest reliability coefficient of 0.87, but they were less reproducible in girls with a test-retest reliability coefficient of 0.76. In Table 13-II we have correlated the physical working capacities expressed as kpm per kilogram minute with the distance run in twelve minutes; the data are for several different groups of boys and girls nine to seventeen years of age. There were significant correlations between PWC$_{170}$ and the twelve-minute distance in the youths studied at the special camps and in boys and girls attending junior and senior high schools; however, the correlation between the twelve-minute run and PWC$_{170}$ per kilogram did not reach statistical significance in the elementary school boys and girls. On anthropometric data alone we are able to predict the PWC$_{170}$ per kilogram with a standard error of less than 15 percent, so that the run added little to the prediction of working capacity in any one subject.

Cooper (13) found a very high correlation between $\dot{V}o_2$ max and the distance run in twelve minutes (0.90). However, his Figure 1 indicates that with a running distance of 1.6 miles, $\dot{V}o_2$ max could range from 40 to 52 ml per kilogram; a patient might thus come from his fair, good, or excellent categories, and the standard error of the $\dot{V}o_2$ max prediction would be at least 14 percent. This is possibly no better than could be achieved by use of height, weight, and skin fold data. The weight of the servicemen in his study ranged from 52 to 123 kg, and it would hardly be surprising if the fat men had both a low $\dot{V}o_2$ max per kilogram and a low twelve-minute run distance.

One military criteria of fitness is the time required to run three miles with boots, helmet, and pack (28). Performance in this type of test is highly dependent on motivation, particularly in the average recruit. On the other hand, when this approach is used in a research situation, Rasch (31) has shown that performance correlates well with the results of the Balke treadmill test (9). Other procedures such as the Harvard step test (27) show a low correlation with both laboratory measures of endurance fitness (21) and endurance running tests (31) and should probably be discontinued.

Strength Testing and Performance in Track and Field

A strain gauge system patterned after that of Asmussen (5) and Lange Andersen (4) was used to measure strength in forty-seven boys and forty-nine girls attending a summer track camp (26). The six strength measurements were hand grip, frontward flexion and backward extension of the trunk, arm push up and

TABLE 13-III

STRENGTH SCORES VERSUS ATHLETIC RESULTS

SIGNIFICANT FACTORS IN MULTIPLE REGRESSION ANALYSIS—GIRLS

Event	r	f*	Significant† t ratios for Individual Regression Coefficients
Decathlon score	.75	4.51	Height, negative for weight, hip flexion, pull down
100 yards	.63	2.25	Height, negative for weight
Discus	.71	3.52	Pull down
Javelin	.84	0.91	Nil
Hurdles	.70	3.26	Height, negative for weight, hip flexion, pull down
Long jump	.67	2.85	Height, negative for weight, pull down
880 yards	.59	1.94	Height, negative for weight
High jump	.48	1.06	Nil
Shot put	.63	2.34	Nil
Cross-country run	.64	2.68	Height, negative for weight

*5% level f = 2.54

†p < .05

pull down, and knee extension. A decathlon competition was also held at the camp. The mean total score in this competition, the mean performances for individual events, and the strength scores are given in Table 13-III.

The ages of the subjects ranged from thirteen to sixteen years. The boys were on the average stronger than the girls in all of the strength tests, although there was some overlap. Multiple regression analyses (Tables 13-IV and 13-V) were used to compare the performance in individual track and field events with body size plus all of the strength measurements; the analysis

TABLE 13-IV

CORRELATION BETWEEN $\dot{V}_{O_2}$ MAX AND ANTHROPOMETRIC DATA*

47 GIRLS, 56 BOYS—9-17 YEARS OF AGE

Parameter	Correlation Coefficient	Standard Error in Prediction of $\dot{V}_{O_2}$ Max (%)
Height and weight—girls	.89	10
Height and weight—boys	.90	14
Weight and skin folds—girls	.91	9
Weight and skin folds—boys	.90	14
Total body potassium—girls	.88	10
Total body potassium—boys	.88	16
Weight, skin folds, PWC_{170}—girls	.94	9
Weight, skin folds, PWC_{170}—boys	.96	.9

TABLE 13-V
CORRELATION BETWEEN PWC_{170} KPM PER KILOGRAM MINUTE
AND TWELVE-MINUTE RUN DISTANCE

Group	Age Range (yr)	Number	Correlation Coefficient	Standard Error in Prediction of PWC_{170} (%)
Girls track camp	13-17	61	.45*	17
Boys track camp	13-17	72	.50*	15
Boys football camp	13-17	67	.61*	14
Elementary school girls	9-10	19	.22	20
Elementary school boys	9-10	19	.26	23
Junior and senior girls	13-17	28	.57*	12
Junior and senior boys	13-17	29	.80*	20

*p <.01

showed that few of the strength values contributed significantly to athletic performance. For the boys the discus throw and shot put were significantly correlated with the isometric strength of the back extensors. Performance in the long jump for unknown reasons showed a positive correlation with the arm push-up strength; this tests the isometric strength of the triceps, biceps, deltoid, and trapezius muscles. No other positive correlations between strength and athletic performance were obtained in the boys.

The girls' performances were positively correlated to height and negatively to weight, significant relationships being established for total decathlon score; 100, 880, and cross-country runs; and the hurdles and long jump. Hip flexion strength was a significant factor in the overall decathlon score and in the hurdles; this measurement tests the strength of the iliopsoas, tensor fasciae latae, sartorius, pectineus, gluteus medius, and quadratus femoris muscles. Arm pull-down strength (which tests the finger flexors, significantly correlated with the decathlon score and the long latissimus dorsi, pectoralis major, serratus anterior, and lower trapezius muscles and is also correlated with body weight) was jump performance.

The strength tests are time consuming and are difficult to standardize and even to reproduce in field situations. They measure the strength of muscle groups in the static, isometric situation, using a movement that is often artificially contrived for ease of standardization. It is perhaps not surprising that the strength thus measured is not highly correlated with athletic performance.

Adamson and Cotes (2) found no correlation between hand grip and response to submaximal and maximal exercise in a group of young men and women; nor did their subjects show any correlation between hand grip, total body potassium, and muscle mass. Explosive force was measured with a force platform; this showed no correlation with submaximal or maximal exercise performance, but it did show a low correlation with the muscle mass of the thigh. In a large group of children studied in this laboratory, a very low correlation was found between grip strength tests, hand and leg lift, and endurance fitness as measured by PWC_{170} and $\dot{V}o_2$ max (20).

Running on the level requires about 3.3 ml per kilogram minute O_2 uptake for each kilometer per hour increase of speed. Thus, the ability to win races of over 800 meters distance is dependent in part on the maximum oxygen uptake, and well-trained distance runners have $\dot{V}o_2$ max values in excess of 70 ml per kilogram minute. On the other hand, sprinters may have $\dot{V}o_2$ max values little better than the average population. Let us suppose that the performance in a two-mile race is compared to the $\dot{V}o_2$ max; if the fitness of the group ranges from the obese professor to an Olympic contender trained for the 10,000 meters run, then the $\dot{V}o_2$ max per kilogram body weight may show a high correlation with running speed. However, the $\dot{V}o_2$ max values of ten runners who were all of international stature would likely be virtually useless in predicting the winner of the next race; so, many other factors, including the psychological, enter the picture. We have compared the running speed in 880-yard races with the aerobic power per kilogram body weight in boys thirteen to sixteen years of age (15). Figure 13-1 shows that while the fastest runners had the highest aerobic power, the correlation between aerobic power and running performance under competitive conditions was of a low order ($r = 0.42$). Possibly the correlation might improve with a longer race.

Falls *et al.* (23) have tried to develop physical fitness test batteries by using a wide range both of physical fitness items and

BOYS (880 YARDS)

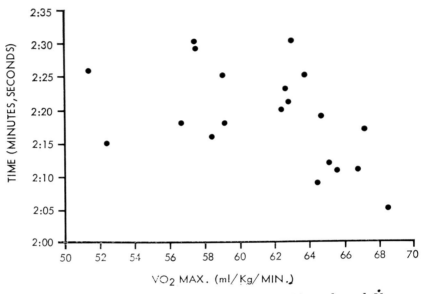

FIGURE 13-1. Relationship between time to run 880 yards and $\dot{V}_{O_2}$ max (milliliters per kilogram minute). Data for boys attending track and field camp.

"pure" physiological variables. They treated their data by factor analysis, with two separate rotations of the axes, and extracted nine factors which accounted for 77 percent of the total common variance. These factors were named athletic fitness, maximum metabolic rate, respiratory capacity, basic height of blood pressure, heart rate response to exercise, expiratory capacity, pulse pressure response, force efficiency and resting heart rate. Attempts were then made to estimate these factors from performance test scores, but whether these statistical manipulations will solve the problems of defining and measuring fitness remains to be seen.

Summary and Conclusions

If nothing else, attempts at correlating various fitness performance tests to supposedly precise physiologic measurements make it clear that most tests are highly specific; the results of one test do not correlate well with the results of another. This is particularly true when athletic performance, such as speed of running, ability to jump, or ability to throw various objects, is correlated with simple measurements of strength, lung function, and cardiorespiratory performance. In the average child the performance of the various athletic functions is so dependent on skill that significant correlations cannot be demonstrated. The exercise physiologist is virtually unable to predict who is going to do well in a given sporting event from basic laboratory tests. In normal children the prediction of maximum oxygen uptake from an endurance run is little better than can be obtained from height, weight, and skin fold measurements, even if the run covers a considerable distance. Performance tests distinguish the obvious and can tell the athlete from the nonathlete but are of limited value in the evaluation of physiologic functions in the average population. Physical performance tests are important in the assessment of overall physical fitness, but they are not a substitute for the measurement of the work capacities of the various organ systems, cardiovascular, musculo-skeletal, pulmonary and others. Correlational studies on the average population offer little in the way of defining fitness; they only serve to make one humble, realizing how complex the problem of fitness really is.

References

1. ADAMS, W.C.: Effect of a season of varsity track and field on selected anthropometric, circulatory and pulmonary function parameters. *Res Quart*, 39:5-15, 1968.
2. ADAMSON, G.T., and COTES, J.E.: Static and explosive muscle force: relationship to other variables. From the Proceedings of the Physiological Society. *J Physiol (London)*, 189:76P-77P, 1967.
3. American Association for Health, Physical Education and Recreation. *Youth Fitness Test Manual*, Washington, D.C. The Association, a Department of the National Education Association, U.S.A. 1958.
4. ANDERSEN, L.: Personal Communication.

5. ASMUSSEN, E., HEEBØLL-NIELSEN, K., and MOLBECH, S.V.: Description of muscle tests and standard values of muscle strength in children. *Communications from the Testing and Observation Institute of the Danish National Association for Infantile Paralysis.* NR5 Suppl. 1-69, 1959.

6. ÅSTRAND, I.: Aerobic work capacity in men and women with special reference to age. *Acta Physiol Scand 49(Suppl.169):* 1-92, 1960.

7. ÅSTRAND, P.O.: *Experimental Studies of Physical Working Capacity in Relation to Sex and Age.* Copenhagen, Munksgaard, 1952.

8. BACHMAN, J.C., and HORVATH, S.M.: Pulmonary function changes which accompany athletic training programs. *Res Quart, 39:* 235-239, 1968.

9. BALKE, B., and WARE, R.W.: An experimental study of physical fitness of Air Force personnel. *US Armed Forces Med J, 10:* 675-688, 1959.

10. BALKE, B.: A simple field test for the assessment of physical fitness. *CARI Report 63-18,* Oklahoma City, Civil Aeromedical Research Institute, Federal Aviation Agency, September, 1963.

11. Canadian Association for Health, Physical Education, and Recreation. *Fitness Performance Test Manual.* Toronto, the Association, 1966.

12. COOLEY, W.W., and LOHNES, P.R.: *Multi Variate Procedures for the Behavioral Sciences.* New York, Wiley and Sons, 1962.

13. COOPER, K.H.: A means of assessing maximal oxygen uptake. *JAMA, 203:*135-138, 1968.

14. COOPER, K.H.: *Aerobics.* Toronto, Bantam Books, 1968.

15. CUMMING, G.R.: Investigations at a Summer Track Camp. Presented at the Sports Medicine Congress—Pan American Games, Winnipeg, 1967.

16. CUMMING, G.R.: Correlation of athletic performance with pulmonary function in 13 to 17 year old boys and girls. *Science & Medicine in Sports,* In press.

17. CUMMING, G.R.: Correlation between the 12-minute run and laboratory measures of endurance fitness. To be published.

18. CUMMING, G.R., and BAILEY, G.: Unpublished data.

19. CUMMING, G.R., GOODWIN, A., BAGGLEY, G., and ANTEL, J.: Repeated measurements of aerobic capacity during a week of

intensive training at a youths' track camp. *Canad J Physiol Pharmacol, 45*:805-811, 1967.

20. CUMMING, G.R., and KEYNES, R.: A fitness performance test for school children and its correlation with physical working capacity and maximal oxygen uptake. *Canad Med Assoc J, 96*: 1262-1269, 1967.

21. CUMMING, G.R., and YOUNG, L.: Physical fitness of nurses. *Canad Nurse, 61(4)*:289-291, 1965.

22. DRAKE, V., JONES, G., BROWN, J.R., and SHEPHARD, R.J.: Fitness performance tests and their relationship to maximum oxygen uptake. *Canad Med Assoc J, 99*:844-848, 1968.

23. FALLS, H.B., ISMAIL, H.S.D., MacLEOD, D.F., WIEBERS, J.E., CHRISTIAN, J.E., and KESSLER, M.V.: Development of physical fitness test batteries by factor analysis techniques. *J Sport Med, 5*:185-197, 1965.

24. FALLS, H.B., ISMAIL, A.H., and MacLEOD, D.F.: Estimation of maximum oxygen uptake in adults from AAHPER youth fitness test items. *Res Quart, 37*:192-201, 1966.

25. GORDON, B., LEVINE, S.A., and WILMAERS, A.: Observations on a group of marathon runners. *Arch Intern Med, 33*:425-434, 1924.

26. GOULDING, D., and CUMMING, G.R.: Unpublished data.

27. JOHNSON, R.E., BROUHA, L., and DARLING, R.C.: A test of physical fitness for strenuous exertion. *Rev Canad Biol, 1*:491-504, 1965.

28. Marine Corps Order 6100.3C, 29 October 1962. Cited by Rasch, P.J. in *Military Medicine, 129*:256-258, 1964.

29. MELLITS, E.D.: In Check: *Human Growth*. Philadelphia, Lea and Febiger, 1968, p.19.

30. OLREE, H., and NELSON, T.: Evaluation of the AAHPER youth fitness test. *J Sport Med, 5*:67-71, 1965.

31. RASCH, P.J., and WILSON, LT. I.D.: The correlation of selected laboratory tests of physical fitness with military endurance. *Milit Medicine, 129*:256-258, 1964.

32. SHEPHARD, R.J.: *Endurance Fitness*. Toronto, U of Toronto Press, 1969, p.29.

Chapter 14

THE PERCEPTION OF PHYSICAL
PERFORMANCE

G. Borg

IN MODERN PSYCHOPHYSICS interest has focussed on methods for so-called ratio-scaling; see for instance, Stevens (21, 23) and Ekman (13, 14). Many modalities have been studied, and a power law seems the most generally applicable if one wishes to describe perceptive variation as a function of stimulus variation. Most ratio-scaling methods work very well within the field of muscular work; in the first experiments of this type, Borg and Dahlström (6, 7) found that the perception of muscular force (pedal resistance) during dynamic bicycle ergometer work lasting less than one minute could be described by a power function having the form $R = c (S + 175)^{1.6}$, where R is the perceived intensity, c is a constant, and S is the stimulus intensity in kpm per minute.

These psychophysical studies were started at Umeå, Sweden, in 1958, and have since expanded to other related fields concerning perception, performance, working capacity, motivation for physical work, psychophysiological problems, and the importance of physical fitness for certain psychological functions. One reason that led us to start this work was a need for a better understanding of how a healthy person adapts to strenuous work and how a sick man adapts to his disease; what does each think about his situation? How does he perceive the stress, the pain, the discomfort, and so on? A decrease of physical working capacity that is perceived by the subject is an important reason for him to see a doctor. Various body sensations, together with experiences from the past as a frame of reference, are prime factors determining behavior in any given situation.

A major aim of physical training is to provide the individual with sufficient reserve strength and stamina to overcome daily physical strain without an incapacitating feeling of fatigue. If physical working capacity declines, the perception of this change does not seem linearly related to the loss of function as measured in the laboratory. Fatigue and the perception of exertion and physical stress thus seemed related to interesting problems, meriting further study. Traditional psychophysics has focussed its attention on problems concerning the determination of absolute and some terminal thresholds of perception, just noticeable differences, Fechnerian* functions, curves relating the intensity of work to sensation and time, and so on. A problem that in my opinion has been too much neglected concerns the levels of perception between the outer limits. There are interesting medium intensity levels such as the preferred intensity (for example, the preferred stimulus ratio, the preferred speed of walking, and so on), and the forced adaptation level.† Such levels, or "zones," should be studied more closely and related to each other and to psychological and stimulus properties.

A picture of a hypothetical effort continuum is shown in Figure 14-1. This is a subjective continuum, running from an absolute minimum to an absolute maximum of effort. The levels or zones of effort are not placed at fixed positions but—when based on many determinations or individuals—give distribu-

*Named after Fechner, a pioneer of psychophysics. He suggested that sensation R was related to the log of stimulus intensity S, according to the equation $R = c \, \text{Log} \, S$.
†This concept is explained below.

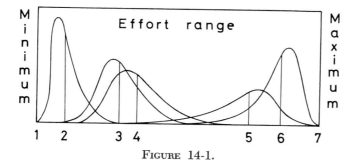

FIGURE 14-1.

tions that may overlap. A minimal effort (1) cannot be measured, or its measurement is not meaningful. Above this is a relative minimum (2), which we may define operationally in connection with resting conditions. The preference level (3) is the preferred intensity for a certain kind of activity. The adaptation level (4) in daily work or leisure activity may correspond with the preference level. But it may also be a forced adaptation level greater than the preferred intensity and within the stress zone (5). When we try to measure the maximal intensity (7), we find it is impossible because of various body defense mechanisms, imperfections of the system, cardiovascular or psychomotor pathologies, mental inhibitions, and so on; we thus measure a somewhat lower level dependent on the volitional state of the individual.

General Perceptive Problems

The main problem we shall deal with here concerns the determination of psychophysical functions during various kinds of physical performances. The scaling methods that we use are not absolutely true ratio methods; they do not yield equidistant scales with a zero point, as the best physical scales would. Nevertheless, the methods are good enough for descriptive purposes, for intermodal and differential comparisons, and to some extent also for studying psychophysiological interrelations. Many experiments have now been performed on subjective force with different ratio settings and estimation methods (2), and they have all given approximately the same function as the one presented above. It is beyond the scope of this chapter to describe the ratio-scaling methods in detail, but as a rough illustration one example may be taken: if you drive a car at 50 mph and then slow down to 25 mph, you will pereceive the change as greater than 50 percent; alternatively, if you drive at 50 mph and then change the speed until you perceive it to be half of 50 mph, you will choose a speed far above 25 mph. The difference between the empirically set ratio value and the theoretical half-value indicates that the relation between perception and stimulus is nonlinear, and the degree of deviation from linearity indicates the nature of the function and the size of the exponent.

Positively accelerating functions with an exponent of about the same size as above (n = 1.6) have been obtained in a later experiment by Sjöberg (18). Hueting (15,16) also found mainly positively accelerating functions, but since he was concerned more with practical applications of his findings, he adapted linear regression curves to the data; this approach may be good enough for the study of individual and group differences. In a study of the subjective force of hand grip, Stevens and Stevens (22) obtained an exponent of 1.7, while for isometric leg force Eisler (12) found an exponent of 1.6.

Isometric contractions are, of course, sustained for only a few seconds. With work of longer duration the stress on the circulatory, respiratory, and other body systems plays an important part in the total perception of exertion, so that one might expect to find different functions, depending on the duration of the work. However, Borg (2) reported about the same exponent during a physical work test of the type described by Sjöstrand (20) and Wahlund (25), where the subject works for six minutes at each of several successive loads on the bicycle ergometer.

A simple method of ratio scaling, which I proposed some years ago, is to use a cognitive reference level, such as the theoretical maximal exertion or the maximal performance, and then have the subject estimate how hard a certain task is as a percentage of this maximum. This method has now been used in several studies from our laboratory, and it has been shown to work very well.

There seem very good possibilities for the comparison of both psychophysiological and physiological and biochemical observations with perceptive variables. However, very few studies have been performed. We know, for instance, that in bicycle ergometer work heart rate rises almost linearly with work load and that lactic acid concentrations increase as about the square of the physical load (2). It should be of interest to study the psychophysiological reactions in more detail and try to "explain" the psychophysical functions.

Perception—Motivation—Performance Capacity

Indirect methods are often employed to estimate an individual's physical working capacity; we make use of physiological responses during submaximal work (for example, Sjöstrand [20], Åstrand [26, 27]). The heart rate is the simplest and a very reliable response to use, but it has the drawback of not being as valid as one might hope, as an indicator of somatic stress. If we know the range of heart rate (from rest to maximum) and the form of the functional variation with physical work, then a correction can be applied (1,5). However, it may be difficult or inconvenient to measure the maximal heart rate, so that this correction cannot always be made. Other stress indicators should therefore also be used. One such indicator is the perceived exertion discussed above. In much the same way that a measurement of physical working capacity is obtained from heart rates at one or several work loads, a capacity measurement can also be derived from ratings of perceived exertion (see below, under the RPE Scale heading).

There are also psychomotor indicators of somatic stress, such as hand-arm-steadiness tests, measurements of reaction-time, and the like. These psychomotor tests might be used directly to study the actual stress or indirectly to estimate the physical working capacity. As such they seem, however, to have a low validity. More direct indications of working capacity are obtained from various measurements of maximal performance. These seem the most valid for field predictions, since in the field, physiological endowments as well as psychological motivation and technique have an important influence on the performance that is achieved.

The maximal performance tests commonly used to determine physical work capacity involve a rigid time-work protocol that is applied to all subjects. The total testing time may thus vary considerably between individuals, causing some inequality in the test situation. It is impossible to obtain perfect equality of total testing time in a behavior test, where maximal performance is the dependent variable and motivation plays an important part. But a fairly good solution of this problem is to choose an initial work load according to either anamnestical, morphological, and physiological data or results on a simple predictive test. The subsequent increase of work load is then gauged from the intensity of the individual's stress reactions during work. If both heart rate and perceived exertion are used as stress indicators and are fed back to a specially programmed steering system, a fairly good subjective equality of testing conditions can be obtained with about the same total test time for each individual (4, 5).

Another way of obtaining subjective equality of testing time in a "motivationally loaded" behavior test is the CSET-method (the Cycling Strength and Endurance Test or CST as it was first called [2]). The loading of an electronic bicycle ergometer is increased continuously according to a predetermined program until the subject cannot pedal any more. This test gives measurements of both dynamic muscular force and capacity for endurance work, where the circulatory and respiratory systems are stressed. A series of threshold values of dynamic maximal strength for brief work (generally about 45 seconds) is determined, and a "work curve" is plotted, relating these threshold values to the duration of activity. This curve is analyzed with regard to various trial levels, the regression of the total curve, and the residual variation; these measurements reflect in different ways a person's muscular force, endurance capacity, and motivation for dynamic physical work. Very high reliability and validity coefficients have been obtained for such data in various studies; for example, a validity coefficient of .62 when wages per day in lumber work was used as a field criterion of working capacity and a validity coefficient of .55 when general military fitness was used as the field criterion.

Motivation influences the results of behavioral tests where performance measurements are used in a way that is often very difficult to estimate. Studies have therefore been performed with the object of measuring work motivation (3,5,11). A motivation model has been worked out in which the difference between "motivation loaded" performance measurements and "nonmotivation loaded" predictions of performance from physical endowments are used as a measure of work motivation. Data may be expressed as deviations from the predictions or residual variance about the regression line relating performance to endowment. The better the physical endowment can be measured and the better we can control technique and other "nonmotivation loaded" factors, the better will the residual variation reflect the degree of motivation of the individual.

The RPE Scale and Some Applications

In most practical situations where it is of interest to measure perceived exertion, a simpler method than the ratio-scaling technique should be used. A scale that gives ratings (R) of perceived (P) exertion (E) has therefore been developed. The first scale had twenty-one points and all the odd values from three to nineteen were anchored with the aid of such verbal expressions as "rather light," "very laborious," and so on. Close correlations have been obtained between ratings and heart rates throughout a work test. In a fairly normal sample of seventy-three men twenty to forty years of age, a correlation coefficient of $r = .85$ was obtained (2).

In order to increase the linearity of the relationship between RPE values and work load and between RPE values and heart rates and at the same time to adjust the ratio of RPE values to heart rates, some modifications of the twenty-one-point scale were made. The scale now consists of fifteen grades from six to twenty, where every second number is accompanied by a written description, as shown in Table 14-I.

The scale is presented in quarto format, and the instruction that the test leader gives the subject is very simple. He is requested to rate the degree of exertion as accurately and naively as possible, either by saying a number, or if for some reason this is impossible, by pointing with his finger at the desired rating value.

The RPE scale is so constructed that the heart rate of a normal, healthy middle-aged man can be predicted if the RPE value is multiplied by 10; thus, $RPE \times 10 = HR$. This equation is roughly correct for medium intensities of physical stress, but of course it should not be taken too literally. There are large deviations from this norm related to difficulties in rating, lack of

TABLE 14-I
THE RPE SCALE (THE SCALE FOR RATING OF
PERCEIVED EXERTION)

6	
7	Very, Very Light
8	
9	Very Light
10	
11	Fairly Light
12	
13	Somewhat Hard
14	
15	Hard
16	
17	Very Hard
18	
19	Very, Very Hard
20	

motivation, and disease (see below). When testing younger men the work test is sometimes interrupted at a heart rate of 170. This corresponds to an RPE of 17. The work load at a heart rate of 170 is often reported (W_{170}); the corresponding W value from ratings is the W_{R17} (as W_{RPE17} is often abbreviated). In several groups of subjects both W_{170} and W_{R17} have been measured or calculated by interpolation. In healthy, normal men both measurements show about the same predictive power when the results from running or skiing competitions, military ratings of the soldiers' endurance, or wages in lumber work are used as the independent criterion of working capacity; correlation coefficients amount to about .50. Since the intercorrelation of the two measurements is of about the same magnitude as the validity coefficients, they complement each other and together give possibilities for a better prediction of working capacity.

The first cross-validation of the rating method outside Sweden was done in Pittsburgh in 1967, when the author was visiting the Human Energy Research Laboratory. Together with Dr. Bruce Noble and Dr. Michael Sherman, a study was made on nineteen healthy male students from the university.* They were eighteen to twenty-four years of age and took part in the required physical

---

*The study was reported at the Annual Meeting of the American College of Sports Medicine, University Park, Pennsylvania, May 3, 1968.

education program. They carried out a modified Sjöstrand bicycle ergometer test, with four minutes work at each of a series of increasing work loads. They also performed a Balke treadmill test, walking at a constant speed of 3.4 mph with a 1 percent increase of grade after each minute of exercise, except the first minute, when the increase was from 0 to 2 percent. During both tests the heart rate and the effort ratings were taken towards the end of each work load. The results from the bicycle test are seen in Figure 14-2. Both heart rates and the RPE values increased fairly linearly with work load. The prediction of a heart rate of 170 from an effort rating of 17 was very good, as shown previously in the Swedish studies. The correlations between heart rates and perceived exertion were very high when all work loads were taken into account; .94 for the bicycle test and .85 for the tread-mill test. There was no significant difference in the correlation between heart rate and effort ratings for the bicycle test and for the treadmill test, suggesting that the relationship between heart rate and perceived exertion may be independent of the kind of

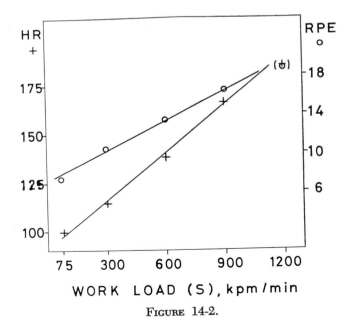

FIGURE 14-2.

work that is performed. The good linearity and high correlations between heart rates and RPE values have subsequently been validated in larger American groups at the Pennsylvania State University (Skinner *et al.* and Bar-Or *et al.*, To be published).

The relationship between heart rate and perceived exertion has also been studied in various types of patients. Patients with vasoregulatory asthenia and to some degree those with arterial hypertension had lower RPE values at a given heart rate than a healthy control group. Patients with coronary heart disease, on the other hand, rated the exertion higher in relation to heart rate, and in general, the RPE values increased more in relation to increase of heart rate in the patient groups than in the healthy controls (Borg and Linderholm, In press).

Borg and Linderholm (8) also found that the relation between RPE values and heart rate changed with age, older people rating the exertion higher in relation to heart rate than young people. The degree of change with age corresponds closely with the decrease of maximal heart rate with age reported by Robinson (17), P.O. Åstrand (26), I. Åstrand (27), and Strandell (24). A formula to correct for changes in the span of heart rate was therefore introduced by Borg and Linderholm (8). The relative reference level (P) then becomes a certain percentage of the heart rate range above the resting value. If 80 percent of the range is used, the reference heart rate becomes 170 for twenty-year-olds and 150 for fifty-year-olds according to the formula $P = 170 - \frac{2}{3}$ (A-20), where A is the age in years. The usefulness of this correction formula is seen when correlations between W_{R17} and W_P are calculated; in age heterogenous groups, the coefficients are substantially higher for W_{R17} values and W_{170} values.

The RPE values may also be helpful when there is doubt about when to interrupt a work test. In order not to stress a subject too hard, a fairly low reference level, for instance a heart rate of 150, is sometimes used. But for some subjects even this level may be too stressful.

When testing an older subject, it happens not too seldom that he cannot continue work at a heart rate of 130 because the exertion is too severe and he feels very fatigued. He will then rate the effort more than fifteen and probably as seventeen or more according to the RPE scale. By collecting effort rating values during submaximal work, it is to some extent possible to predict when the test should be interrupted.

Preference and Adaptation Levels

In a study of lumber workers (2), a preferred intensity of bicycle ergometer work was determined along with several measurements of physical working capacity. The subjects had to set a level which they felt was equivalent to one hour's lumber work. They were allowed to adjust the work load by manipulation of a handle for about one-half a minute prior to taking a reading. An intratest reliability coefficient for the preference levels was calculated and found to be r_{tt} .90. The mean preference levels for all subjects was about 50 percent of maximum. This is of interest, as it coincides rather well with the physical stress an individual can endure for a longer time. A significant correlation of about .35 was also obtained between the preference levels and the wages earned by individual workers.

Adaptation levels are now being studied in this laboratory. The subject has, for example, to adjust the work load during six minutes of exercise on a bicycle ergometer, so that the intensity of exertion is felt to be the same throughout the test, for instance, 50 percent of a maximal effort. Preliminary results seem to show that the work load selected initially decreases very rapidly, but it then levels off to a steady state (adaptation) level according to a simple exponential function.

Some Applications to Physical Training

I think it is astonishing how well most people can modify the intensity of exercise as a result of their perception of exertion and fatigue. When the intensity feels too severe, a person slows down until he has recovered enough to increase his intensity again. Soon, he slows down again, and the process is repeated. Self-determined pacing is especially developed in well-conditioned individuals.

During recent years various conditioning prescriptions have been developed. They are sometimes fairly complicated and often use physical terms, for instance, the patient is advised he should run at a certain physical speed. Of course, there is a need for studies using such prescriptions. But as a general rule, I think we can make it much easier for our subjects. And we have to make it easy if we are to get people to exercise. If we combine a simple counting of the pulse rate with ratings of how we feel, I think we can construct a good conditioning prescription in most cases. Sometimes this simple method may be difficult to use. People who have not had much experience of training or who have no reference for what is hard and what is moderate work may find it difficult to modify their behavior. But I feel sure it should be very easy to train even an inexperienced subject to concentrate on how he feels and thus to give him a good frame of reference for perception; it is merely necessary to have him practice rating the perceived exertion and correlating this with heart rate, so that he will learn the level of perceived exertion that is just right for him. This has the advantage that when he increases his working capacity, he does not need to change his reference level but can continue to jog or perform other types of exercise at about the same subjective intensity.

In a simple training situation the maximal performance capacity increases. This has the effect of decreasing subjective responses to a given submaximal intensity of effort. The direction of change of these submaximal responses with the change in terminal performance intensity is self-evident, but the degree of change is not easy to predict. In Figure 14-3 a model (1,5) is shown for the evaluation of the effect of training intensity. The points of origin on the S and R axes are a and b, while S_t and R_t are the upper limits. If we know the increase in maximal performance (S_t) and the form of the stimulus-response function, we can also predict the change in submaximal response. However, if the form of the function is changed with training or a or R_t is changed, this has to be taken into account.

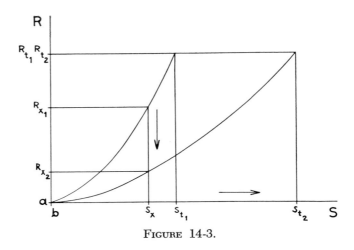

FIGURE 14-3.

I would like to close this chapter with a short comment on some observations I made when visiting the United States. At the Pennsylvania Rehabilitation Center we made a study of the physical working capacity of a mixed group of young male patients, and we found that the capacity—measured both from heart rates and RPE values in a bicycle ergometer test—was very much below that of Swedish groups. The ordinary American students also had values some 20 percent lower than Swedish students. One immediate conclusion is that patients in a rehabilitation program ought to get better endurance conditioning. The difference between Swedish and American young males might—at a guess— be due to a general difference of activity level, which is found even in the preschool years. At most of the places I visited in the United States, I found the children to be less physically active than Swedish children: they also played games that seemed less demanding with regard to endurance. So, the main reason why there are so many overweight boys and girls in America might be due not to overeating but to lack of exercise.

References

1. Borg, G.: Interindividual scaling and perception of muscular force. *Kungl Fysiograf Sällsk Lund Förh*, 31:117-125, 1961.

2. BORG, G.: *Physical Performance and Perceived Exertion.* Gleerups, Lund, 1962.

3. BORG, G.: Bestämning av motivationens inverkan på fysisk prestation. *Nord Psykiat T, 18:*591-596, 1964.

4. BORG, G.: Ett flexibelt arbetsprov med styrning av arbetsbetingelserna. *Psykol Und, Klin Psykol Lab, Umeå Univ, 5:*1-14, 1967.

5. BORG, G.: The three effort continua in physical work. *Proceedings of the XVIth International Congress of Applied Psychology,* Amsterdam, 18-22 Aug. 1968, p.394-397. Reprint, Amsterdam, Swets & Zeitlinger, 1969.

6. BORG, G., and DAHLSTRÖM, H.: Psykofysisk undersökning av arbete på cykelergometer. *Nord Med, 62:*1383-1386, 1959,

7. BORG, G., and DAHLSTRÖM, H.: The perception of muscular work. *Umeå Vetensk Bibl Skriftserie, 5:*1-26, 1960.

8. BORG, G., and LINDERHOLM, H.: Perceived exertion and pulse rate during graded exercise in various age groups. *Acta Med Scand, 472:*194-206, 1967.

9. BORG, G., and LINDERHOLM, H.: Exercise performance and perceived exertion in patients with coronary insufficiency, arterial hypertension and vaso-regulatory asthenia. In press.

10. BORG, G., EDSTRÖM, C-G., and MARKLUND, G.: Arbetsmotivation. Differensen mellan observerade och förväntade fysiska prestationer. *Psykol Und Klin Psyk Lab, Umeå Univ, 6:*1-24, 1967.

11. BORG, G., EDSTRÖM, C-G., and MARKLUND, G.: Betydelsen av belastningsökningens hastighet vid bestämning av terminal trösklar för fysiskt arbete. *Psykol Und, Klin Psyk Lab, Umeå Univ,* No. 2, 1968.

12. EISLER, H.: Subjective scale of force for a large muscle group. *J Exp Psychol, 64:*253-267, 1962.

13. EKMAN, G:. Some aspects of psychological research. In Rosenblith, W. (Ed.): *Sensory communication.* New York, John Wiley, & Son, 1961.

14. EKMAN, G.: Two generalized ratio scaling methods. *J Psychol, 45:*287-295, 1958.

15. HUETING, J.E.: An attempt to quantify sensations of general physical fatigue. *1st Intern Congress of Psychol of Sport,* Rome, 1965. Reprint of proceedings.

16. HUETING, J.E., and SARPHATI, H.R.: Measuring fatigue. *J Appl Psychol, 50:*535-538, 1966.

17. ROBINSON, S.: Experimental studies of physical fitness in relation to age. *Arbeitsphysiol, 10*:251, 1938.
18. SJÖBERG, H.: Relation between different arousal levels enduced by graded physical work and physiological efficiency. *Report Psychol Lab, Univ Stockholm, No. 251, 1968.*
19. SJÖBERG, H.: Psykisk prestationsförmåga och fysisk aktivering. *Psykol Inst, Stockholm Univ,* 1969.
20. SJÖSTRAND, T.: Changes in the respiratory organs of workmen at an ore smelting works. *Acta Med Scand (Suppl.), 196*:687-699, 1947.
21. STEVENS, S.S.: On the psychophysical law. *Psychol Rev, 64*:153, 1957.
22. STEVENS, S.S.: Cross-Modality validation of subjective scales for loudness, vibration and electric shock. *J Exp Psychol, 57*:201-209, 1959.
23. STEVENS, S.S.: Psychophysics of sensory function. In Rosenblith, W. (Ed.): *Sensory communication.* New York, John Wiley & Son, 1961.
24. STRANDELL, T.: Circulatory studies on healthy old men. From the Dept. of Clin. Physiol., Karolinska sjukhuset, Stockholm. 1964, Norstedt, also published as *Suppl. 414* to *Acta Med Scand,* 1964.
25. WAHLUND, H.: Determination of the physical working capacity. *Acta Med Scand (Suppl. 215),* 1948.
26. ÅSTRAND, P.O.: *Experiment Studies of Physical Working Capacity in Relation to Age and Sex.* Copenhagen, Munksgaard, 1952.
27. ÅSTRAND, I.: Aerobic work capacity in men and women with special reference to age. *Acta Physiol Scand (Suppl.)169*:1-92, 1960.

Chapter 15

MEASUREMENT AND INTERPRETATION OF EXERCISE ELECTROCARDIOGRAMS

P. M. Rautaharju, H. Friedrich, and H. Wolf

Introduction

QUANTITATIVE measurement and interpretation of the ECG response to exercise still remains a relatively demanding task despite several man years of effort invested by a number of research groups. While visual monitoring of the ECG during exercise may be adequate from the point of view of the safety of the subject, there is convincing evidence that quantitative analysis of the exercise records is not feasible without computer-aided measurements.

The seriousness of the problem is well illustrated in a recent report of a technical group on exercise electrocardiography (3). The tests conducted by the group indicate that the percent of electrocardiograms classified as abnormal by fourteen readers from a series of records taken immediately *after exercise* ranged from five to fifty-eight. This tenfold interobserver difference in the number of records classified as abnormal is not necessarily as critical as one might at first conclude. It can be attributed not only to random measurement errors but also to possible differences in measurement biases for various human readers and differences in the criteria used when calling a record abnormal. Much more alarming is the large intra-observer or repeat variability. The repeat variability was tested on five readers, using a set

Note: This work was supported through research grants from the Canadian Heart Foundation and the Medical Research Council, Ottawa. The exercise records used in analysis of the program performance were collected in cooperation with Dr. M.J. Karvonen, Dr. B.S. Djordjevic, Dr. N. Kimura, Dr. R. Buzina, Dr. H. Blackburn, and Dr. A. Keys in cardiovascular field studies supported through U.S.P.H.S. Grant No. HE-04997 to Dr. Keys.

of 152 postexercise records. Two attempts were made to classify the records into categories of normal, borderline, or abnormal, and all five readers changed their interpretation in over one-half of the records at the second reading.

The development of automatic computer programs for analysis of resting electrocardiograms has been perhaps the most significant area of progress in medical computer applications. Unfortunately, one of the major drawbacks of all presently available ECG measurement programs is a loss of measurement precision if the signal is noisy. This has made it impossible to utilize available programs for analysis of exercise records. One way to alleviate this problem is to use various noise reduction schemes; these reduce the noise level below the critical value so that conventional wave recognition techniques and already available programs can then be used for analysis and interpretation of the exercise electrocardiogram. Various averaging techniques have turned out to be most useful for this purpose.

It would, however, be a serious error to expect that averaging will take care of all measurement problems in exercise electrocardiography. Modern tape recording and computer technology have brought us extremely powerful tools, but at the same time they have brought us a host of new and, to many investigators, unfamiliar problems which often lead to frustrating disappointments. Some of these unexpected problems—and some remedies to them—will be discussed in this chapter. We shall first define our goal rather dogmatically and then proceed step-by-step, considering the problems which we have to solve. Some consideration will also be given to the practical question whether the investigator should acquire a special purpose computer or rely on general purpose digital computers that may already be available to him.

Performance Requirements

Guaranteed Measurement Precision

Let us assume that we wish to measure some defined ECG amplitudes in the ST segment of the electrocardiogram with a guaranteed measurement precision of 25μv and secondly, that we wish to identify the onset and the offset of the QRS complex with a precision of 10 msec. This is in accordance with the tentative guidelines proposed recently by a technical group for the standardization of exercise electrocardiography (23). The guaranteed measurement precision as defined in this context implies that in 95 percent of measurements the measurement error is less than specified, despite the presence of expected levels of random or periodic noise in the record. The requirement of 25μv precision in ST amplitude measurements seems sensible, since the most commonly used diagnostic criterion of an abnormal ECG response is an ST segmental depression of 0.1 mV (100μV).

A precision of 25μV rms poses some problems for the data acquisition system. It is especially important that the specifications recommended by the American Heart Association Instrumentation Committee should be rigidly enforced (25). A low frequency cutoff of 0.05 Hz is needed; this is equivalent to a time constant of 3.6 seconds in the conventional direct writing electrocardiographs, and if the requirement is not met, unpredictable distortions of the ST segment far exceeding the 25μV limit may take place (2). This rules out use of the majority of commercially available telemetering systems for quantitative ECG analysis and interpretation.

The specifications for the data acquisition system set by the American Heart Association Standardization Committee are minimum standards and in many regards they represent a compromise between cost and performance. Consider, for instance, the 40 dB signal to noise ratio recommended for the tape recording system. Making some allowance for baseline fluctuations, we can assume that the system has to accommodate a 5 mV signal for either polarity or a total linear dynamic range of 10 mV before amplification. A 40 dB signal to noise ratio implies that we can expect a noise level in the recorded signal equivalent to 100μV peak-to-peak at the source. Consequently, the inherent noise in a tape recorder meeting generally accepted performance specifications may already be up to four times as large as the required measurement precision.

The requirement of identifying the QRS onset and offset with a guaranteed precision of 10 msec implies that we have to sample the signal at least two hundred times per second. If components of the ECG signal in the frequency band from 0.05 to 100 Hz are to be studied, then a sampling rate of five hundred samples per second per lead is desirable. It is imperative to filter the records before sampling, that is, before analog-to-digital conversion. In our example the best compromise would be to use a low pass filter which starts attenuating rather sharply at 100 Hz and transmits only a negligible amount of power at 500 Hz. Unless this is done, noise in the band near the sampling frequency and its higher harmonics can "fold back" and generate unexpectedly large components of low frequency noise which cannot afterwards be separated from the signal. This error is due to the so-called aliasing error. A lower sampling rate is adequate if the investigator is interested only in low frequency components of the signal (for example, the ST segment), but a corresponding lower cutoff frequency must then be selected for the filter.

It is also quite important to use buffer amplifiers for each channel before the signals are fed to the so-called mixing resistor networks of the electrocardiograph; this avoids the serious signal distortion that would otherwise be caused by high skin-electrode resistance (25, 29).

Noise Tolerance Requirements

The quality of exercise ECG records has substantially improved during the last few years with improved electrodes and recording techniques. Careful subject preparation and noise reduction before recording is still by far the most important step to improved measurement precision when the records are later processed.

To obtain more specific guidelines in setting performance requirements for measurement programs, the noise content was measured from the exercise records of 291 subjects. The exercise was at 85 percent of the predicted maximum heart rate. The average noise level was $32\mu V$ rms (Table 15-I), and in 5 percent of the records the noise level exceeded $60\mu V$ rms.* In our previous report (32) the average value of 60 Hz hum measured from three-minute exercise records was $34\mu V$ peak-to-peak with a minimum

TABLE 15-I

THE NOISE LEVEL IN THE ELECTROCARDIOGRAMS OF 291 MIDDLE-AGED MALE SUBJECTS RECORDED DURING SUBMAXIMAL EXERCISE TEST WITH A BICYCLE ERGOMETER*

	Average Noise Level	Upper Limit of Noise Range 95%	98%
Resting records	19	32	40
Exercise records	32	60	72

*Beckman biopotential electrodes were used with careful skin-electrode preparation techniques. The noise level (microvolts rms) was measured from the ST segment.

of 4μV and a maximum of 340μV. The total noise level (random and periodic) ranged from 60μV to 915μV rms. The noise values listed in Table 15-I are substantially smaller; this is due to the elimination of low frequency baseline fluctuations, using linear baseline interpolation and "straightening" from beat to beat.

The 50μV noise tolerance should be considered as a minimum requirement. Tentative standards of noise tolerance and precision proposed by a technical group (23) include a) 60 cycle interference up to 100μV rms; b) periodic or aperiodic low frequency base line shifts with a slope up to 1 mV per second; c) 100μV rms random noise in the bandwidth 0.1 to 100 Hz; and d) recognition and rejection of portions of the signal affected by "spikes" of short duration, sudden bursts of white noise, and other sudden transients detrimental to accurate measurement.

Noise Reduction by Averaging

General Considerations

The general principle of averaging is extensively used both in radar technology and in neurophysiological and electroencephalographic studies of evoked responses. If the noise is random with respect to the repetitive signal, one can expect an improvement in the signal to noise ratio proportional to the square root of the number of signal transients, providing that they are properly "aligned" and coherently added in the computer memory.

Averaging techniques were developed for electrocardiography

*A noise level of 32μV rms implies that 95 percent of the noise "spikes" span a range of 128μV peak-to-peak.

in 1961-1962, while the author was a graduate student in Dr. Otto H. Schmitt's laboratory at the University of Minnesota (21). The feasibility and many of the limitations of this approach were documented during these early years (19,20,22,29). There has been a gradual but substantial improvement in the procedures employed both in special purpose devices and in general purpose digital computer techniques, although many problems remain to be solved. The reader is advised to consult particularly the 1966 methodological article of Bruce *et al.* (10) and the extensive monograph of Blomqvist (6) published in 1965.

In general, averaging from signals such as the ECG, which are not exactly periodic, requires the following steps:

1. Filtering of the signal before sampling to avoid the aliasing error.
2. Elimination of extrasystoles and excessively noisy segments of the signal.
3. Sampling of the signal (analog-to-digital conversion) and transfer to the computer memory.
4. "Alignment" of selected complexes for coherent addition in the computer memory. This is often referred to as "triggering" and involves finding some definable "fiducial" point within the QRS complex as a common reference point for alignment.
5. Normalization, that is, division of the sum of the numerical values at each sampling point by the number of complexes added.
6. Calibration of the amplitudes of the averaged signal (in millivolts or microvolts, referring to the source before amplification).
7. Display of the averaged signal with transfer of numerical values for quantitative measurement, analysis, and interpretation visually or by a computer.

Averaging With Special Purpose Digital Computers

A wide variety of averaging computers have been commercially introduced since the CAT computer of the former Mnemotron Corporation opened the biomedical market in the beginning of the 1960's. The price for equivalent performance has dropped to less than one-third in eight years, and some of these fine counting and measuring instruments can now be purchased for less than many of the more advanced electronic desk calculators or high performance oscilloscopes.

Most averaging computers do not provide built-in filters, and many investigators have experienced trouble with the aliasing error introduced by high frequency noise.

Many averaging devices have built-in trigger circuits, but none have logic circuits for elimination of extrasystoles or gross artefacts. Averaging of inhomogeneous transients is one of the main sources of errors (19), since one extrasystole or a gross artefact is enough to ruin the results. Relatively simple logic circuits can be used with reasonable success (19, 33), but visual monitoring is usually still essential.

Analog-to-digital conversion is often done with surprisingly low resolution, and the achievement of adequate precision depends on accumulation of a sufficient number of complexes. Sampling is programmed simply by knobs and switches. The number of samples which can be taken from each transient varies from 250 to 4000 with different models of computer. A total sampling period of 500 msec is usually necessary for ECG measurement (from the P wave to at least the peak of the T wave). This means that a computer which can accommodate 250 samples uses 2-msec sampling intervals. This sampling rate, 500 samples per second, is definitely adequate. A correspondingly larger number of memory addresses is needed, and a higher total sampling rate must be used if more than one ECG lead is averaged simultaneously. In practice the sampling is usually not simultaneous but is multiplexed between the input channels—this produces a lag which must be corrected if quantitative comparisons between leads are desired. Alignment of the complexes prior to averaging is based on a trigger signal derived from the QRS complex. If the alignment is not exact, a smoothing error occurs (19, 22). Cross correlation techniques can be used to minimize the smoothing error (7), but it is rarely significant in analysis of the ST segment. An adequately consistent time reference point can thus be derived from the QRS complex, using relatively simple amplitude of slope triggering circuits.

It may be necessary to sample the signal both before and after the trigger point. This is no problem with general purpose digital computers, but averaging computers do not ordinarily have a buffer memory where values preceding the trigger point could be temporarily stored.* This difficulty can be overcome with magnetic tape recording techniques by introducing a delay between the signal used for triggering and the signal used for averaging (10, 13, 21, 22).

Continuous normalization of the signal, that is, true averaging, is a definite advantage, and this feature is incorporated in one recent computer which also has a built-in calibration system.

Early enthusiastic reports on the use of special purpose averaging computers for exercise ECG processing have not made the procedure as popular as one might have expected. One possible reason is that a relatively high level of technical skill is required for quality control. The necessary continuous visual monitoring is tedious and unreliable. Further processing of the records with digital computers is almost always necessary, and data transfer or interfacing of special purpose devices can become rather complicated. Many of these problems could be overcome with further minor improvements in design; it is thus possible that special purpose devices will be increasingly used in the future, at least as preprocessors in conjunction with more versatile programmable computers.

Selective Averaging With General Purpose Digital Computers

Several investigators are currently working in this area, including Sheffield at the University of Alabama, Van der Groeben at Stanford Medical School, and Blomqvist at Southwestern Medical School in Dallas. Some features of the program developed by the Biophysics Group of Dalhousie Medical School will be de-

---

*Most of the deficiencies listed above have been eliminated in a new averaging computer introduced by a French manufacturer since preparation of this manuscript.

TABLE 15-II
SUMMARY OF THE DALHOUSIE EXERCISE
ECG ANALYSIS PROGRAM

Step 1:	A/D conversion of 24 seconds of group A bipolar leads (HE,HC,HA,HM,HI and HF).
Step 2:	Generation of group B derived leads (X,Y, and Z components of the Frank leads, spatial magnitude curve R, and smoothed difference function D).
Step 6:	Data reduction: Identification of the J-point and the H-point obtain measurements with timing and wave typing parameters.
Step 4:	Quality control and selective averaging of group A leads collecting 16 "best" QRS-ST complexes.
Step 5:	Generation of group C leads (the averaged Frank leads and 12 bipolar leads in direction of lower left anterior octant).
Step 6:	Data reduction: Identification of the J-point and the H-point and representation of the ST segment with 4 first terms of the Chebyshev polynomials.
Step 7:	Grading of the ECG response to exercise using decision rules listed in Table 15-III.

scribed to demonstrate certain advantages of this technique. (Table 15-II)

Selection of Leads

At least two, and ordinarily six, bipolar leads are recorded simultaneously and analyzed as a group. The neck electrode (H) is used as a common reference, and potential differences, HF, HE, HC, HA, HM, and HI, are recorded between H and locations F, E, C, A, M, and I as specified by Frank (13). The reasons for this choice of leads will be discussed in the section on "selection of variables for analysis."

Filtering and Analog-to-Digital Conversion

The records are filtered before analog-to-digital conversion, using a low pass filter with an upper cutoff frequency of 125 Hz and a 24 dB per octave slope of attenuation for frequencies above that. Frequencies of less than 100 Hz are not normally filtered to avoid signal distortion.

Quality Control and Selective Averaging

Quality control is perhaps the most demanding part of the program, and there are still some weaknesses in it. The prime philosophy is to spot artefacts and noisy segments visually and

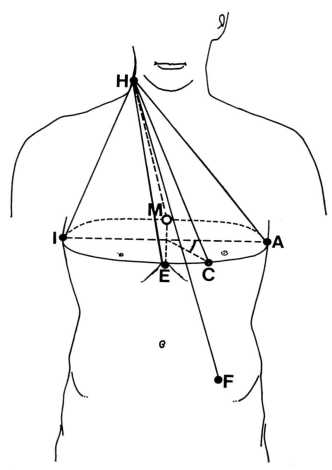

FIGURE 15-1. Electrode positions for exercise ECG leads. Six potential differences or "bipolar" leads are recorded simultaneously (HI,HE,HC,HA, HM and HF), using the neck electrode (H) as a common reference point. Several other bipolar leads (IA,ME, etc.) and the X,Y,Z components of the Frank leads are also derived by electronic or digital computation. The criteria for an abnormal ST segment listed in Table 15-III are valid for leads which are electrically oriented in the direction of the lower-left-anterior octant.

to employ filtering and other noise reduction schemes only when absolutely necessary. Gross artefacts are rejected, and extrasystoles are identified. The adequacy of quality control is checked at the end of the program by measuring the residual noise level in the ST-T segment.

The basic idea of selective averaging is to choose from the forty-eight QRS-ST complexes that are available sixteen complexes which closely resemble each other and are as noise free as possible. Ordinarily the bipolar signals are synthesized to yield the X, Y, and Z components of the Frank leads; thus, both magnitude and orientation measurements can be used to rule out extrasystoles and artefacts. The procedure works, however, with any two or three simultaneously recorded bipolar ECG signals, and these need not necessarily be orthogonal.

One critical point in any averaging program is selection of the time reference point. The maximum amplitude of the spatial magnitude curve is used as one time reference point in the Dalhousie program, but additional verification is based on the single lead with the highest QRS complex. Averaging is done separately for each of the six bipolar components. A two-second segment of the Frank X, Y, and Z leads is then generated Fig 15-2 and this is processed with the original Mayo-IBM measurement program to obtain timing parameters. The program is described elsewhere (32). The averaged complexes are plotted for visual reference, and the program provides plots with arrows and timing marks for immediate verification that the measurement program has performed with adequate accuracy.

Selection of Variables for ST Analysis

The six bipolar leads shown in Figure 15-1 permit the electronic or digital computation of numerous additional bipolar leads like IE, IC, and IA. Leads HE, HC, and HA can be used to synthesize leads CR_2, CR_4, and CR_6 (6), which are commonly used as exercise leads in Sweden, and any conventional leads can also be derived from them with good accuracy. The combination of the selected six leads gives directly the components of the Frank orthogonal leads, if a minor correction is made to allow for

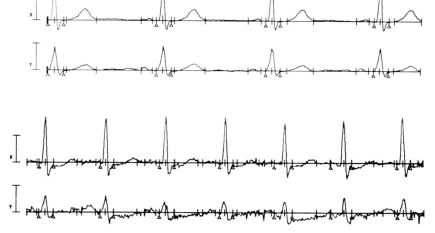

FIGURE 15-2. The X and Y components of the Frank lead system, generated from the six bipolar leads shown in Figure 15-1. The resting record is at the top, and the bottom traces are recorded at a heart rate of 155 per minute (85% of the predicted maximum for a 40-year-old subject). Beat-by-beat linear baseline correction has substantially reduced low-frequency noise which is the largest source of error in visual measurements.

location of the F electrode in the left lower abdomen instead of the left leg.

The Dalhousie program selects from a group of twelve bipolar leads directed towards the left-lower-anterior octant the lead with the most "ischemic" ST segment for interpretation and grading of the ECG response to exercise. Although a vast array of amplitude and wave form information is analyzed for research purposes, a radical data reduction is possible for ST analysis resulting from extensive redundancy in the source data (24). The reduced program identifies two time reference points from the ST segment, the J point, and the H point. The J point is the QRS-ST junction, and the H point is halfway between the J point and the maximum T. These referecnce points can be determined in the conventional way from any lead, but a much improved precision is achieved by using such computer auxiliary functions as the spatial magnitude curve and its smoothed approximate derivative.

The wave form of the ST segment between the J and the H points is approximated, using the first four terms of the Chebyshev polynomials as a curve fitting procedure (20). The four co-efficients represent, in a condensed form, all relevant wave form and amplitude information contained in the ST segment; the curve fitting procedure is also an efficient final step in noise reduction. The first coefficient gives the average voltage for the first half of the ST segment; the second coefficient, the slope; the third coefficient describes the amount of convexity or concavity of the segment; and the fourth coefficient tells, roughly speaking, to what extent the segment is "S-shaped" and in what direction. Finally, the root mean square of deviations from the approximated function is a good measure of residual noise in the averaged signal. Simulation tests using this procedure indicate that random noise can be measured to within $10 \mu V$ rms.

A final step in data reduction is to use the criteria listed in Table 15-III. This classification follows to a large extent the procedure proposed by Punsar *et al.* (18); they use a revised version of the Minnesota code (4,28) and classify the ST segment into thirteen subcategories. The Dalhousie program is based on two to five binary decisions, using the slope of the first half of the ST segment and one amplitude measurement. Attempts to use the

TABLE 15-III

TENTATIVE DECISION RULES FOR GRADING THE ST SEGMENT
WAVE FORM INTO EIGHT SUBCATEGORIES*

Category	Code	Criteria		
		Slope mV/sec		J or H amplitude mV
Ischemic	1	$SL \leq 0$	and	$H \leq -0.200$
	2	$SL \leq 0$	and	$H \leq -0.100$
	3	$SL \leq 0$	and	$H \leq -0.050$
Borderline	4	$SL \leq 1$	and	$J \leq -0.200$
	5	$SL \leq 1$	and	$J \leq -0.100$
Junctional	6	$SL > 1$	and	$J \leq -0.200$
	7	$SL > 1$	and	$J \leq -0.100$
Normal	8	$SL \leq 0$	and	
	OR			$H > -0.050$
		$SL > 0$	and	$J > -0.100$

*The slope (SL) is determined for the first half of the ST segment between points J and H. J is the amplitude of the QRS-ST junction, and H is the amplitude of the ST segment half-way between the J-point and the maximum T voltage.

onset of the T wave as a time reference point for ST classification as suggested by Punsar *et al.* were unsuccessful because of unacceptably large measurement errors and difficulty in defining the start of the T wave. From the electrophysiological point of view, this is not surprising, since the demarcation between the slow and fast phases of repolarization is unclear even at the cellular level. The present program classifies the ST segment into eight categories (Table 15-III). It is likely that with further experience the number of meaningful categories can be further reduced.

The Performance of the Selective Averaging and Measurement Program

The performance of the Dalhousie program was recently tested in a field study of 146 subjects. Submaximal exercise was performed on a bicycle ergometer at 85 percent of the predicted maximal heart rate (15). Reasons for unsuccessful performance are given in Table 15-IV. In eleven of the subjects the target heart rate could not be reached, either for medical reasons or because the subject was uncooperative. Two records had to be rejected because of technical errors. Of the remaining 133 records, 14 had to be rejected because of program failures; in ten of these the timing error at the QRS onset and QRS offset exceeded 10 msec. A failure rate of 10 percent, although not fully satisfactory, is reasonably good, considering our rather stringent criteria for failure and the relatively poor quality of the records obtained

TABLE 15-IV

PROGRAM FAILURES IN THE ANALYSIS OF 146 SUCCESSIVE
SUBMAXIMAL EXERCISE TESTS DURING A FIELD STUDY*

	No. of Subjects
Exercise test incomplete for medical reasons	11
Technical recording errors	2
QRS onset error > 10 msec	6
QRS offset error > 10 msec	4
Other program failures	3
Excessive residual noise	1
Total No. of completed exercise tests	133
Total No. of program failures	14 = 10.5%

*The subjects were men 45 to 65 years of age, a random sample of a total population. The target heart rate was 85% of the predicted maximum.

under difficult field conditions. Further program revisions will undoubtedly reduce the failure rate, but it will be difficult to achieve a fully satisfactory performance in all cases.

The noise tolerance of the program was evaluated using a computer simulation procedure. A "library" of 252 records was generated from twelve 24-second electrocardiograms which were all of relatively high quality. Random and 60 Hz noise were then separately added to each record in increasing amounts of up to 100µV rms, and the computer findings at each noise level were compared with measurements made on noise free records.

It was verified that selective averaging of sixteen complexes reduced the level of random noise to one-quarter of the initial level, irrespective of the magnitude of the noise (at least up to 100 µV rms). However, it did not reduce 60 Hz hum effectively when this exceeded 50µV rms. Consequently, a digital filter (15) was incorporated into the program if the level of 60 Hz interference exceeded 50µv.

With these provisions the guaranteed measurement precision of 10 msec for QRS onset and offset and 25µV for J point amplitude could be achieved, at least up to noise levels of 80µV rms. Noise within the levels expected in exercise records is thus no longer the limiting factor for program performance. The remaining program failures are due primarily to weaknesses in the point recognition logic, particularly with "difficult" ECG patterns.

The Problem Areas and the Future Prospects

In diagnostic and therapeutic applications, exercise tests must be carefully monitored by a qualified physician. The occurrence of even short runs of successive extrasystoles is most important. Monitoring should probably be continued for several minutes after exercise. An exercise response can be classified as abnormal with the occurrence of three or more *successive* extrasystolic beats (12). The occurrence of ventricular tachycardias is an unavoidable although a relatively small risk in ordinary application of exercise tests; it is conceivable that in the future, exercise tests will be used as a physiological way of eliciting potentially hazardous arrhythmias and testing the efficiency of various therapeutic measures in the individual patient.

A great deal of work is still required to devise fully automated and efficient exercise ECG analysis programs. For the convenience of the investigator and for the safety of the patient, the program should operate very close to real time and from remote locations through teleprocessing (30). Several systems of this kind will be available in the near future.

A good quality data acquisition system is necessary. This may cost from five thousand to fifteen thousand dollars, depending on the number of channels and on the quality desired. For computer processing the investigator at present has a choice of either investing five thousand to fifteen thousand dollars in a special purpose averaging computer or of relying on a general purpose digital computer which may cost him two dollars or more per exercise record processed. Both of these approaches have their advantages and disadvantages, as discussed above.

One area largely neglected in the past is the development of exercise testing procedures for female subjects. A serious effort should be made to design and test a suitable lead system for females.

There seems general agreement that the segmental ST segment depression has substantial value in the prediction of potential myocardial ischemia (16,27). Simonson (31) and Doan *et al.* (11) have shown that ischemic segmental ST depression cannot be produced in normal young persons even by the most severe exercise. The percent of abnormal responses increases markedly with age. Thus, Bruce (9) found that in maximum exercise tests on clinically normal American male subjects, the prevalence of ischemic response rose from 0 percent in the group of men under thirty-five years to 28 percent in the age group fifty to fifty-four years. The age-specific increase was substantially less in Chinese men from Taipei.

The percentage of abnormal responses increases with the imposition of a greater work load. In the clinically normal group of men analyzed by the Seattle group (9,11,12), the maximal exercise test produced nine times as many positive responses as

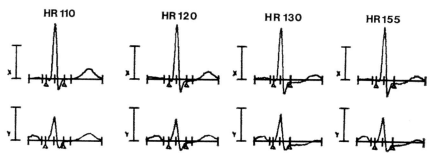

FIGURE 15-3. Changes in the ST segment amplitudes and wave form during a graded submaximal exercise test. At a heart rate of 130 per minute, there is a junctional ST segment depression of 90μV in X lead and of 120μV in Y lead. The average slope of the first half of the ST segment is approximately 0.22 mV per second in both leads. A junctional depression of 150μV would be obtained in a frontal plane lead with an elevation angle of about 36 degrees. The response shown here at heart rates 130 and 155 would be classified into category 5 (borderline response), since the ST slope is less than 1 mV per second but the J depression exceeds 100μV.

the conventional Master double two step test. However, the risk to the subject may increase with increasing load, and it is likely that submaximal tests—for instance, at the level of 85 percent of the predicted maximum heart rate (15)—will remain more generally accepted than the maximum capacity test (Fig 15-3).

Basic electrophysiological mechanisms underlying the ischemic response are not known. Generalized hypoxia does not necessarily aggravate the ST segment response to exercise; thus, Blomqvist found no significant difference of response to maximal exercise at sea level and at a simulated altitude of 4000 meters (6).

There is usually electrical activity present during the ST interval, and this produces ST segment elevation in leads that are oriented in the posterior-anterior direction. In the normal and abnormal subjects analyzed by Blomqvist, the ST segment changes were not significant in the Z direction. In general, ischemic ST segment deviations result from net forces directed to the right and upwards, and they give rise to ST segment depression in leads oriented to the left and downwards. Seven electrodes (and a ground) are required to record the six bipolar leads described in this article. This leaves the investigator a large variety of options for selection of bipolar, orthogonal, or resolved leads in any direction desired. The wave form of the ST segment in any scalar lead depends on the spatial orientation of the ST vectors; thus, the ST segment may look completely normal in one lead but quite ischemic in another lead which has a slightly different orientation (24). The magnitude of ST segment depression that is observed depends heavily on the "sensitivity" and orientation of the lead (1).

Ischemic changes are probably not limited to the ST segment. Vectorcardiographic aspects of the QRS changes and changes in the T loop were recently discussed by Isaacs *et al.* (14).

The significance of junctional ST depression is unknown, and reports are conflicting (1, 26). The magnitude of junctional depression increases with heart rate (6). It is often speculated that junctional depression is the earliest manifestation of myocardial ischemia and that it gradually evolves into the segmental ischemic ST pattern (11, 12, 22). A major effort is still required to establish more sensitive criteria for the detection of ischemia and to validate the prognostic significance of abnormal responses.

References

1. Astrand, I.: Exercise electrocardiograms in a 5 year follow-up study. *Acta Med Scand, 173*:257-268, 1963.
2. Berson, A.S., and Pipberger, H.V.: The low frequency response of electrocardiographs, a frequent source of recording errors. *Amer Heart J, 71*:779-789, 1966.
3. Blackburn, *et al.*: The exercise electrocardiogram: Differences in interpretation. Report by a technical group on exercise electrocardiography. *Amer J Cardiology, 21*:871-880, 1968.
4. Blackburn, H., Keys, A., Simonson, E., Rautaharju, P.M., and Punsar, S.: The electrocardiogram in population studies. A classification system. *Circulation, 21*:1160-1175, 1960.
5. Blackburn, H., Taylor, H.L., Okamoto, N., Rautaharju, P.M., Mitchell, P.L., and Kerkhof, A.C.: Standardization of the exercise electrocardiogram. A systematic comparison of chest lead configurations employed for monitoring during exercise. In Karvonen, M.J., and Barry, A.J. (Eds.): *Physical Activity*

and the Heart. Springfield, Charles C Thomas, 1967, pp.101-133.

6. BLOMQVIST, G.: The Frank lead exercise electrocardiogram. A quantitative study based on averaging technique and digital computer analysis. *Acta Med Scand, 178*:5-98, 1965.

7. BRANDON, C.W., and BRODY, D.A.: Time alignment in the averaging of electrocardiographic signals. *Proc 8th Internat Conf on Med and Biol Engineering.* Chicago, Session 16-1, 1969.

8. BRODY, A.J.: Master two-step exercise test in clinically unselected patients. *JAMA, 171*:1195-1198, 1959.

9. BRUCE, R.A.: Comparative prevalence of segmental ST depression after maximal exercise in healthy men in Seattle and Taipei. In Karvonen, M.J., and Barry, A.J. (Eds.): *Physical Activity and the Heart.* Springfield, Charles C Thomas, 1967, pp. 144-158.

10. BRUCE, R.A., MAZZARELLA, J.A., JORDON, J.W., and GREEN, E.: Quantitation of QRS and ST segment responses to exercises. *Amer Heart J, 71*:455-466, 1966.

11. DOAN, A.E., PETERSON, D.R., BLACKMON, J.R., and BRUCE, R.A.: Myocardial ischemia after maximal exercise in healthy men. A method for detecting potential coronary heart disease? *Amer Heart J, 69*:11-21, 1965.

12. DOAN, A.E., PETERSON, D.R., BLACKMON, J.R., and BRUCE, R.A.: Myocardial ischemia after maximal exercise in healthy men. A one year follow-up of physically active and inactive men. *Amer J Cardiol, 17*:9-10, 1966.

13. FRANK, E.: An accurate, clinically practical system for spatial vectorcardiography. *Circulation, 13*:737-749, 1956.

14. ISAACS, J.H., WILBURNE, M., MILLS, H., KUHN, R., COLE, S.L., and STEIN, H.: The ischemic T loop during and following exercise—a vector-electrocardiographic (VECG) study. *J Electrocardiology, 1*:57-76, 1968.

15. LESTER, F.M., SHEFFIELD, L.T., and REEVES, T.J.: Electrocardiographic changes in clinically normal older men following near maximal and maximal exercise. *Circulation, 36*:5-14, 1967.

16. MASTER, A.M., and ROSENFELD, I.: Clinical application of the two step exercise test. *JAMA, 178*:283-289, 1961.

17. MATTINGLY, T.W.: The post exercise electrocardiogram. Its value in the diagnosis and prognosis of coronary arterial disease. *Amer J Cardiol, 9*:395-409, 1962.

18. PUNSAR, S., PYÖRALA, K., and SILTANEN, P.: Classification of electro-cardiographic ST segment changes in epidemiological studies of coronary heart disease. *Ann Med Intern Fenn, 57*:53-63, 1968.

19. RAUTAHARJU, P.M.: Deterministic type wave form analysis in electrocardiography. *Ann NY Acad Sci, 128*:939-954, 1966.

20. RAUTAHARJU, P.M.: Hybrid and small special purpose computers in electrocardiographic, ballistocardiographic and pulse wave research. *Ann NY Acad Sci, 126*:906-918, 1965.

21. RAUTAHARJU, P.M.: Quantitative spatial vector analysis of electro-cardiographic data by electronic computer means. Ph.D. Thesis, Univ. of Minn., 1963.

22. RAUTAHARJU, P.M., and BLACKBURN, H.: The exercise electro-cardiogram; experience in analysis of noisy cardiograms with a small computer. *Amer Heart J, 69*:515-552, 1965.

23. RAUTAHARJU, P.M., *et al.*: Report of a technical group on per-formance specifications for automated exercise ECG analysis programs. Tentative requirements for noise tolerance and pre-cision. Chapter 15. In Blackburn, H. (Ed.): *Measurement in Exercise Electrocardiography.* Springfield, Charles C Thomas, 1969.

24. RAUTAHARJU, P.M., WINTER, D.A., WONG, A.Y.K., and BLACKBURN, H.: Computer analysis of the exercise electrocardiogram. In Manning, G.W., and Ahuja, S.P. (Eds.): *Electrical Activity of the Heart.* Springfield, Charles C Thomas, 1969, pp.287-303.

25. Report on committee on electrocardiography, American Heart Association. Recommendations for standardization of leads and of specifications for instruments in electrocardiography and vector-cardiography. *Circulation, 35*:583-602, 1967.

26. ROBB, G.P., and MARKS, H.H.: Latent coronary artery disease: Determination of its presence and severity by the exercise electrocardiogram. *Amer J Cardiol, 13*:603-618, 1964.

27. RUMBALL, C.A., and ACHESON, E.C.: Latent coronary heart disease detected by electrocardiogram before and after exercise. *Brit Med J, 1*:423-428, 1963.

28. The Scandinavian Committee on ECG classification: The Minne-sota code for ECG classification. Adaptation to CR leads and modification of the code for ECG's recorded during and after exercise. *Acta Med Scand (Suppl. 148),* 1967.

29. SCHMITT, O.H.: Averaging techniques employing several simul-

taneous physiological variables. *Ann NY Acad Sci, 115*:952-975, 1964.

30. SHEFFIELD, L.T., PERRY, M.D., BURDESHAW, J.S., CONROY, D.V., and LARKIN, L.N.: Application of computer techniques to the graded exercise EKG test for ischemic heart disease. *Proc 7th Internat Conf on Med and Biol Engin.* Stockholm, Sweden, 1967, p.103.
31. SIMONSON, E.: Use of the electrocardiogram in exercise tests. *Amer Heart J, 66*:552-565, 1963.
32. SMITH, R.E., and HYDE, C.M.: Computer analysis of the electrocardiogram in clinical practice. In Manning, G.W., and Ahuja, S.P. (Eds.): *Electric Activity of the Heart.* Springfield, Charles C Thomas, 1969, pp.305-315.
33. WINTER, D.A., RAUTAHARJU, P.M., and WOLF, H.K.: Measurement and characteristics of over-all noise content in exercise electrocardiograms. *Amer Heart J, 74*:324-331, 1967.
34. WINTER, D.A., and TRENHOLM, B.G.: Reliable triggering for exercise electrocardiograms. *IEEE Trans on Biomed Engineering. Vol. BME 16*:75-79, 1969.

SECTION FOUR

THE INFLUENCE OF AGE, HEALTH, AND ENVIRONMENT ON WORKING CAPACITY

Chapter 16

THE WORKING CAPACITY OF SCHOOLCHILDREN

Roy J. Shephard

Introduction

THE WORKING CAPACITY of schoolchildren in general and pre-adolescent schoolchildren in particular has received rather less study than that of adults. However, it is of considerable interest. Young children are naturally active and thus closer to their potential ceiling of fitness than adults; regional differences of performance between children may thus have greater genetic significance than corresponding differences between adults. It is further suspected that the growth hormone of the anterior pituitary and testosterone are both involved in the anabolic response to prolonged training; other factors being equal, the response to a training regime is thus likely to be greater in the child than in the adult. Finally, schoolchildren are, in general, cooperative subjects with a fair amount of uncommitted time; the possibility of obtaining a random sample of the population is thus much greater than for adults.

The present article cannot pretend to cover the whole of this interesting area of study. It is strongly biased by information

Note: The opinions expressed here are the personal views of the author. However, much of the experimental work on which these opinions are based was carried out jointly with members of an International Biological Programme working party (66).

The work described in this chapter has been supported in part by research grants from the Directorate of fitness and Amateur Sport, the Ontario Heart Foundation, and the World Health Organization. Thanks are also due to the directors of the various laboratories concerned for the release of staff to participate in the I.B.P. working party.

319

collected by the I.B.P. working party (66), and technical details regarding methodology are covered more fully in the article cited.

Methodology

Choice of Exercise Machine

As in the adult, the choice of laboratory procedure for the assessment of working capacity lies between a step, bicycle ergometer, and treadmill test. It is not always easy to persuade children to climb a staircase with a consistent rhythm, and problems may also arise from differences of leg length. A step test is thus rarely used for children.

The bicycle ergometer is quite popular, especially with boys; at present, many preadolescent children over the age of five or six also own some form of bicycle, although with the trend to apartment living, this percentage is rapidly declining, particularly in the large cities. If the child is ten years of age or older, an adult ergometer can be used with appropriate adjustment of saddle height. In younger children it is necessary to obtain a bicycle ergometer with adjustable crank length, a shortened saddle pillar, and reduced frictional loading (40). If the child is under the age of five, modifications of the task concept are also desirable (5); for instance, the ergometer may be attached to a toy such as a pedal car. Children are generally able to perform maximum exercise on a bicycle ergometer without complaints of leg fatigue; however, at high work loads the intended rhythm is not always maintained (6), and there may be a tendency to lift the body weight off the bicycle seat, with consequent variations in both the efficiency and the upper limit of performance.

Treadmill exercise seems well tolerated by children (66). Maximum effort tests may be a little frightening for some children, but the maximum thus attained is more certainly limited by central factors than is the case in bicycle ergometer exercise.

Choice of Test Procedure

As with adults the level of cardiorespiratory fitness and thus of working capacity may be assessed in several ways. The maximum oxygen intake may be measured directly, it may be predicted from submaximum measurements of pulse rate and oxygen consumption or work rate, the work performed at a specified pulse rate may be reported (the PWC_{170}), or the slope of the pulse rate/oxygen consumption line (the oxygen pulse) may be calculated.

Theoretically, the most satisfactory procedure is the direct measurement of maximum oxygen intake. After a suitable warm-up exercise, subjects commence to run at 90 to 100 percent of their anticipated aerobic power; the slope or speed of the treadmill is adjusted every two minutes (64, 66) or alternatively at subsequent attendances (6) until two successive increments of work load fail to increase oxygen consumption by a specified amount. The standards proposed for adults—150 ml per minute (71) or 54 ml per minute (48) seem inappropriate, but the present author's suggestion (2 ml/kg min increment of oxygen consumption for a 5% or 10% increment in work load) would permit a similar definition of the oxygen plateau for children of differing body size.

In practice it is by no means easy to persuade nonathletic children to progress through the necessary sequence of tests before complaining of exhaustion, and even if this can be accomplished, a substantial proportion of school-age subjects apparently fail to reach an oxygen plateau (6, 23).

Alternatively, the maximum oxygen intake can be predicted from submaximum measurements of pulse rate and oxygen consumption, using extrapolation procedures of the type proposed for adults (Åstrand nomogram, Margaria nomogram, Maritz extrapolation). The linear relationship between heart rate and oxygen consumption needed for extrapolation is fairly well maintained in children (Fig. 16-1 and Ref. 23), but there does seem an asymptote at a pulse rate of about 180 per minute (Fig. 16-1). The pulse rate to which extrapolation should proceed is debatable. Åstrand reported a maximum pulse rate of about 210 per minute (6), but others have consistently observed pulse rates of 195 to 200 per minute in exhausting tests (66,54,74,67,17). It could be argued that Åstrand's children were better motivated

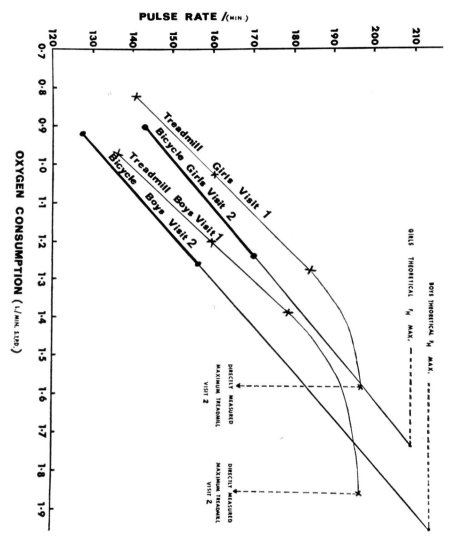

FIGURE 16-1. The relationship between pulse rate and oxygen consumption. Data obtained by I.B.P. working party (66) on children ten to twelve years of age. At the first visit submaximum exercise was performed on a treadmill. At the second visit submaximum exercise was performed on a bicycle ergometer and maximum exercise on a treadmill. The "theoretical" maximum heart rates are taken from the data of Åstrand (6).

and therefore reached higher pulse rates; however, his terminal lactate concentrations were closely similar to those found by the I.B.P. team (66). The reason for the high pulse rates in the Swedish series is thus obscure.

The age correction factors for the Åstrand nomogram (7) are compatible with the Swedish data, being equivalent to the assumption of a maximum pulse rate of 212 per minute in an eleven-year-old boy and 208 per minute in a girl of the same age. However, the nomogram also assumes that the pulse rate at 50 percent of aerobic power is 128 per minute in male subjects and 135 per minute in females; in children the 50 percent pulse rates are substantially higher than this (Fig. 16-1). If these theoretical problems are ignored, the age-corrected nomogram in fact gives a fair prediction of aerobic power in children (66). The I.B.P. team found this to be true in those making a strenuous maximum effort (arterial lactate 2 minutes after exercise greater than 80 mg/100 ml) and in those making an average effort (arterial lactate 60-80 mg/100 ml). The maximum oxygen intake as predicted from the response to submaximum treadmill exercise was just slightly less than the directly measured value (discrepancy 0.01 liter/min STPD in the boys, and 0.11 liter/min STPD in the girls).

When a linear extrapolation of the Maritz type was carried out on the same data (Fig. 16-1), the discrepancy between the directly measured and the predicted maximum oxygen intake was much larger, especially if the observed maximum pulse rate (195/min) rather than the theoretical maximum (210/min) was used as a basis of extrapolation. It is well recognized that if submaximum tests are to be used in this manner, the various factors which may influence the pulse rate at rest and in moderate work (anxiety, a high environmental temperature, and recent feeding) be either avoided or minimized. In the I.B.P. series (66) the room temperature was cool, and tests were conducted several hours after feeding, but anxiety was probably a factor especially at the first visit. At the second visit the children were exercised on a bicycle ergometer, and the maximum oxygen intake predicted from submaximum exercise was then 10 percent greater than at the first visit. Much of this difference was undoubtedly due to a lessening of anxiety; the average resting pulse rate also decreased from 88 per minute to 81 per minute in the boys and from 97 per minute to 83 per minute in the girls.

If the oxygen consumption is to be predicted from the work performed, tests are usually carried out on a bicycle ergometer on the basis that the efficiency of effort is relatively constant during this type of work. This view is questionable even in the adult, and in view of the known influences of unmeasured oxygen debt, body weight, state of training, pattern of effort, speed, and load upon efficiency (23,36,9), it is hardly warranted to assume that efficiency is 23 percent in the child as in the adult. Indeed, specific studies in children (Table 16-I) suggest that in general, the net efficiency (after allowance for basal metabolism) is in the

TABLE 16-I

THE NET MECHANICAL EFFICIENCY OF BICYCLE ERGOMETER
WORK IN CHILDREN

Subjects	Age Range (yr)	Net Efficiency (%)[*]	Author
M, F	6-14	20.6 ± 1.5	Bengtsson (11)
M	7-9	18.4	Taylor *et al.* (70)
	9-11	22.8	
	12-15	17.9	
F	6-9	17.3	Bal *et al.* (8)
	10-12	19.3	
	12-14	19.0	
M, F	7-18	15.6	Mellerowicz (47)
F	9-11	14.5 180 kg-m/min	Hollmann *et al.* (38)
		18.0 300	
		20.1 240 kg-m/min	
M	10-12 (N = 17)	20.1 240 kg/min	I.B.P. Study (66)
	(N = 9)	25.6 360	
	(N = 26)	22.2 420-450	
	(N = 2)	22.8 540-600	
F	10-12 (N = 25)	19.4 240	
	(N = 9)	22.7 360	
	(N = 21)	22.8 420-450	
	(N = 4)	26.6 540-600	

[*]After allowance for basal metabolism of 50 kcal/hour. Note that most children have a substantial oxygen consumption while sitting "at rest" on the bicycle ergometer. A rather higher mechanical efficiency (about 25%) is obtained if calculations are based on the *slope* of the oxygen consumption/work performance line (5, 57).

range 19 to 20 percent. Our data (66) support this view for moderate work loads, but at the higher intensities of effort (where some anaerobic work may occur) the efficiency approaches the supposed adult value of 23 percent.

Partly because of the uncertainties introduced by extrapolation of submaximum test data to a predicted maximum oxygen intake, some authors have preferred to report their results in directly measured or interpolated form (the PWC_{170}, Ref. 40, or the Leistungs-pulsindex, Ref. 56). The main objection to this approach is that the relationship between PWC_{170} and maximum performance depends upon the maximum pulse rate of the individual. Results are, in general, comparable for children of a given age group but may not be comparable from one age to another.

Field Tests of Working Capacity

The two field tests commonly proposed to sample endurance in children are the 300-yard run (16) and the 600-yard walk-run (1). Neither are sufficiently prolonged for this purpose, and the correlation between test scores and the directly measured aerobic power is poor (24). There would thus seem a place for a test such as the twelve-minute run (18); preliminary observations suggest that the distance boys can run in this time closely reflects their aerobic power (Cooper, personal communication to author). Since children are usually available in large schools, it is also practical to carry out simple bicycle ergometer tests on substantial segments of a population, and indeed this has been done in Sweden and in Canada (40).

Maximum Oxygen Intake Data

The Basis of Standardization

In order to compare results obtained on children of differing body size, it is usual to express the maximum oxygen intake per kilogram of body weight (54). Åstrand (6) also plots maximum oxygen intake relative to body surface area and to height and points out the disadvantage of the latter two parameters; both yield nonlinear relationships. Thus, although height, weight, and surface area standardization all permit comparisons over a limited span of body sizes (74,3,11,56), only weight is satisfactory over the broad range from childhood to adult life.

This article follows the traditional viewpoint, and oxygen intake, working capacity, and other parameters of interest are expressed relative to body weight. The residual influence of maturity seems relatively unimportant, at least in the preadolescent child. This point may be tested in terms of the coefficients of correlation between aerobic power and "age discrepancy" (the difference between calendar and radiographic age of the individual). The coefficients for our population of children ten to twelve years of age are as follows:

		Coefficient Relating "Age Discrepancy" to	
		(a) Aerobic Power (Liters/min STPD)	(b) Aerobic Power (ml/kg min STPD)
Boys	r =	0.38 ± 0.21	− 0.24 ± 0.22
Girls	r =	0.50 ± 0.19	0.00 ± 0.22

The "age discrepancy" is significantly related to absolute aerobic power, but the relationship is not significant when aerobic power is expressed per unit of body weight.

Normal Values

The normal standards of aerobic power reported from different parts of the world are summarized in Table 16-II. In the case of the boys, results have been pooled over the age range of six to eighteen years. Individual investigators have shown some age differences, but these are not reproducible from one laboratory to another and thus seem of doubtful practical significance. The mean aerobic power of boys is surprisingly constant at 48 to 50 ml per kilogram minute, the two main exceptions being the studies of Åstrand (6) and of Rodahl et al. (55). Åstrand studied the "best," "rather good," and "poor" members of school classes. He also comments that exceptionally fat children did not participate and that all subjects were rather well trained. His group is thus somewhat biased in favor of individuals with a high level of aerobic power. The group studied by Rodahl et al. (55)

TABLE 16-II

NORMAL STANDARDS OF MAXIMUM OXYGEN INTAKE

Author	Nation	Sex	Age (yr)	Maximum Oxygen Intake (ml/kg min STPD)
Seliger *et al.* (59)	Czechoslovakia	M	11	51.2*
Sprynarova (67)	Czechoslovakia	M	11-13	49.1
Cumming (20)	Canada	M	6-18	49.4
Shephard *et al.* (66)	Canada	M	10-12	48.0
Robinson (54)	U.S.A. (1938)	M	6-16	49.2
Morse *et al.* (49)	U.S.A. (1949)	M	10-17	49.0
Rodahl *et al.* (55)	U.S.A. (1959)	M	10-18	32.0
Brown (15)	U.S.A. (1960)	M	9-12	50.9
Kramer *et al.* (44)	U.S.A. (1961)	M	10-16	48.0
Åstrand (6)	Sweden	M	6-18	56.4
Hollmann *et al.* (37)	Germany	M	12-16	46.0
Andersen (4)	Norway (Lapps)	M	10-16	53.5
Ceretelli *et al.* (17)	Italy	M	8-18	49.9
Cumming (20)	Canada	F	6-8	50.5
Åstrand (6)	Sweden	F	6-8	51.5
Ceretelli *et al.* (17)	Italy	F	8-16	45.0
Wilmore *et al.* (74)	U.S.A. (1967)	F	7-13	51.0
Cumming (20)	Canada	F	10-16	40.6
Shephard *et al.* (66)	Canada	F	10-12	38.7
Åstrand (6)	Sweden	F	10-16	48.8
Andersen (4)	Norway (Lapps)	F	10-16	45.4
Rodahl *et al.* (55)	U.S.A. (1959)	F	10-16	29.0

*Students at special gymnastic school

were very unfit; however, the values recorded are so low that it also seems likely that some of the group failed to achieve their maximum oxygen intake.

In view of recent talk about the deterioration in national fitness, it is worth noting that recent figures for the aerobic power of United States (15, 44) and Canadian (20, 66) boys do not show any substantial deterioration relative to the Bostonian children studied by Robinson in 1938 (54).

Most authors agree that the aerobic power per unit of body mass is larger in younger than in older girls. Accordingly, data for girls six to eight years of age has been distinguished from that for girls ten to sixteen years of age (Table 16-II). Again, the group studied by Åstrand (6) had an unusually large aerobic power, and that studied by Rodahl *et al.* (55) was particularly poor. However, there were also discrepancies in the results from other laboratories; Canadian and Norwegian girls (66,20,4) had a poorer performance than Italian girls (17) and one recent group of U.S. girls (74) of the same age.

Physical Working Capacity (PWC_{170})

A selection of "normal" values from the world literature is given in Table 16-III; other normal series are quoted by Andersen (5). The reported figures vary substantially from one laboratory to another, and this is particularly disturbing when the aerobic power of all boys seems so similar. The variation may be attributable in part to errors of ergometer calibration, in part to differences in environmental conditions, and in part to the use of non-random population samples.   ,

The only attempts to use a deliberate randomly selected population are seen in two recent Canadian surveys (40,66). When the bicycle ergometer was taken to school premises, virtually 100 percent participation was secured (40). However, when the parents of children in the same schools were asked to complete a formal letter of consent and children were transported to the laboratory for a longer series of tests, the proportion of participants dropped to about 35% (66). If the desirable element of "free choice" is permitted both the child and his legal guardians, it is often difficult to obtain a satisfactory percentage of an initial random sample; the investigator must be content to identify any bias in those tested and to examine the effect of this bias upon his experimental results.

In the Canadian series the laboratory figures for the PWC_{170} were some 10 percent larger than those obtained in the field (40, 66). It is possible that by emphasizing the right of parents to refuse a test, the segment of the population examined was of above average cardiorespiratory fitness. However, this is unlikely on two counts: a) The parents of participants did not consider their children to be unusually fit for their age, and b) the laboratory studies were restricted to Metropolitan Toronto, whereas the field study was drawn from both urban and rural schools across Canada. Some factors of technique may have been more closely controlled in the laboratory, but the main basis of the

TABLE 16-III
NORMAL STANDARDS FOR P.W.C.$_{170}$

Author	Nation	Sex	Age (yr)	PWC$_{170}$ (kg-m/min)	PWC$_{170}$ (kg-m/min/ kg)
Cumming (21)	Canada	M	11	474	13.9
		M	11-12	384	
CAHPER (40)	Canada	M	7-9	347	12.5
		M	10-11	460	13.0
		M	12-13	605	13.7
		M	14-17	799	13.4
Shephard *et al.* (66)	Canada	M	10-12	546	14.1
Rodahl *et al.* (55)	U.S.A.	M	8	282	9.7
		M	10	330	9.3
		M	12	472	10.6
Adams (2)	U.S.A.	M	11	650	14.1
Bengtsson (11)	Sweden	no sex	7-9	309	
		difference	10-12	468	
Adams (3)	Sweden				
	(town)	M	11	569	15.8
	(country)	M	11	624	16.0
Rutenfranz (56)	Germany	M	8-9	502	17.2
		M	10-12	732	19.1
Blümcheu *et al.* (13)	Germany	M	8-10	450	
Seliger *et al.* (59)	Czecho-slovakia	M	11	564	16.5*
Cumming (21)	Canada	F	11	497	11.6
		F	11-12	300	7.7
CAHPER (40)	Canada	F	7-9	276	10.3
		F	10-11	349	10.1
		F	12-13	434	9.6
		F	14-17	454	8.4
Shephard *et al.* (66)	Canada	F	10-12	417	11.2
Rodahl *et al.* (55)	U.S.A.	F	8	262	9.3
		F	10	294	8.4
		F	12	368	8.1
Adams (2)	U.S.A.	F	11	488	11.1
Wilmore and Sigerseth (74)	U.S.A.	F	7-9	380	12.5
		F	10-11	470	12.7
		F	12-13	620	12.7
Adams (3)	Sweden				
	(town)	F	11	423	11.8
	(country)	F	11	518	12.3
Bengtsson (11)	Sweden	no sex	7-9	309	
		difference	11	468	
Rutenfranz (56)	Germany	F	9	414	14.8
		F	10-12	518	15.0
Hollmann *et al.* (38)	Germany	F	9-11	319	8.9

*Students attending special gymnastic school

difference is probably that children were "habituated" by their previous visit to the laboratory; their physiological response to a submaximum exercise load was thus distorted relatively little by anxiety. This view is supported by a) the decrease in resting pulse rates from the first to the second visit (see Methodology section of this article) and b) the 10 percent difference between the first (treadmill) and the second (bicycle ergometer) predictions of aerobic power (Fig. 16-1).

Very low PWC_{170} values were obtained by Rodahl *et al.* (55); this supports in part the small maximum oxygen intake found in their population.

Blood Lactic Acid and Oxygen Debt

The maximum levels of blood lactate found in the I.B.P. treadmill experiments (78.7 $\pm$ 28.2 mg/100 ml in the boys, 77.1 $\pm$ 25.4 mg/100 ml in the girls; Ref. 66) are slightly greater than those reported by Morse *et al.* (49) and correspond closely with those found by Åstrand (6). They differ from the adult response (64, 65) in two respects: a) The peak concentration is lower, and b) the decline in concentration after stopping exercise is more rapid. The present author's figures for children ten to twelve years of age are 80.1, 73.3, and 69.9 mg/100 ml two, four, and six minutes after ceasing maximum exercise. The faster decline in the children may reflect a) the lower peak lactate concentration and b) a more rapid transport of lactate from the active muscles to the capillaries of the finger tip.

Several possible explanations may be offered for the lower peak lactate concentrations in childhood: a) The "on-transient" of oxygen consumption at the beginning of exercise may have a faster time-constant in the child, b) the buffering capacity of the blood may be somewhat lower than in the adult, and c) the children may be less willing to sustain maximum exertion than are young adults.

Whichever of these explanations is correct, the low lactate levels are substantiated by a small "oxygen debt." The total excess oxygen consumption in the first eleven minutes following maximum exercise was 2.44 liters STPD in the boys, and 1.76 liters STPD in the girls, compared with some 7.5 liters in adult men (46). When the excess oxygen consumption was plotted semilogarithmically and alactate and lactate components of the oxygen debt were distinguished, a fair correlation was found between the lactate "debt" and the directly measured blood lactate concentrations (for the boys r = 0.61 ± 0.19 and for the girls r = 0.64 ± 0.18).

In the submaximum treadmill exercise, accumulation of lactate was much less marked in children than in adults. Even at 80 percent of maximum aerobic power, the lactate concentration was only 21.9 mg per 100 ml. This confirms the view that peripheral limitation of oxygen intake is less common in children than in adults.

The Influence of Obesity

The procedure of relating maximum oxygen intake or working capacity to body weight penalizes the obese individual. In many respects the penalty is justified, since the energy cost of most activities is markedly influenced by the body weight of the individual. Nevertheless, it seems worth enquiring how far the poor performance of certain regional groups is attributable to obesity and a relative rather than an absolute deficiency of active tissue.

Table 16-IV summarizes weight/height ratios for a variety of populations. A minimum standard for healthy children is provided by Robinson's data for boys living at an orphanage in 1938 (54). Many of the older tables of normal data (39, 52, 68) quote not much larger ratios; however, recent series are substantially heavier, some from the United States by as much as 40 to 50 percent. Part of the explanation for this increase lies in earlier maturation of the children; a weight/height ratio that would have been appropriate for a thirteen-year-old child in 1938 is now seen in a boy of eleven or twelve. It is difficult to attribute any deterioration of fitness to the increased weight/height ratios, since the ratios were not particularly large in the series of Rodahl *et al.* (55), where aerobic power was poor, and

TABLE 16-IV

BODY WEIGHT AND WEIGHT/HEIGHT RATIOS OF SCHOOLCHILDREN (KG/CM)

Author	Nation	Age (yr)	Boys		Girls	
			Body Weight (kg)	Weight/Height Ratio (kg/cm)	Body Weight (kg)	Weight/Height Ratio (kg/cm)
Cumming et al. (21)	Canada	11-12	37.0	0.253	40.0	0.272
CAHPER (40)	Canada	11	37.7	—	36.2	—
Shephard et al. (66)	Canada	10	36.0	0.252	33.7	0.240
		11	38.6	0.264	38.0	0.254
		12	40.5	0.274	42.9	0.275
Robinson (54)	U.S.A. (1938)	10.5	29.5	0.215	—	—
Stuart et al. (68)	U.S.A. (1946)	11	35.2	0.244	35.7	0.247
Rodahl et al. (55)	U.S.A. (1959)	10	35.8	0.254	35.3	0.252
		12	44.8	0.294	45.3	0.294
Adams et al. (2)	U.S.A. (1961)	11	46.0	0.303	44.0	0.297
Wilmore et al. (74)	U.S.A. (1967)	10-11	—	—	37.0	0.259
		12-13	—	—	49.0	0.308
Holt (39)	U.K.	10	—	0.231	—	0.231
		11	—	0.241	—	0.241
		12	—	0.253	—	0.253
Provis and Ellis (52)	U.K.	11.5	33.4	0.236	33.8	0.239
Adams et al. (3)	Sweden (urban)	11	36.0	0.245	36.0	0.247
	(rural)	11	39.0	0.265	42.0	0.278
Astrand (6)	Sweden	11	36.7	0.249	34.1	0.241
Seliger et al. (59)	Czechoslovakia	11.5	34.2	0.242	—	—
Sprynarova (67)	Czechoslovakia	10.9	37.1	0.257	—	—
Rutenfranz (56)	Germany	11	38.7	0.262	38.5	0.266
Hollmann et al. (38)	Germany	11	—	—	35.5	0.246

very large ratios are seen in the recent series of Wilmore and Sigerseth (74), where aerobic power was good.

Studies in this laboratory (66) have shown a body fat content of 15.6 percent in boys, and 20.7 percent in girls. Whether this percentage could usefully be reduced is a matter of debate. Many carnivorous mammals have a much lower fat content than this; rather lower values are also found in adult male (10.6%) but not female (20.3%) physical education students (73). On the other hand, it is possible to meet the weight for height standards of the Society of Actuaries with as much as 30 percent body fat (51).

Thus, although the present generation of children is heavier than those of the prewar era, it is by no means proven that the degree of obesity is sufficient to have an adverse influence on either working capacity or life expectancy.

The Oxygen Conductance Equation in Childhood

The conductance equation for the prediction of maximum aerobic power is discussed elsewhere in this volume. In short, the overall conductance of oxygen ($\dot{G}_{O_2}$) can be partitioned into two significant series terms representing alveolar ventilation ($\dot{V}_A$) and blood transport ($\lambda\dot{Q}$). Thus:

$$\frac{1}{\dot{G}_{O_2}} = \frac{1}{\dot{V}_A} + \frac{1}{\lambda\dot{Q}}$$

Certain specific features of this equation as it relates to children will be noted in the present article.

In general, the child's oxygen transport proceeds rather better in the gas phase and rather poorer in the blood phase than would be the case in an adult. The maximum exercise ventilation of our children ten to twelve years of age has averaged 52.1 liters per minute STPD or 1.37 liters per kilogram minute (66); this is larger than the figure of about 1.0 liters per kilogram minute found in sedentary adults and more comparable with the value of ~ 1.6 liters per kilogram minute found in adult athletes. Morse *et al.* (49) and Wilmore and Sigerseth (74) also report figures of ~ 1.4 liters per kilogram minute in children ten to eleven years of age, while Astrand's children (6) reached values as large as

1.6 liters per kilogram minute. On the other hand, the lung capacity, forced expiratory volume, and maximum voluntary ventilation are not outstanding in children (19,27,66,63); presumably, children can use a larger fraction of their ventilatory reserve without reaching the limits imposed by the sensation of dyspnea and an excessive consumption of oxygen in the respiratory muscles. In our experience (10) the alveolar ventilation of children is some 79 percent of the external ventilation during near maximal exercise; this again compares favorably with the figure of 75 percent we have found for adults; it may reflect the lesser length of the thorax and consequent greater uniformity of alveolar perfusion.

Information on the maximum cardiac output of preadolescent children is limited. We (10) have used a CO_2 rebreathing procedure, pushing children to a level of exercise where an apparent plateau of stroke volume was reached (mean pulse rate 152/min in the boys and 168/min in the girls). Based on the plateau reading (46 ml in children ten to twelve years of age), a cardiac output of 9.0 liters per minute would be reached at a pulse rate of 195 per minute and 9.7 liters per minute at a pulse rate of 210 per minute. These figures are small relative to the maximum cardiac output found by acetylene rebreathing in the adult (61). Possibly the stroke volume increases beyond the apparent plateau; possibly there are also systematic errors in the CO_2 rebreathing method of measuring cardiac output (28). However, the radiographic heart volume is also small relative to body weight. Our data (66) show a mean cardiac volume of 9.8 ml per kilogram in boys and 9.6 ml per kilogram in girls, and this conforms well with a recent study from Cologne (15); it contrasts with figures of 11.4 to 11.7 ml per kilogram for older boys and men and 14.8 ml per kilogram for athletes (53, 3) and supports the view of a "hypokinetic" heart in childhood (10).

The hemoglobin level of children is less than in adult men. Our figures (66) of 14.1 gm per 100 ml for Canadian boys and girls are confirmed by more extensive studies from the United Kingdom (30,60,69) and from Sweden (6). The solubility factor λ is thus proportionately reduced from about 1.16 in the adult to about 1.05 in the preadolescent child.

There is no published information on the maximum arterio-venous oxygen difference in children. Our data (10) show values of 10.1 ml per 100 ml and 13.3 ml per 100 ml at loads of 280 and 420 kg per minute, respectively. These loads correspond to 47 and 67 percent of aerobic power; thus, the relationship of arteriovenous oxygen difference to the intensity of exercise seems similar to that found in the adult (65), and there is every reason to suppose that the maximum arteriovenous difference reaches *at least* the adult figure of 16 ml per 100 ml; indeed, a difference of 17.5 ml per 100 ml would be required to deliver 1.7 liters of oxygen per minute with a cardiac output of 9.7 liters per minute.

The approximate form of the conductance equation for an eleven-year-old child is thus:

$$\frac{1}{G_{O_2}} = \frac{1}{0.79(52.1)} + \frac{1}{1.05(9.7)} = \frac{1}{41.2} + \frac{1}{10.2}$$

In other words, blood transport is approximately four times as important as alveolar ventilation in determining the overall conductance of oxygen.

It is shown elsewhere in this book that diffusion of oxygen does not normally impose a significant limitation upon oxygen conductance, either in the lungs or in the tissues. The maximum diffusing capacity of the child's lung is at least as great as in the adult, whether related to body weight or to oxygen consumption (66); thus, terms related to diffusion can be ignored in the child as in the adult.

Variations in Working Capacity

Sociological Factors

Several authors have argued that since aerobic power is in-fluenced by the level of habitual activity, a greater maximum oxygen intake should be found in a rural than in an urban society. In Sweden (3) this expectation was justified, and the PWC_{170} per kilogram of body weight was greater in rural than in urban children (Table 16-III). A similar trend was apparent in Canada;

the absolute aerobic power of children fourteen to eighteen years of age was 8.9 percent larger in the males and 5.9 percent larger in the females; relative to body weight the differences were 5.1 and 3.4 percent, respectively (41). However, in both Canada and Sweden the differences observed were of marginal statistical significance. This may reflect several confounding factors: a) Hard physical work and prolonged walking are diminishing characteristics of rural life. b) Increased physical activity out of school may be offset by poorer facilities for recreation within rural schools. c) In Canada at least the standard of living is much lower in rural areas.

Seasonal Factors

There is no general agreement on changes in working capacity over the school year. Åstrand (personal communication to author) noted an improvement during the school year, with deterioration during the summer vacation. On the other hand, Adams *et al.* (3), also studying Swedish children, found an improvement of working capacity during the school holidays, particularly in those with a low initial level of cardiorespiratory fitness. In Canada no signicant seasonal effects are found in schoolchildren (Cumming: personal communication to author). The intensity of activity in and out of school and the relative restrictions on physical activity imposed by climatic conditions are so variable from one region of the world to another that it would indeed be surprising if any useful generalizations could be made.

Training

Training is generally held to improve aerobic power, but this is difficult to demonstrate in young children, possibly because the majority are already at or near their potential maximum working capacity. The response of adults to a training regime is influenced markedly by the initial fitness of the subjects (62). Saltin *et al.* (58) were able to improve the aerobic power of young athletes by only 4 percent as a result of participation in a very vigorous training programme.

In children significant differences of aerobic power can be demonstrated between those who are active in sports and those who are not (for instance, 3, 50). However, it is less certain that the relationship is causal. Šprynarova (67) and Ulbrich (72) have each followed children "longitudinally," commencing at the age of eleven. Children entering specific sports programmes had a higher initial aerobic power than nonparticipants, and this difference was not accentuated by systematic training for one hour twice per week. Cumming (personal communication to author) was also unable to find any improvement of aerobic power as a result of either participation in a variety of school gymnastic programmes or a period of intensive training at a youths' track camp (25). It would seem that boys with an aerobic power of 48 to 50 ml per kilogram minute are close to their potential and that the rewards of training are small; presumably the greater aerobic power of selected athletes has a large genetic component.

The situation is a little different in most girls. Certainly, Canadian girls with an aerobic power of less than 40 ml per kilogram minute have a poor standard of cardiorespiratory fitness, and the maximum working capacity of girls can be increased by attachment to a special school where the emphasis is upon gymnastics (38).

It is of course difficult to separate the influences of endogenous physical endowment and of environment. Even before the age when specialized training is undertaken, the unfit child may have adopted interests and attitudes leading to a lower level of habitual activity (29), and such attitudes rather than a true genetic limitation may account for both a poor initial level of cardiorespiratory fitness and a limited response to a training regime.

Hormonal Factors

Space does not permit a detailed discussion of the relationships between hormone secretion and the growth of working capacity. However, a brief survey will be made of some recent developments.

It is well recognized that either administration of growth hormone (31) or natural overproduction, as in acromegaly (42), lead to abnormal development of the body musculature. However, the influence of the growth hormone on body development seems relatively independent of the training process. Work-induced hypertrophy can occur in hypophysectomized animals (32), and administration of growth hormone leads to an equal increase of weight in innervated and denervated muscles (33). It has further been suggested that growth hormone increases muscle bulk without increasing its strength (12). Muscular activity alters the relative proportions of soluble and myofibrillar proteins (35) and increases the percentage of mitochondrial protein (Edington, personal communication to author), whereas administration of growth hormone leads to a more uniform increase in all the protein constituents of a muscle (34).

In summary, the effect of growth hormone seems to increase the size of skeletal muscle by the same relative factor, whether they are atrophying from denervation or undergoing hypertrophy secondary to an increased work load. Growth hormone acts as a "linear amplifier" for other anabolic processes (33). Thus, unless these other and more fundamental anabolic processes are more susceptible to physical activity in the child, there would seem a need to revise the doctrine that cardiorespiratory training is produced more easily in the child than in the adult.

References

1. AAHPER: American Association for Health, Physical Education and Recreation. *Youth Fitness Test Manual,* Washington, D.C. The Association: a department of the National Education Association, U.S.A., 1958.
2. ADAMS, F.H., LINDE, L.M., and MIYAKE, H.: The physical working capacity of normal school children. I. California. *Pediatrics, 28*:55-64, 1961.
3. ADAMS, F.H., BENGTSSON, E., BERVEN, H., and WEGELIUS, C.: The physical working capacity of normal schoolchildren. II. Swedish city and country. *Pediatrics, 28*:243-257, 1961.
4. ANDERSEN, K.L.: Physical, fitness—studies of healthy men and women in Norway. In Jokl, E., and Simon, E. (Eds.): *International Research in Sport and Physical Education.* Springfield, Charles C Thomas, 1964.

5. ANDERSEN, K.L.: In W.H.O. Handbook of Exercise Methodology, To be published, 1970.

6. ÅSTRAND, P-O.: *Experimental Studies of Physical Working Capacity in Relation to Sex and Age.* Copenhagen, Munksgaard, 1952.

7. ÅSTRAND, I.: Aerobic work capacity in men and women with special reference to age. *Acta Physiol Scand, 49 (Suppl. 169)*, 1960.

8. BAL, M.E.R., THOMPSON, E.M., MCINTOSH, E.M., TAYLOR, C.M., and MACLEOD, G.: Mechanical efficiency of cycling of girls six to fourteen years of age. *J Appl Physiol*, 6:185-188, 1953.

9. BANISTER, E.W., and JACKSON, R.C.: The effect of speed and load changes on oxygen intake for equivalent power outputs during bicycle ergometry. Unpublished report, Simon Fraser University, British Columbia, 1967.

10. BAR-OR., O., SHEPHARD, R.J., and ALLEN, C.: Exercise Cardiac Output of 10-13 year old children. *Proceedings 16th Annual Meeting, American College of Sports Medicine,* Atlanta, 1969.

11. BENGTSSON, E.: The working capacity in normal children, evaluated by sub-maximal exercise on the bicycle ergometer and compared with adults. *Acta Med Scand, 154*:91-109, 1956.

12. BIGLAND, B., and JEHRING, B.: Muscle performance in rats, normal and treated with growth hormone. *J Physiol (London), 117*: 129-136, 1951.

13. BLUMCHEU, G., ROSKAMM, H., and REINDELL, H.: Herzvolumen und Korperliche Leistungsfahigkeit. *Kreislaufforschung, 55*: 1012-1016, 1966.

14. BOUCHARD, C., HOLLMANN, W., and HERKENRATH, G.: Developpement du volume cardiaque et de la capacité physique au travail et leurs relations avec le niveau de maturité biologique chez les garçons de huit à dixhuit ans. C.A.H.P.E.R. National Convention, Montreal, 1967.

15. BROWN, S. R.: Factors influencing improvement in the oxygen intake of young boys. Ph.D. Thesis, Universitiy of Illinois, Urbana, Ill., 1960.

16. C.A.H.P.E.R.: Canadian Association of Health, Physical Education and Recreation (1966). *Fitness Performance Test Manual.* The association, Toronto, Ontario, 1966.

17. CERETELLI, P., AGHEMO, P., and ROVELLI, E.: Morphological and

physiological observations in schoolchildren in Milan. *Med Dell Sport (Milan)*, 2:109-121, 1963.

18. COOPER, K.: Aerobics. New York, Evans, 1968.
19. COTES, J.E.: *Lung Function. Assessment and Application in Medicine.* Oxford, Blackwell Scientific Publications, 1965.
20. CUMMING, G.R.: Current levels of fitness. *Canad Med Assoc J,* 96:868-877, 1967.
21. CUMMING, G.R., and CUMMING, P.M.: Working capacity of normal children tested on a bicycle ergometer. *Canad Med Assoc J,* 88:351-355, 1963.
22. CUMMING, G.R., and DANZIGER, R.: Bicycle ergometer studies in children. *Pediatrics, 32:*202-208, 1953.
23. CUMMING, G.R., and FRIESEN, W.: Bicycle ergometer measurements of maximal oxygen uptake in children. *Canad J Physiol,* 45:937-946, 1967.
24. CUMMING, G.R., and KEYNES, R.: A fitness performance test for schoolchildren and its correlation with physical working capacity and maximal oxygen uptake. *Canad Med Assoc J, 96:* 1262-1269, 1967.
25. CUMMING, G.R., GOODWIN, A., BAGGLEY, G., and ANTEL, J.: Repeated measurement of aerobic capacity during a week of intensive training at a youths' track camp. *Canad J Physiol Pharmacol, 45:*805-811, 1967.
26. DEMPSEY, J.A., REDDAN, W., BALKE, B., and RANKIN, J.: Work capacity determinants and physiologic cost of weight—supported work in obesity. *J Appl Physiol, 21:*1815-1820, 1966.
27. DEMUTH, G.R., HOWATT, W.F., and HILL, B.M.: The growth of lung function. *Pediatriacs, 35 (Suppl.),* 161-218, 1965.
28. DENISON, D., EDWARDS, R.H.T., JONES, G., and POPE, H.: Comparison of rebreathing estimates with direct measurements of mixed venous P,co_2 and PA,co_2 in man. *UK Physiol Soc,* April 1969, pp.77-78.
29. DURNIN, J.V.G.A.: Activity patterns in the community. In: International Symposium on physical activity and cardiovascular health. *Canad Med Assoc J, 96:*882-885, 1967.
30. ELWOOD, P.C., WITHEY, J.L., and KILPATRICK, G.S.: Distribution of haemoglobin level in a group of schoolchildren, and its relation to height, weight, and other variables. *Brit J Prev Soc Med, 18:*125-129, 1964.
31. EVANS, H.M., SIMPSON, M.E., and LI, C.H.: The gigantism pro-

duced by injection of pituitary growth hormone. *Growth,* 12:15-32, 1948.

32. GOLDBERG, A.L.: Work-induced growth in skeletal muscle or normal and hypophysectomized rats. *Amer J Physiol, 213*:1193-1198, 1967.

33. GOLDBERG, A.L., and GOODMAN, H.M.: Relationship between growth hormone and muscular work in determining muscle size. *J Physiol, 200*:655-666, 1969.

34. GREY, B.J., and YOUNG, F.G.: The influence of growth hormone on the composition of rat muscle. *J Endocr, 10*:179-183, 1954.

35. HAMOSH, M., LESCH, M., BARON, J., and KAUFMANN, S.: Enhanced protein synthesis in a cell-free system from hypertrophied skeletal muscle. *Science, NY, 158*:935-937, 1967.

36. HENRY, F.M., and DeMOOR, J.: Metabolic efficiency of exercise in relation to work load at constant speed. *J Appl Physiol, 2*:481-487, 1950.

37. HOLLMANN, W., BOUCHARD, C., and HERKENRATH, G.: Die Entwicklung des Kardiopulmonalen Systems bei Kindern und Jugendlichen des 8 bis 18 Lebensjahres. *Sportarzt, 7*:255, 1965.

38. HOLLMANN, W., SCHOLTZMETHNER, R., GRUNEWALD, B., and WERNER, H.: Untersuchungen zur Ausdauerverbesserung 9 bis 11 jahriger Madchen im Rahmen des Schulsonderturnens. *Die Liebeserziehung 10,* Koln, Germany, 1967.

39. HOLT: Data on body weight of children in the U.K. Quoted by Sheldon, W. *Diseases of Infancy and Childhood.* London, Churchill, 1948.

40. HOWELL, M.L., and MacNAB, R.B.J.: *The Physical Work Capacity of Canadian Children Aged 7 to 17.* Toronto, Canadian Association for Health, Physical Education and Recreation, 1968.

41. HOWELL, M.L., MacNAB, R.B.J., GREEN, H.J., HYDE, R.C., and NORMAN, R.W.: Work capacity tests in the Secondary Schools of Alberta: Age and sex differences, rural and urban differences, and population means. 16th C.A.H.P.E.R. Convention, Fredericton, N.B., 1965.

42. KNOBIL, E.: The pituitary growth hormone: some physiological considerations. In Zarrow, M. (Ed.): *Growth in Living Systems.* New York, Basic Books, 1961.

43. KONIG, G., REINDELL, H., KEUL, J., and ROSKAMM, H.: Untersuchungen uber das Verhaltes von Atmung und Kreislauf im

Belastungsversuch bei Kindern und Jungendlichen im alter von 10-19 Jahren. *Int Z Angew Physiol, 18*:393-434, 1961.

44. KRAMER, J.D., and LURIE, P.R.: Maximal oxygen consumption. *Amer J Dis Child, 108*:283-297, 1964.

45. MacNAB, R.B.J., HOWELL, M.L., NORMAN, R.W., HYDE, R.C., and GREEN, H.J.: The Astrand maximal and sub-maximal bicycle ergometer test: validity, reliability, intra and interindividual differences. Paper presented at 16th C.A.H.P.E.R. Convention, Fredericton, N.B., 1965.

46. MARGARIA, R.: Anaerobic metabolism in muscle. In: Proceedings of International Symposium on Physical Activity and Cardiovascular Health. *Canad Med Assoc J, 96*:770-774, 1967.

47. MELLEROWICZ, H.: *Ergometrie*. Munchen, Urban & Schwarzenberg, 1967.

48. MITCHELL, J.H., SPROULE, B.J., and CHAPMAN, C.: The physiological meaning of the maximum oxygen intake test. *J Clin Invest, 37*:538-547, 1958.

49. MORSE, M., SCHULTZ, F.W., and CASSELS, D.E.: Relation of age to physiological responses of the older boy (10-17 years) to exercise. *J Appl Physiol, 1*:683, 1949.

50. NORMAN, R.W.K.: Age differences in the work capacity of Alberta Secondary School students as measured by the Astrand predicted maximal oxygen intake test. Unpublished report, Fitness Research Unit, University of Alberta, 1967.

51. NORRIS, A.H., LUNDY, T., and SHOCK, N.W.: Trends in selected indices of body composition in men between the ages of 30 and 80 years. *Ann NY Acad Sci, 110*:623-639, 1963.

52. PROVIS, H.S., and ELLIS, R.W.B.: An anthropometric study of Edinburgh schoolchildren. *Arch Dis Chil, 30*:328-337, 1955.

53. REINDELL, H., KONIG, K., ROSKAMM, H., and KEUL, J.: *Mkurse Artzl Fortbild, 4*, 1959. Quoted by Mellerowicz (47).

54. ROBINSON, S.: Experimental studies of physical fitness in relation to age. *Arbeitsphysiol, 10*:251-323, 1939.

55. RODAHL, K., ÅSTRAND, P-O., BIRKHEAD, N.C., HETTINGER, T., ISSEKUTZ, B., JONES, D.M., and WEAVER, R.: Physical work capacity. A study of some children and young adults in the United States. *Arch Environ Health, 2*:499-510, 1961.

56. RUTENFRANZ, J.: Entwicklung und Beurteilung der korperlichen Leistungsfahigkeit bei Kindern und Jugendlichen. *Bibliotheca Paediatrica 82.* Supplement to *Ann Pediat,* Basel, Karger, 1964.

57. RUTENFRANZ, J., and MOCELLIN, R.: Investigations on children and youths regarding the relationship between various parameters of the physical development and the working capacity. *2nd International Seminar for Ergometry*, Berlin, Germany, 1967.

58. SALTIN, B., BLOMQVIST, G., MITCHELL, J.H., JOHNSON, R.L., WILDEN-THAL, K., and CHAPMAN, C.B.: Response to exercise after bed rest and after training. A longitudinal study of adaptive changes in oxygen transport and body composition. *Amer Heart Assoc Monograph, 23*:1-78, 1968.

59. SELIGER, V., and PACHLOPNIKOVA, I.: Vergleichende ergometrische Untersuchungen bei den Gymnastikturnern. *2nd International Seminar for Ergometry*, Berlin, Germany, 1967.

60. SHEPHARD, R.J.: The influence of age on the haemoglobin level in congenital heart disease. *Brit Heart J, 18*:49-54, 1956.

61. SHEPHARD, R.J.: The heart and circulation under stress of Olympic conditions. *JAMA, 205*:150-155, 1968.

62. SHEPHARD, R.J.: Intensity, duration, and frequency of exercise as determinants of the response to a training regime. *Int Z Angew Physiol, 26*:258-271, 1969.

63. SHEPHARD, R. J.: Prediction formulas and some normal values in pulmonary physiology: Man. Handbook of Respiration and Circulation, American Physiological Society: In preparation, 1970.

64. SHEPHARD, R.J., ALLEN, C., BENADE, A.J.S., DAVIES, C.T.M., DI PRAMPERO, P.E., HEDMAN, R., MERRIMAN, J.E., MYHRE, K., and SIMMONS, R.: The maximum oxygen intake: An international reference standard of cardio-respiratory fitness. *Bull WHO, 38*:757-764, 1968.

65. SHEPHARD, R.J., ALLEN, C., BENADE, A.J.S., DAVIES, C.T.M., DI PRAMPERO, P.E., HEDMAN, R., MERRIMAN, J.E., MYHRE, K., and SIMMONS, R.: Standardization of sub-maximal exercise tests. *Bull WHO 38*:765-776, 1968.

66. SHEPHARD, R.J., ALLEN, C., BAR-OR, O., DAVIES, C.T.M., DEGRÉ, S., HEDMAN, R., ISHII, K., KANEKO, M., LACOUR, J.R., DI PRAMPERO, P.E., and SELIGER, V.: The working capacity of Toronto school children. *Canad Med Assoc J, 100*:560-566, 705-714, 1969.

67. ŠPRYNOROVA, S.: Development of the relationship between aerobic capacity and the circulatory and respiratory reaction to moder-

ate activity in boys 11-13 years old. *Physiol Bohemoslov, 15*: 253-264, 1966.

68. STUART, H.C., and MEREDITH, H.V.: Use of body measurements in the school health program. *Amer J Public Health, 36*:1365-1373, 1946.

69. TANNER, J.M.: *Growth at Adolescence.* 2nd Ed. Oxford, Blackwell Scientific Publication, 1962.

70. TAYLOR, C.M., BAL, M.E.R., LAMB, M.W., and MACLEOD, G.: Mechanical efficiency of cycling of boys seven to fifteen years of age. *J Appl Physiol, 2*:563-570, 1950.

71. TAYLOR, H.L., BUSKIRK, E., and HENSCHEL, A.: Maximal oxygen intake as an objective measure of cardiorespiratory performance. *J Appl Physiol, 8*:73-80, 1955.

72. ULBRICH, J.: Development of inter-individual variations of pulse rate in juveniles work. *Teor Praxa Těl Vých, 16*:24-26, 1968.

73. VON DÖBELN, W.: Human Standard and maximal metabolic rate in relation to fat-free body mass. *Acta Physiol Scand, 37(Suppl. 126),* 1956.

74. WILMORE, J.H., and SIGERSETH, P.O.: Physical work capacity of young girls 7-13 years of age. *J Appl Physiol, 22*:923-928, 1967.

Chapter 17

EXERCISE PERFORMANCE OF
CARDIAC PATIENTS

M. H. FRICK

Reduced ability to perform physical exercise is inherent in almost all types of heart disease. This deviation from normal, whether spontaneously expressed by the patients or found out by the use of leading questions, has provided the basis for the subjective grading of disability in heart disease (4, 31). Since there is a wide interindividual range in the thresholds for different sensations as well as a lack of uniformity of daily exertion, it is not surprising that the information obtained is neither exact nor comparable. To obtain more valid data, objective testing procedures have been developed and are described elsewhere in this book.

The spectrum of heart disease is very wide, ranging from rarities to the more common conditions that form the bulk of the diagnostic categories seen in a cardiac laboratory. The main types of disease can be analyzed as groups and will be so considered here.

Congenital Heart Disease

In the *nonobstructive* variety, atrial septal defect (ASD), patent ductus arteriosus (PDA), and ventricular septal defect (VSD) constitute the majority of cases. After the early exclusion by nature of cases incompatible with life, a number of children reach the age when testing of their exercise performance becomes possible. Using age and weight matched control series, it can be shown that the majority of children with ASD, PDA, or VSD have a lower exercise performance than the normal average (1, 8, 15). Increasing pulmonary arterial pressure is

345

TABLE 17-I

A COMPARISON BEWEEN PHYSICALLY INACTIVE AND ACTIVE FEMALE PATIENTS, BOTH GROUPS
HAVING LEFT-TO-RIGHT SHUNTS WITHOUT PULMONARY HYPERTENSION

Groups		Age (yr)	BSA Meters²	PWR_{150} (kpm/min)	HV (ml)	SP_{PA} (mm Hg)	PF/SF (ratio)	PVR (units)
Physical inactivity (N = 5)	Mean	28	1.54	265	818	22	2.0	0.8
	Range	16-39	1.49-1.64	200-300	540-1430	16-28	1.1-3.2	0.2-1.3
Regular excess of physical activity (N = 5)	Mean	30	1.70	680	998	25	3.4	0.8
	Range	20-39	1.53-1.80	400-795	855-1135	20-30	2.2-4.8	0.3-1.5

Abbreviations used: BSA = body surface area, PWR_{150} = physical working rate at heart rate 150, HV = heart volume, SP_{PA} = systolic pressure in pulmonary artery, PF = pulmonary flow, SF = systemic flow, PVR = pulmonary vascular resistance.

associated with decreasing performance, suggesting that restriction of pulmonary flow is one determinant (22). Left or right ventricular failure occurs with relatively low frequency.

In adult life these patients present a wide range of exercise performance (10, 37, 40). The following factors, in order of frequency, can be coupled with impairment: a) a high pulmonary arterial pressure because of either excessive left-to-right shunting or high pulmonary vascular resistance, b) left or right ventricular failure, c) advanced age, and d) physical inactivity (10). The last item is worth emphasizing, since it is frequently iatrogenic and patients taking regular exercise often have excellent fitness despite a considerable left-to-right shunt (Table 17-I). On the other hand, it is not known whether excess activity promotes the development of pulmonary vascular disease. If there

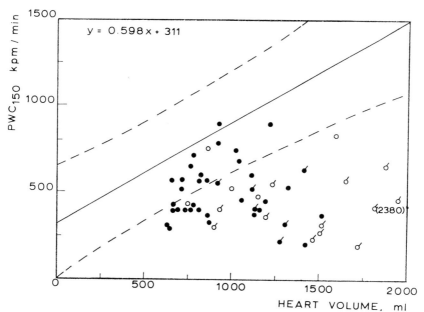

FIGURE 17-1. Relation between physical working rate (PWC$_{150}$) and heart volume in patients with atrial septal defect. Normal regression and its 95 percent tolerance limits are shown. Filled symbols: patients under thirty-five years. Open symbols: patients over thirty-five years. Symbols with tail: pulmonary hypertension.

is long-standing left-to-right shunting or pulmonary vascular disease since birth, the cross-sectional area of the pulmonary vasculature is reduced and the quantum of accepted flow is correspondingly diminished. When the mean resting pulmonary arterial pressure exceeds 60 mm Hg, the increase of pulmonary flow with exercise becomes significantly restricted (45). However, whereas patients with ASD can quite often considerably increase the pulmonary flow upon exertion despite evident pulmonary vascular disease, the increase is smaller in cases with PDA, VSD, and the Eisenmenger syndrome (6).

Elevated left-sided diastolic pressures seldom contribute to the rise in pulmonary arterial pressure upon exertion (44) except in patients of advanced age who often exhibit atrial fibrillation (40).

The wide scatter in the exercise performance of cardiac patients has led to the use of some additional reference standards, known from studies on healthy subjects to be related to exercise

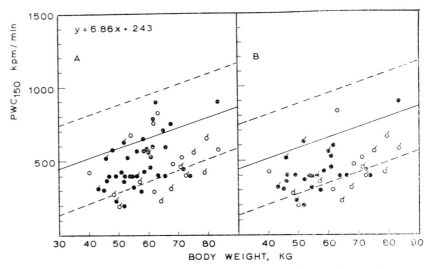

FIGURE 17-2. *A:* Relation between PWC$_{150}$ and body weight in the same patients as in Figure 17-1. Normal regression and its 95 percent tolerance limits are shown. *B:* Relation between PWC$_{150}$ and body weight in the patients who have a low PWC$_{150}$/heart volume ratio.

performance. The most frequently used one is heart volume (34). Figures 17-1 and 17-2 illustrate the apparent discrepancy that was found in a series of fifty-six patients with ASD when the physical working rate was related to heart volume and body weight, respectively. Eighty-nine percent of the patients had low exercise performance in relation to heart volume but only 18 percent in relation to body weight. This indicates that patients with "physiologically" poor performance can still exercise with the same ease as healthy subjects of similar weight. In the majority of cases the heart volume decreases after corrective surgery, but this is a slow process that may take up to two years to complete (26). The exercise performance generally improves in parallel with this, shifting the physical working rate-heart volume relation towards normal. However, in very large hearts irreversible overstretching of the myocardial fibers can be in-

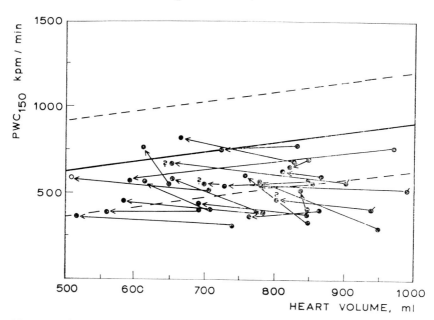

Figure 17-3. Prooperative and postoperative relationships in patients with atrial septal defect and a preoperative heart volume of less than 1000 ml. Mean follow-up time, 2½ years. Seventy percent of the cases had normal PWC_{150}/heart relation after surgery.

volved; this is suggested by the sequence of events in patients
with moderately and greatly enlarged hearts (Fig. 17-3 and 17.4).

Since dyspnea is a main factor in exercise impairment,
respiratory abnormalities may contribute to disability. Restrictive
or obstructive ventilatory impairments have been found infrequently in the absence of left ventricular failure or paren-
chymatous lung disease (7, 10, 40, 41, 47). In a number of cases
the lung compliance is reduced (48). This is clearly associated
with hyperkinetic pulmonary hypertension but not necessarily
with impaired ventilatory function (7). The ventilatory drive
and dyspnea upon exertion have continued an enigma. In some
cases with right-to-left shunting, systemic hypoxemia would
appear to be the logical explanation. On the other hand, no
definite correlation has been found between the oxygen tension

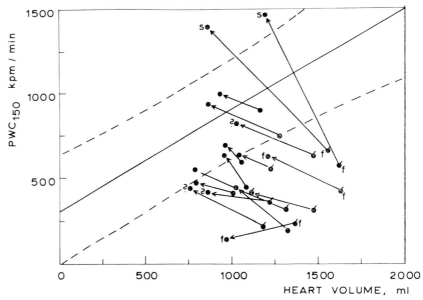

FIGURE 17-4. Preoperative and postoperative relationships in patients with
atrial septal defect and a preoperative heart volume of over 1000 ml. Fifty
percent of the cases still have a low PWC_{150} in relation to heart volume
after a follow-up of 2½ years. f: atrial fibrillation. s: sinus rhythm. Symbols
with tail: pulmonary hypertension. ?: pulmonary arterial pressure not
known.

and allied parameters in arterial blood and the level of ventilation (13, 47), although an increase in the oxygen content of inspired air prolongs the duration of tolerable exercise (5). Even the data on the occurrence of excess ventilation in patients with left-to-right shunts are at variance (35, 41, 47). In cases where pulmonary venous hypertension is evoked by exercise, hyperventilation has occurred, as in patients with mitral stenosis (14).

The patients affected with the *obstructive* variety of congenital heart disease are mainly those with pulmonary stenosis (PS), coarctation of the aorta (CoA), and aortic stenosis (AS). Children with PS have reduced exercise performance (8, 15). Measurements of right ventricular pressures indicate that the peak pressure determines the exercise limit (22). In adults with PS the exercise performance is related to the severity of the stenosis assessed on the basis of either the peak right ventricular pressure (20) or the valve area (23). Only the severe cases (peak pressure >100 mm Hg or valve area <0.33 cm^2 m^2 BSA) have a depressed cardiac output-oxygen consumption relation during exercise and an impaired exercise performance. Postoperative studies show that the cardiac output-oxygen consumption relation is still abnormal during exercise; a large oxygen extraction capacity of the periphery has been suggested as the adaptative mechanism (24). In patients with PS, exercise causes an excessive ventilation. This response is not consequent on changes in blood chemistry (12) and is without valid explanation.

About 80 percent of children with CoA have reduced exercise performance (15), but adults with this lesion frequently show no impairment, their exercise performance being in proper relation to both body weight and heart volume and sometimes compatible with top-class athletic achievements (33). This age-dependent difference may arise from a quantitatively dissimilar formation of collateral vessels. In adults, contrary to expectations, true claudication is rarely seen (9). The central circulation in CoA is characterized by a high resting cardiac output and a normal response to exercise, frequently by elevated pulmonary capillary venous pressures upon exertion and often by an excessive rise of brachial arterial pressure on effort (46). After early infancy, left ventricular failure is rarely encountered up to the age of thirty years unless the disease is complicated by AS; the latter is the most frequent associated lesion and is due to congenital biscuspid valves.

The majority of children with AS are subjectively asymptomatic (27) although the systolic pressures in the left ventricle can be very high during exercise (22). Objective testing shows that about 60 percent of these children have exercise impairment (15). The exercise performance of adults with AS is similar to that in the acquired form of the disease considered below.

Acquired Valvular Disease

Acquired pulmonary stenosis may not be as rare as earlier assumed (39), but obstruction or regurgitation at aortic (AS, AI) and mitral orifices (MS, MI), alone or in combination, are the lesions most often encountered. In AS the exercise impairment is caused not only by dyspnea and cardiac pain but also by syncope, dizziness, general weakness, and leg exhaustion which can be poorly quantitated in physiological terms. The symptoms are often unpredictable and not always reproducible in repeated tests. The gradient across the valve remains more or less fixed from rest to exercise (38). In some patients the aortic pressure behaves "paradoxically," failing to show the normal increment with exercise. An effective stroke volume is maintained through high peak systolic and end-diastolic pressures in the left ventricle. Aging changes the relation of peak systolic to end-diastolic pressure and decreases the stroke volume-heart volume ratio (25). Dyspnea is associated with pulmonary venous hypertension due to the high end-diastolic pressures in the left ventricle (12). The same applies to AI.

MS is probably the most "malignant" valvular heart disease, leading to marked exercise impairment. Some patients complain of a cardiac pain that can be indistinguishable from angina pectoris. The mechanism is not established, but the pain is probably of extracardiac origin, since the coronary arteries appear normal in the majority of cases (3).

Dyspnea is the major factor reducing exercise performance.

If the total pressure gradient between the pulmonary artery and the left ventricle is subdivided, then the gradient across the pulmonary vasculature is more significantly related to impairment than the gradient across the mitral valve (11). This reflects the importance of pulmonary vascular disease arising from pulmonary venous hypertension and resulting in low diffusion capacity, ventilation-perfusion imbalance, and reduced lung compliance and conductance (49). Although, in general, patients with mitral valve disease suffer from exercise impairment, they range widely in their exercise performance. In MI, performance is influenced by the amount of regurgitant flow. In pure MS, myocardial factors and atrial fibrillation play a role. It has been suggested that one of the early adaptative mechanisms is a reduction of cardiac output, and that initially this is not mediated through an elevated pulmonary vascular resistance (21). This would signify that there is an adaptative increase in the oxygen extraction capacity of the periphery similar to that suggested for patients with pulmonary stenosis (24). The unresponsiveness of cardiac output to successful valvulotomy (16) is in accord with this reasoning.

Coronary Artery Disease

Four main symptoms limit exercise in patients with coronary heart disease: a) angina pectoris, b) dyspnea associated with angina or ischemic ECG changes, c) dyspnea without evidence of ischemia, and d) a host of arrhythmias.

While the mechanism of ischemic pain is still open to discussion, progress has been made in the clarification of various factors determining coronary flow and myocardial oxygen consumption (Table 17-II). Attempts to apply to man knowledge

TABLE 17-II
FACTORS DETERMINING CORONARY FLOW

O_2 Demand	O_2 Supply
Heart rate	Aortic pressure
Ventricular systolic pressure and its time integral	Coronary vessel resistance
	Collateral pathways
Ventricular volume	O_2 in arterial blood
Fiber shortening velocity	Neurohumoral factors
Neurohumoral factors	

obtained from animal experiments have been quite successful. A rate-pressure product, based on heart rate, aortic pressure, and ejection time has reproducibly and accurately demonstrated the exercise limit for angina in a given patient (36). A definite threshold for angina can also be demonstrated by atrial pacing (42). Reproducible thresholds are found in the majority of patients, but some cases behave unpredictably. Apparently the size of the left ventricular cavity (influencing the tension in the wall), myocardial contractility, and neurovegetative equilibrium are the responsible factors. The frequently occurring asynchrony of contraction (18) and maldistribution of flow within the myocardium are additional factors that can change the oxygen demand/supply ratio in a manner which cannot be calculated from hemodynamic indices.

In addition to anginal pain, patients often feel dyspnea on exertion, and this may be the only symptom despite clear ECG evidence of ischemia. Elevated pulmonary capillary venous pressures are often recorded during angina induced by exercise (30). However, the prevailing concept that every attack of angina is associated with left ventricular failure might not be correct. During muscular exercise the left ventricle is facing an enhanced inflow, and in coronary artery disease the compliance of the ventricular wall is changed because of fibrosis and scarring. The elevated end-diastolic pressures are not found as a rule when angina is induced by atrial pacing (32, 42), and their occurrence in exercise need not denote failure but simply stiffness of the wall. Both alternatives, however, lead to elevated pressures in the pulmonary veins.

Dyspnea without signs of ischemia is found in patients with clinically established heart failure, high left ventricular end-diastolic pressures upon exertion, and no detectable ischemic area. The slope of the relation between cardiac output and oxygen consumption during exercise is similar to that in healthy subjects, but the magnitude of maximum flow is reduced (28). In addition to the effect of reduced contractile muscle mass, a second cause of the restricted forward flow can be the papillary muscle dysfunction that frequently complicates coronary artery disease (17).

Many arrhythmias can compromise exercise. Among these, multiple ventricular extrasystoles can cause unpleasant sensations that limit exercise in sensitive patients. Bradyarrhythimas limit exercise, mainly because the stroke output is reduced. The exercise heart rate must exceed 80 beats per minute for the maximal oxygen uptake to be reached (43).

Conclusions

A number of circulatory and ventilatory factors can be linked to the exercise limitation of cardiac patients in the main diagnostic groups. The most understandable and clear cut is angina pectoris. Data relating to dyspnea are more controversial and better elucidated in diseases affecting the left heart than in diseases with pulmonary vascular involvement, whether the latter has been present since birth or is secondary to excessive flow. Additional factors complicating the analysis are obesity (2), atrial fibrillation (19), and systemic arterial hypertension (50).

In mitral stenosis the pressure gradient across the pulmonary vascular bed is as well related to excess ventilation (29) as it is to exercise impairment (11). A similar gradient exists in pulmonary vascular diseases from other causes, and it is tempting to suggest that stimulation of pulmonary stretch receptors is the common trigger for the ventilatory drive. However, since excess ventilation also occurs in patients with pulmonary stenosis, this cannot be the only mechanism.

The oxygen cost of ventilation is relatively small at low ventilatory rates but increases disproportionately at high rates (5) and may thus become the crucial point breaking the exercise. Ventilatory drive, however, is not synonymous with dyspnea; the latter is a subjective sensation and can be felt at very different ventilatory rates. Research to unravel this problem must include the study of psychological factors and the behavior of the higher integrating centers in addition to the physiological variables briefly portrayed in this article.

References

1. ADAMS, F.H., and DUFFIE, E.R., JR.: Physical working capacity in children with heart disease. *Lancet, 81*:493-496, 1961.

2. ALEXANDER, J.K.: Obesity and cardiac performance. *Amer J Cardiol, 14*:860-865, 1964.

3. BJÖRK, L., and CULLHED, I.: Coronary arteriography in valvular heart disease. *Acta Med Scand, 185*:531-534, 1969.

4. Committee on Medical Rating of Physical Impairment. Guides to the evaluation of permanent impairment. The cardiovascular system. *JAMA, 172*:1049-1060, 1964.

5. COTES, J.E.: Exercise limitation in health and disease. *Brit Med Bull, 19*:31-35, 1963.

6. DAVIES, H., and GAZETOPOULOS, N.: Haemodynamic changes on exercise in patients with left-to-right shunts. *Brit Heart J, 28*:579-589, 1966.

7. DAVIES, H., and GAZETOPOULOS, N.: Lung function in patients with left-to-right shunts. *Brit Heart J, 29*:317-326, 1967.

8. DUFFIE, E.R., and ADAMS, F.H.: The use of the working capacity test in the evaluation of children with congenital heart disease. *Pediatrics, 32*:757-768, 1963.

9. FRICK, M.H., and HALONEN, P.I.: Coarctation of the aorta. A study based on 110 patients. *Ann Med Intern Fenn, 49*:137-150, 1960.

10. FRICK, M.H., PUNSAR, S., and SOMER, T.: The spectrum of cardiac capacity in patients with nonobstructive congenital heart disease. *Amer J Cardiol, 17*:20-26, 1966.

11. FRICK, M.H.: Cardiac capacity in mitral valve disease. In Denolin, H., König, K., Messin, R., and Degré, S. (Eds.): *Ergometry in Cardiology*. Mannheim, Boehringer, 1968, pp.109-115.

12. GAZETOPOULOS, N., DAVIES, H., and DEUCHAR, D.: Ventilation in relation to arterial and venous blood chemistry in heart disease. *Brit Heart J, 28*:16-31, 1966.

13. GAZETOPOULOS, N., and DAVIES, H.: Ventilatory response to exercise in patients with left-to-right shunts. *Brit Heart J, 28*:590-598, 1966.

14. GAZETOPOULOS, N., DAVIES, H., OLIVER, C., and DEUCHAR, D.: Ventilation and haemodynamics in heart disease. *Brit Heart J, 28*:1-15, 1966.

15. GOLDBERG, S.J., MENDES, F., and HURWITZ, R.: Maximal exercise capability of children as a function of specific cardiac defects. *Amer J Cardiol, 23*:349-353, 1969.

16. GRANATH, A.: Mitral valvulotomy. A clinical and haemodynamic

pre- and postoperative study. *Acta Med Scand (Suppl. 433)*, 1965.

17. HEIKKILÄ, J.: Mitral incompetence as a complication of acute myocardial infarction. *Acta Med Scand (Suppl. 475)*, 1968.

18. HERMAN, M.V., HEINLE, R.A., KLEIN, M.D., and GORLIN, R.: Localized disorders in myocardial contraction. Asynergy and its role in congestive heart failure. *New Eng J Med*, 277:222-232, 1967.

19. HORNSTEN, T.R., and BRUCE, R.A.: Effects of atrial fibrillation on exercise performance in patients with cardiac disease. *Circulation*, 37:543-548, 1968.

20. HOWITT, G.: Haemodynamic effects of exercise in pulmonary stenosis. *Brit Heart J*, 28:152-160, 1966.

21. HUGENHOLZ, P.G., RYAN, T.J., STEIN, S.W., and ABELMAN, W.H.: The spectrum of pure mitral stenosis. Hemodynamic studies in relation to clinical disability. *Amer J Cardiol*, 10:773-784, 1962.

22. HUGENHOLZ, P.G., and NADAS, A.S.: Exercise studies in patients with congenital heart disease. *Pediatrics*, 32:769-775, 1963.

23. IKKOS, D., JONSSON, B., and LINDERHOLM, H.: Effect of exercise in pulmonary stenosis with intact ventricular septum. *Brit Heart J*, 28:316-330, 1966.

24. JONSSON, B., and LEE, S.J.K.: Haemodynamic effects of exercise in isolated pulmonary stenosis before and after surgery. *Brit Heart J*, 30:60-66, 1968.

25. JONSSON, B.: Effect of exercise in aortic stenosis before and after surgery. In: Symposium on Rehabilitation of Noncoronary Heart Disease. Höhenried, W. Germany, 1969, In press.

26. KÖNIG, K.: Bewegungstherapie zur Rehabilitation nach Herzoperationen. *München Med Wschr*, 110:1832-1845, 1968.

27. LANDTMAN, B., and WALLGREN, E.I.: Congenital aortic stenosis in children. *Ann Paediat Fenn*, 2:259-271, 1956.

28. MALMBORG, R.O.: A clinical and hemodynamic analysis of factors limiting cardiac performance in patients with coronary heart disease. *Acta Med Scand (Suppl. 426)*, 1965.

29. McGREGOR, M.: A short comment. In: International Symposium on Physical Activity and Cardiovascular Health. *Canad Med Assoc J*, 96:757, 1967.

30. MÜLLER, O., and RØRVIK, K.: Haemodynamic consequences of coronary heart disease with observations during anginal pain

and on the effect of nitroglycerin. *Brit Heart J, 20*:302-310, 1958.

31. New York Heart Association, the Criteria Committee: *Diseases of the Heart and Blood Vessels. Nomenclature and Criteria for Diagnosis.* 6th Ed. Boston, Little Brown & Co., 1964.

32. O'Brien, K.P., Higgs, L.W., Glancy, L., and Epstein, S.E.: Hemodynamic accompaniments of angina: A comparison during angina induced by exercise and by atrial pacing. *Circulation, 39*:735-743, 1969.

33. Punsar, S., and Laustela, E.: Kasuistischer Bericht über ungewöhnliche physische Leistungsfähigkeit trotz Aortenkoarktation. *Zschr Kreislaufforsch, 46*:913-917, 1957.

34. Reindell, H., König, K., and Roskamm, H.: *Funktionsdiagnostik des gesunden und kranken Herzens.* Stuttgart, Georg Thieme, 1967.

35. Ressl, J., Kubis, M., Lukl, P., Vykydal, J., and Weinberg, J.: Resting hyperventilation in adults with atrial septal defect. *Brit Heart J, 31*:118-121, 1969.

36. Robinson, B.F.: Relation of heart rate and systolic blood pressure to the onset of pain in angina pectoris. *Circulation, 35*:1073-1083, 1967.

37. Sandøe, E.: *Congenital Isolated Ventricular Septal Defect.* Copenhagen, Munksgaard, 1963.

38. Schmutzler, H.: Der Wert der Arbeitsbelastung für die Funktionsdiagnostik erworbener Herzfehler. *Anglo German Med Rev, 4*:209-223, 1967.

39. Seymour, J., Emanuel, R., and Pattinson, N.: Acquired pulmonary stenosis. *Brit Heart J, 30*:776-785, 1968.

40. Siltanen, P.: Atrial septal defect of secundum type in adults. *Acta Med Scand (Suppl. 497),* 1968.

41. Sloman, G., and Gandevia, B.: Ventilatory capacity and exercise ventilation in congenital and acquired cardiac disease. *Brit Heart J, 26*:121-128, 1964.

42. Sowton, E., Balcon, R., Cross, D., and Frick, M.H.: Measurement of the angina threshold using atrial pacing. *Cardiovasc Res, 1*:301-307, 1967.

43. Sowton, E.: The relationship between maximal oxygen uptake and heart rate in patients treated with artificial pacemakers. *Cardiologia, 50*:15-22, 1967.

44. Stephens, N.L., Shafter, H.A., and Bliss, H.A.: Hemodynamic

and ventilatory effects of exercise in the upright position in patients with left-to-right shunts. *Circulation, 24*:99-106, 1964.

45. SWAN, H.J.C., MARSHALL, H.W., and WOOD, E.H.: The effect of exercise in the supine position on pulmonary vascular dynamics in patients with left-to-right shunts. *J Clin Invest, 37*:202-213, 1958.

46. TAYLOR, S.H., and DONALD, K.W.: Circulatory studies at rest and during exercise in coarctation of the aorta before and after operation. *Brit Heart J, 22*:117-139, 1960.

47. WESSEL, H.U., KEZDI, P., and CUGELL, D.W.: Respiratory and cardiovascular function in patients with severe pulmonary hypertension. *Circulation, 24*:825-832, 1964.

48. WILHELMSEN, L.: Pulmonary mechanics and pulmonary circulation in heart disease. *In* Müller, C. (Ed.): *Conference on Pulmonary Circulation.* Oslo, Universitetsforlaget, 1965, pp.169-179.

49. WILHELMSEN, L.: Lung mechanics in rheumatic valvular disease. *Acta Med Scand (Suppl. 489)*, 1968.

50. WONG, H.O., KASSER, I.S., and BRUCE, R.A.: Impaired maximal exercise performance with hypertensive cardiovascular disease. *Circulation, 39*:633-638, 1969.

Chapter 18

MAXIMUM EXERCISE AT MEDIUM ALTITUDE

JOHN A. FAULKNER

Pioneer work on the respiratory and cardiovascular response to exercise at altitude was carried out by Zuntz and his students in Germany (50), by Douglas and Haldane on Pikes Peak, Colorado (16), by the personnel of the Harvard Fatigue Laboratory at Leadville and Mt. Evans, Colorado (13, 20), and in Chile (12). Until 1964 the emphasis was on the physiological responses of man to altitudes of at least 3000 m; studies were made at rest or during submaximum exercise (14, 37, 49) with application to mining, military operations, mountaineering, aviation, and space science.*

The assignment of the 1968 Olympic Games to Mexico City (2300 m) shifted the interest of scientists to maximum exercise at medium altitude. The proceedings of two international symposia, held in 1966 at Albuquerque, New Mexico (24) and Milan, Italy (33), have summarized the findings of these investigations. At the time of these symposia, predictions were made as to what would happen in Mexico City, and athletes were advised as to how they should train for maximum performance at medium altitude. The effects of a 2300 m altitude on performance and on the physiological response to maximum exercise may now be reevaluated in terms of the Olympic results. Craig (12) has made an excellent postmortem evaluation of performances in track,

---

*For a more complete review of the early literature, see Balke (3), Dill (12), and Dill et al. (14, p.861).

Note: The author wishes to thank Dr. Bruno Balke and Dr. Elsworth R. Buskirk, both for stimulating his initial interest in physiological research at altitude and also for their critical evaluation of this manuscript.

These studies were carried out with support from Contracts DA-49-193-MD-2709 and DA-79-193-MD-2446 and National Institutes of Health Research Grant GM-12554.

field, and swimming events at Mexico City relative to the existing world records and of the accuracy with which physiologists predicted the outcome. Because a more precise estimate of the effect of altitude on maximum performance and a more complete interpretation of the physiological mechanisms involved can be made for running than for swimming or field events, the present discussion will be limited to data on running.

Running Performance

Olympic records in running normally average about 1 percent slower than the existing world record at all distances (Fig. 18-1). The running record for the 1968 Olympics were at considerable variance with the usual pattern (11). World records were equalled or bettered in events up to 800 m. In both the 200 m and

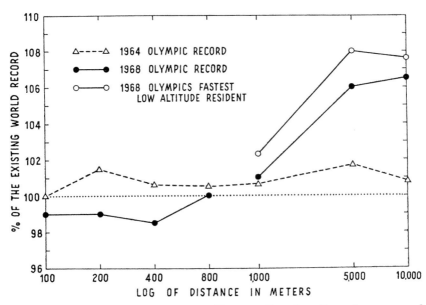

FIGURE 18-1. The 1964 and 1968 Olympic Running Records compared to the existing World Records at the time of the Olympics. The existing World Record is represented as 100 percent. Since the existing world record was divided into the Olympic Record × 100, a percentage greater than 100 represents a slower time.

400 m sprints all three medal winners equalled or bettered the world record. In the 1500 m race surprisingly a new Olympic record was set, and the time was only 1 percent slower than the world record. However, in the 5000 m and 10,000 m runs Olympic records were not set, and the winning times were 6 percent slower than the world marks. The predicted decrements in performance at 2300 m relative to performance at low altitude were in remarkably good agreement with the actual results of the Olympic Games (11). The average error was a 1 percent over-estimation of the decrement in performance at altitude.

Physiological Basis of Maximum Performance

Since the immediate event in the contraction of skeletal muscle is the hydrolysis of ATP (36), a reduced oxygen tension does not directly affect the conversion of chemical energy to mechanical work. However, the reduced oxygen tension does affect the ability of specific types of skeletal muscle cells to rephosphorylate ATP.

On the basis of structural and functional characteristics, skeletal muscle cells may be classified as red, intermediate, or white (Table 18-I). Although most mammalian muscles are com-posed of mixed proportions of all three fiber types, a motor unit

TABLE 18-I

THE CHARACTERISTICS THAT TEND TO BE ASSOCIATED WITH
EACH OTHER IN THE SKELETAL MUSCLE CELLS OF
A GIVEN MOTOR UNIT

Characteristic	*Muscle*	
Color	Red	White
Axon diameter	Small	Large
Cells per motor unit	Few	Many
Recruitment	Often	Seldom
Contraction time	Slow	Fast
Tension per fiber	Low	High
Myoglobin concentration	High	Low
Blood flow	High	Low
Mitochondrial density	High	Low
Resting metabolism	High	Low
Oxidative phosphorylation	High	Low
Glycolytic energy	Low	High
Natural actomyosin ATPase activity	Low	High
Fatiguability	Slow	Fast

is a homogeneous collection of a single fiber type (27). Because the motor units composed of white fibers are innervated by large diameter neurons with a high threshold for stimulation, they are recruited infrequently for rapid powerful contractions (27). If the recruitment of white fibers is sustained, they fatigue very rapidly (19). The motor units composed of red fibers are innervated by small diameter neurons that have a low threshold for stimulation (27). Therefore, the red fibers are recruited frequently. The red fibers are suited structurally and functionally to long sustained contractions of low tension and they fatigue very slowly (19).

The recruitment of red fiber and white fiber motor units during running may be described on the basis of Henneman and Olson's data (27). During running at any speed red fiber motor units are recruited continuously. At the running velocity used in distance events, there is little or no recruitment of white fiber motor units. When runs are made at an intermediate tempo, white fibers are recruited infrequently, so that recovery is possible between contractions. Consequently, total body metabolism is mainly aerobic. In sprint running and during the faster phases of middle distance events, the white fiber motor units are recruited more and more frequently. If the rest periods between contractions are too short, recovery is not completed and fatigue occurs. Fatigue occurs rapidly in the sprint events because the white fibers can hydrolyze ATP faster than it can be synthesized and creatine phosphate concentration decreases (7). In middle distance events the frequent recruitment of white fiber motor units and the dependence of white fibers on glycolysis for the phosphorylation of ATP (42) result in high blood lactate concentrations (34).

The performance of white fiber motor units is not affected by the decreased oxygen tension at altitude, since resynthesis of ATP in these fibers is by anaerobic processes even at sea level. When running for five minutes or longer at the maximum possible speed, even at low altitudes the maximum cardiac output and maximum arteriovenous oxygen difference are reached, and oxygen transport limits the metabolism of skeletal muscle cells (21). Aerobic metabolism must, therefore, be reduced by any decrease in atmospheric oxygen tension. Since red fiber motor units resynthesize ATP by oxidative phosphorylation, a decrease in atmospheric and thus tissue oxygen tension affects red fiber metabolism more severely than white fiber metabolism. However, the white fibers also are affected and probably require a longer recovery period between twitches at medium altitude than at low altitude; in consequence, the recruitment of white fiber motor units cannot be cycled as rapidly in endurance events at medium altitude as in endurance events at low altitude.

Oxygen Debt

Altitude does not appear to affect either the energy stores in skeletal muscle cells or the ability of skeletal muscle cells to generate energy anaerobically. The oxygen debt following maximum exercise is not diminished from low altitude control values, either at medium (5) or at high altitude (8). Blood lactate concentrations appear to be about the same during and after maximum exercise regardless of the altitude, at least up to 4000 m (28); however, there are conflicting data (13, 20) possibly because of individual variability and/or the type of test used. Since brief, powerful contractions of the white fibers are primarily dependent on stored energy and/or the regeneration of energy by anaerobic processes, the maximum performance in sprint and middle distance events up to 800 m is not impaired by a lowered oxygen tension. In sprint running, performance is actually enhanced because of the diminished air resistance (31).

Maximum Oxygen Uptake

Maximum oxygen uptake decreases linearly with decreases in ambient oxygen tension (8, 9, 13, 23, 33, 38). If the maximum oxygen uptake at low altitude is expressed as 100 percent, the percentage decrease in maximum oxygen uptake is approximately four percent for each 5 mm Hg decrease in oxygen tension or a 1 percent decrease for each 100 m increase in altitude (Fig. 18.2). The individual variability, which is great at all altitudes, increases with increasing altitude (31). The variability has been attributed to differences in age (8), physical fitness (25, 43), resident altitude before exposure to the test altitude (23), and the type of test during which maximum oxygen uptake was measured (23).

Dill (13) has described four degrees of acclimatization which are obtained by exposure to a given altitude for thirty minutes, a few weeks, a few months, and a lifetime. The data presented in Figure 18-2 were obtained on highly trained, low altitude residents during the first week at altitude and after two to seven weeks at altitude. They are roughly comparable to Dill's second and third degrees of acclimatization. It is interesting that during the first minutes of exposure, impairment of maximum oxygen uptake is not as great as during the first week of exposure (15). The degree of impairment during the first thirty minutes is approximately equal to that of the acclimatized runners in Figure 18-2.

The maximum oxygen uptake reflects the capacity for oxidative phosphorylation, a process which occurs predominantly in red fibers (42). Since at low altitude oxygen is the reactant that limits maximum performance in endurance running, cycling,

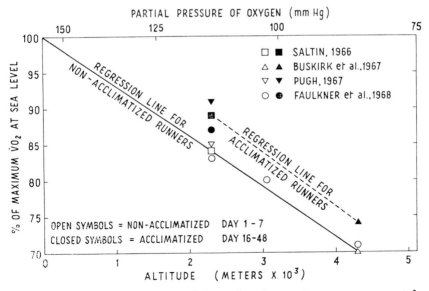

FIGURE 18-2. The percentage of low altitude maximum oxygen uptake observed at 2300 m, 3100 m, and 4300 m.

swimming, or any muscular activity that involves large masses of red fibers, the decrease in oxygen tension with increasing altitude would be expected to cause further decreases in maximum oxygen uptake.

Hemoconcentration occurs during the first few days at altitude because of a decrease in the plasma volume (8, 41). After seven days at 2300 m the plasma volume decreased 8 percent (E. R. Buskirk, personal communication), the hematocrit increased 4 percent, and the hemoglobin concentration increased 10 percent (22). The same period of exposure to 4300 m resulted in a 16 percent decrease of plasma volume, a 6 percent increase of hematocrit, and a 20 percent increase of hemoglobin concentration (8). The hemoconcentration results in a return of the oxygen content of arterial blood to its normal low altitude value (Table 18-II).

When maximum work is performed under conditions which simulate an altitude of 4000 m (45), no change of plasma volume occurs, and in maximum work oxygen carriage by unit volume of blood is decreased 25 percent. Under these conditions, heart rate, stroke volume, and cardiac output are the same as at sea level. The decrease of maximum oxygen uptake at simulated altitude is due completely to the decrease in the arteriovenous oxygen difference.

After early acclimatization to 4000 m, when the plasma volume is decreased and the oxygen content of unit volume of arterial blood at rest is the same as at sea level, a 30 percent decrease of maximum oxygen uptake (8, 23, 44) is seen as under conditions of simulated altitude. However, the decrease in maximum oxygen uptake after early acclimatization is due in part to a 20 percent decrease of cardiac output, and the arteriovenous oxygen difference is decreased by no more than 15 percent (44). A diminished stroke volume, possibly resulting from the decrease in plasma volume or the increased viscosity of the blood, is the major cause of the decreased cardiac output (44). If the cardiac output in maximum exercise at 2300 m was diminished in proportion to the decrease in plasma volume, the 14 percent decrease in maximum oxygen uptake seen at this altitude would be attributable to a 10 percent decrease in cardiac output and a 3 percent decrease in arteriovenous oxygen difference.

The decrease of arteriovenous oxygen difference during maximum work at altitude results from a greater decrease in arterial oxygen tension (44) than usually occurs during maximum work at low altitude and an increase in the mixed venous oxygen content. The latter may reflect that a smaller portion of the mixed venous blood is coming from skeletal muscle beds with an extremely low oxygen content, and relatively more is coming from other tissues.

Cellular Adaptation

Oxygen delivery and oxygen utilization under hypoxic conditions are modified by changes at the cellular level. Valdivia (47) has reported that the capillary density in the skeletal muscle of guinea pigs born and raised at high altitude is significantly greater than that of controls born and raised at low altitude. A 16 percent increase in the myoglobin concentration of human skeletal muscle (40) and an increase of 15 percent in the heart, 22 percent in the diaphragm, and 25 percent in the gastrocnemius of rats (1) would also facilitate oxygen transport and oxygen storage (26). At altitude an increase of the myoglobin concentration in white fibers might well be critical for the rapid restoration of high energy phosphate concentrations following contraction.

Reynafarje (40) has reported enhanced activity of the NADH-oxidase, TPNH-cytochrome c reductase, and transhydrogenase enzyme systems, and Mager *et al.* (32) have observed a change in the LDH isozyme concentrations with a decrease in the heart subunit to the muscle subunit ratio. The decrease in this ratio indicates a relative shift from aerobic to anaerobic metabolism. An increased capacity for glycolysis and an increased ATPase activity in heart, diaphragm, and some skeletal muscles are found in guinea pigs raised or moved to high altitude when such animals are compared to low altitude controls; this also suggests a cellular adaptation to environmental hypoxia (46).

The oxygen dissociation curve of the high altitude natives is shifted to the right relative to that of low altitude natives; this was first reported by Aste-Salazar and Hurtado in 1944 (3) and was confirmed by Hurtado in 1966 (29). It indicates a decrease affinity of hemoglobin for oxygen. Because the curve is displaced, the change in oxygen tension between arterial and venous blood occurs on its steeper part. Therefore, for a given decrease of oxygen tension, more oxygen is released to the tissues, while for a constant tissue oxygen uptake the oxygen tension gradient between arterial and venous blood is less (29). Benesch and Benesch (6) and Chanutin and Curnish (10) have demonstrated that the affinity of hemoglobin for oxygen is inversely related to the 2,3-diphosphoglycerate (DPG) concentration. The DPG concentration is higher in the red blood cells of subjects who move to high altitude than in control values obtained at low altitude (30); it is also higher in high altitude natives than in low altitude natives (17). Since an increase in DPG has been observed after sixty minutes of strenuous exercise at low altitude (18), the interactions among DPG, hemoglobin, and oxygen tension have the potential to affect maximum performance at altitude (Table 18-II).

Training at Medium Altitude

There has been considerable controversy concerning the effect of training at altitude on the maximum oxygen uptake, both at altitude and on subsequent return to sea level (4, 5, 8, 22, 23, 25, 38, 43). However, every investigation of runners native to low altitude who trained at medium or high altitude reports some improvement in maximum oxygen uptake. The average improvement for world class runners is 5 percent (Fig. 18-2); this is not statistically significant because of the great individual variability. The initial decrease of maximum oxygen uptake at 2300 m (3% to 19%) and the range of subsequent improvement (0% to 20%) make a simple interpretation of the data most difficult (23, 31); one major factor appears to be the state of training in the test used to measure maximum oxygen uptake.

Recent data suggests that the training of cellular mechanisms is highly specific, supporting previous observations that maximum

TABLE 18-II

HEMOGLOBIN AND 2,3-DIPHOSPHOGLYCERATE CONCENTRATIONS AND BLOOD GASES
AT REST AND IN MAXIMUM EXERCISE AT DIFFERENT ALTITUDES

Altitude (m)	Bar. Press. (mm Hg)	State	Hb	DPG (μmols/gm Hb)	$Pa,_{O_2}$ (mm Hg)	Saturation (%)	$Ca,_{O_2}$ (ml/liter)
0	740	Rest	15.1	12.02	105	97	196
		Exercise	—	—	98	96	194
2300	580	Rest	16.6	—	75	93	206
		Exercise	—	—	70	87	193
3100	520	Rest	17.2	12.79	67	90	207
		Exercise	—	—	57	85	196
4300	420	Rest	18.2	—	52	84	205
		Exercise	—	—	45	70	171

Note: Portions of this table were obtained from References 17, 23, 25, 38 and 41.

oxygen uptake may vary greatly when measured during different activities such as running, bicycling, and swimming (21). The maximum oxygen uptake of runners bicycling (5, 8, 22, 38, and 43) might be significantly less than their maximum oxygen uptake running. Under these circumstances training data are questionable, since runners may increase their maximum oxygen uptake during repeated tests on a bicycle ergometer and yet show no change in their maximum oxygen uptake running. This problem would not arise if the precaution were observed of training runners on the bicycle ergometer before taking them to altitude.

College runners and swimmers may not increase their maximum oxygen uptake during four years of strenuous training at sea level even though significant improvements of performance occur (unpublished data). Apparently, there is a maximum aerobic capacity for a given individual, and once that capacity has been attained, no further increase will occur. Probably subjects who improved their aerobic capacity at altitude had not reached their potential and those who did not show any change were already maximally trained. Changes in maximum oxygen uptake on return to low altitude merely reflect the changes that occurred at altitude.

Regardless of changes in maximum oxygen uptake, runners learn to run at a better pace through training at a given altitude. At low altitudes runners have extremely uniform lap times in one-, two-, and three-mile runs (23). During the first time trials at medium altitudes, lap times are quite variable. Eleven of fourteen college runners ran their best time trial performances over one- to three-mile distances between the twenty-fifth and fortieth day at 2300 m (23). However, when the performance at altitude was improved by better pacing, performance on return to sea level was unchanged.

Saltin (43) has observed that the more highly trained subjects may have a greater percentage decrement in maximum oxygen uptake at altitude than less well trained subjects. Grover *et al.* (25) concluded that their data on high school runners from Leadville, Colorado (3100 m) supported this contention because the decrease in maximum oxygen uptake of high school runners was 25 percent, compared to predictions of 17 percent by Pugh *et al.* (38) and 23 percent by Margaria and Cerretelli (35). The greater than expected decrease in the data of Grover *et al.* is more likely due to their use of a treadmill test rather than the bicycle ergometer tests used by the other two groups (23). When the percentage decrement of maximum oxygen uptake reported in the various altitude studies (2300-4300 m) is plotted against the maximum oxygen uptake at sea level, there is no obvious relationship.

Chronic Adaptation to Altitude

Although hemoconcentration is attained through a decreased plasma volume in the first few days of acclimatization to altitude, the red cell mass does not begin to increase for several months (41). Burskirk *et al.* (8) did not observe any change in red cell mass after forty-eight days of exposure to 4000 m. After four months the plasma volume was not significantly different from normal low altitude values. However, eight months of acclimatization to high altitude result in significant increases in red cell mass and plasma volume. Because of these increases the oxygen carrying capacity of the blood and the total blood volume are equivalent to sea level values (41). The increase in total blood volume relative to the early stages of acclimatization may contribute to an increased cardiac output in maximum work through an increase in the mean circulatory filling pressure. Such a mechanism might explain why the percentage decrement of maximum oxygen uptake is smaller after eight or more months of residence at high altitude than during the first weeks or months at high altitude.

Because most highly trained runners reside at low altitude, it has been difficult to make comparisons with high altitude runners (25). Chronic adaptation to high altitude does not appear to enhance endurance performance at low altitude. However, the results of the distance events in the 1968 Olympic Games clearly demonstrated that in endurance competitions at medium altitudes world class athletes who have spent a lifetime at medium or high altitude have a physiological advantage over men who reside at low altitude. During maximum performance at medium altitude the permanent high altitude resident has a higher oxygen carrying capacity, a higher cardiac output, a higher arteriovenous oxygen difference, and a higher maximum oxygen uptake than a low altitude resident of comparable training. Intermittent training sessions at medium altitude improve the endurance performance of highly trained, low altitude residents primarily through improved pacing. In events of more than three minutes duration (1500 m and longer), both low and high altitude residents will run faster times at low altitude than at high altitude.

References

1. ANTHONY, A., ACKERMAN, E., and STROTHER, G.: Effects of altitude acclimatization on rat myoglobin. Changes in myoglobin content of skeletal and cardiac muscle. *Amer J Physiol, 196(3):* 512-516, 1959.

2. ASTE-SALAZAR, H., and HURTADO, A.: The affinity of hemoglobin for oxygen at sea level and at high altitudes. *Amer J Physiol, 142:*733-743, 1944.

3. BALKE, B.: Cardiac performance in relation to altitude. *Amer J Cardiol, 14:*796-810, 1964.

4. BALKE, B., DANIELS, J.T., and FAULKNER, J.A.: Training for maximum performance at altitude. In Margaria, R. (Ed.): *Exercise at Altitude.* New York, Exerpta Medica Foundation, 1967, pp.179-186.

5. BALKE, B., NAGLE, F.J., and DANIELS, J.T.: Altitude and maximum performance in work and sports activity. *JAMA, 194:*646-649, 1965.

6. BENESCH, R., and BENESCH, R.E.: The effect of organic phosphates from the human erythrocyte on the allosteric properties of hemoglobin. *Biochem Biophys Res Commun, 26(2):*162-167, 1967.

7. BERGSTROM, J.: Local changes of ATP and phosphorylcreatine in human muscle tissue in connection with exercise. In Chapman, C.B. (Ed.): *Physiology of Muscular Exercise.* Amer. Heart Assoc. Monograph No. 15, 1967, pp.91-96.

8. BUSKIRK, E.R., KOLLIAS, J., PICON-REATEGUI, E., AKERS, R.F., PROKOP, E.K., and BAKER, P.: Physiology and performance of track athletes at various altitudes in the United States and

Peru. In Goddard, R.F. (Ed.): *International Symposium on Effects of Altitude on Physical Performance.* Chicago Athletic Institute, 1966.

9. CERRETELLI, P., and MARGARIA, R.: Maximum oxygen consumption at altitude. *Int Z Angew Physiol, 18*:460-464, 1961.

10. CHANUTIN, A., and CURNISH, R.R.: Effect of organic and inorganic phosphates on the oxygen equilibrium of human erythrocytes. *Arch Biochem Biophys, 121*:96-102, 1967.

11. CRAIG, A.B., JR.: Olympics 1968: A post-mortem. *Med Sci in Sports,* In press.

12. DILL, D.B.: *Life, Heat and Altitude.* Cambridge, Harvard U.P., 1938.

13. DILL, D.B.: Physiological adjustments to altitude changes. *JAMA, 205*:747-753, 1968.

14. DILL, D.B., ADOLPH, E.F., and WILBER, C.G. (Eds.): *Handbook of Physiology: Adaptation to the Environment, Section 4.* Washington, D.C., American Physiological Society, 1964.

15. DILL, D.B.: Work capacity in acute exposures to altitude. *J Appl Physiol, 21*:1168-1176, 1966.

16. DOUGLAS, C.G., HALDANE, J.S., HENDERSON, R., and SCHNEIDER, E.C.: Physiological observations made on Pikes Peak, Colorado, with special reference to adaptation to low barometric pressures. *Phil Trans Roy Soc, 203B*:185, 1913.

17. EATON, J.W., BREWER, G.J., and GROVER, R.F.: Role of red cell 2, 3-diphosphoglycerate in the adaptation of man to altitude. *J Lab Clin Med, 73(4)*:603-609, 1969.

18. EATON, J.W., FAULKNER, J.A., and BREWER, G.J.: Increased 2,3-diphosphoglycerate (DPG) in the human red cell during muscular exercise. *Physiologist, 12*:212, 1969.

19. EBERSTEIN, A., and SANDOW, A.: Fatigue in phasic and tonic fibers of frog muscle. *Science, 125*:383, 1961.

20. EDWARDS, H.T.: Lactic acid in rest and work at high altitude. *Amer J Physiol, 116*:367, 1936.

21. FAULKNER, J.A.: Muscle Fatigue. In Briskey, E.J., Cassens, R.G., and Marsh, R.R. (Eds.): *The Physiology and Biochemistry of Muscle as a Food.* Madison, Univ. of Wisconsin Press, 1970, Vol. II.

22. FAULKNER, J.A., DANIELS, J.T., and BALKE, B.: Effects of training at moderate altitude on physical performance capacity. *J Appl Physiol, 23*:85-89, 1967.

23. FAULKNER, J.A., KOLLIAS, J., FAVOUR, C.B., BUSKIRK, E.R., and BALKE, B.: Maximum aerobic capacity and running performance at altitude. *J Appl Physiol, 24(5)*:685-691, 1968.
24. GODDARD, R.F. (Ed.): *International Symposium on Effects of Altitude on Physical Performance.* Chicago, Athletic Inst., 1966.
25. GROVER, R.F., REEVES, J.T., GROVER, E.B., and LEATHERS, J.E.: Muscular exercise in young men native to 3,100 m altitude. *J Appl Physiol, 22(3)*:555-564, 1967.
26. HEMMINGSEN, E.A.: Enhancement of oxygen transport by myoglobin. *Comp Biochem Physiol, 10*:239-244, 1963.
27. HENNEMAN, E., and OLSON, C.B.: Relations between structure and function in the design of skeletal muscles. *J Neurophysiol, 28*:581-598, 1965.
28. HERMANSEN, L., and SALTIN, B.: Blood lactate concentration during exercise at acute exposure to altitude. In Magaria, R. (Ed.): *Exercise at Altitude.* New York, Exerpta Medica Foundation, 1967, pp.48-53.
29. HURTADO, A.: Acclimatization to high altitudes. In Weihe, W.H. (Ed.): *The Physiological Effects of High Altitude.* New York, The Macmillan Company, 1964, pp.1-17.
30. LENFANT, C., TORRANCE, J., ENGLISH, E., FINCH, C.A., REYNAFARJE, C., RAMOS, J., and FAURA, J.: Effect of altitude on oxygen binding by hemoglobin and on organic phosphate levels. *J Clin Invest, 47*:2652-2656, 1968.
31. LLOYD, B.B.: Theoretical effects of altitude on the equation of motion of a runner. In Margaria, R. (Ed.): *Exercise at Altitude.* New York, Exerpta Medica Foundation, 1967, pp.65-72.
32. MAGER, M., BLATT, W.F., NATALE, P.J., and BLATTEIS, C.M.: Effect of high altitude on lactic dehydrogenase isozymes of neonatal and adult rats. *Amer J Physiol, 215(1)*:8-13, 1968.
33. MARGARIA, R. (Ed.): *Exercise at Altitude.* New York, Excerpta Medica Foundation, 1967.
34. MARGARIA, R.: Aerobic and anaerobic sources in muscular exercise. In Margaria, R. (Ed.): *Exercise at Altitude.* New York, Excerpta Medica Foundation, 1967, pp.15-22.
35. MARGARIA, R., and CERRETELLI, R.: Physiological aspects of life at extreme altitude. In Tromp, S.W. (Ed.): *Biometeorology.* London, Pergamon Press, 1962.
36. NEEDHAM, D.M.: Biochemistry of muscle action. In Bourne, G.H. (Ed.): *Structure and Function of Muscle. Vol. II. Biochemistry and Physiology.* New York, Academic Press, 1960, pp.55-104.

37. *Proceedings of the Symposium on Human Adaptability to Environments and Physical Fitness.* Madras, India, Defense Inst. of Physiology and Allied Sciences, 1966.

38. PUGH, L.G.C.E.: Athletes at altitude. *J Physiol (London), 192*: 619-646, 1967.

39. PUGH, L.G.C.E., GILL, M.B., LAHIRI, S., MILLEDGE, J.S., WARD, M.P., and WEST, J.B.: Muscular exercise at great altitudes. *J Appl Physiol, 19*:431-440, 1964.

40. REYNAFARJE, B.: Myoglobin content and enzymatic activity of muscle and altitude adaptation. *J Appl Physiol, 17(2)*:301-305, 1962.

41. REYNAFARJE, C.: Hematologic changes during rest and physical activity in man at high altitude. In Weihe, W.H. (Ed.): *The Physiological Effects of High Altitude.* New York, The Macmillan Company, 1964, pp.73-83.

42. ROMANUL, F.C.: Capillary supply and metabolism of muscle fibers. *Arch Neurol, 12*:497-509, 1965.

43. SALTIN, B.: *Mexico City Olympic stad ett hojdfysiologiskt experiment.* Stockholm, Framtiden, 1966.

44. SALTIN, B., GROVER, R.F., BLOMQVIST, C.G., HARTLEY, L.H., and JOHNSON, R.L., JR.: Maximal oxygen uptake and cardiac output after 2 weeks at 4,300 m. *J Appl Physiol, 25(4)*:400-409, 1968.

45. STENBERG, J., EKBLOM, B., and MESSIN, R.: Hemodynamic response to work at simulated altitude, 4,000 m. *J Appl Physiol, 21(5)*: 1589-1594, 1966.

46. TAPPAN, D.V., REYNAFARJE, B., POTTER, V.R., and HURTADO, A.: Alterations in enzymes and metabolites resulting from adaptation to low oxygen tensions. *Amer J Physiol, 190(1)*:93-98, 1957.

47. VALDIVIA, E.: Total capillary bed in striated muscle of guinea pigs native to the Peruvian mountains. *Amer J Physiol, 194(3)*: 585-589, 1958.

48. WELCH, H.G., and STAINSBY, W.N.: Oxygen debt in contracting dog skeletal muscle *in situ. Respiration Physiol, 3*:229-242, 1967.

49. WEIHE, W.H. (Ed.): *The Physiological Effects of High Altitude.* New York, The Macmillan Company, 1964.

50. ZUNTZ, N., LOEWY, A., MUELLER, F., and CASPARI, W.: *Hoehenklima und bergwanderungen in ihrer wirkung auf den menschen.* Berlin-Leipzig, Bong, 1906.

Chapter 19

EXERCISE IN HOT ENVIRONMENTS

P. F. IAMPIETRO

Introduction

THE ABILITY OF MAN to exercise (work) successfully in hot environments depends ultimately on his abilitiy to dissipate the extra heat produced by the working muscles in the face of an increased ambient heat gain (or a decreased capacity to lose heat). Long-term exercise in hot environments obviously requires that periods of low metabolic demand be interspersed with periods of high demand so that the body heat content can be maintained within physiologically acceptable limits. Short-term work at high energy levels (for instance, running in athletic contests) can be tolerated by storing the extra heat in the body and dissipating it after the exercise is over (23).

While most exercise or sports programs are conducted in environments which allow activity at relatively high metabolic levels without undue strain on the temperature regulating and cardiovascular systems, there are occasions when individual exercise programs, athletic contests, and sports (particularly football games in the southern part of the United States) are conducted under conditions which can lead to decreased performance and even heat injury or death (20, 21, 22, 25).

The avenues of heat exchange open to man are modified by the exercise he performs as well as by environmental and other factors such as clothing, equipment, sex, age, and body composition. A consideration of the physical avenues of heat exchange and their relative importance during exercise in a "cool" and in a "hot" environment may be of value in assessing man's physiological tolerance and performance capabilities in these environments.

376

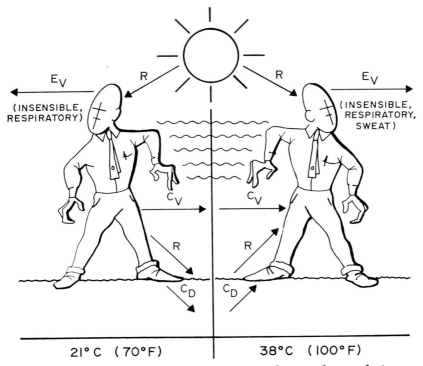

FIGURE 19-1. The physical avenues of heat exchange of man during exposure to a cool and a warm environment. R: radiation. C_D conduction. C_V: convection. E_V: evaporation.

Physical Avenues of Heat Exchange

All heat exchange between man and his environment occurs by one of four avenues—conduction, convection, radiation, and evaporation. Figure 19-1 shows diagrammatically the direction of heat flow in a cool and in a hot environment.

Heat transfer by conduction (exchange of thermal energy through or between objects in physical contact) is not an important avenue of exchange in man under most circumstances, since only small areas of the body surface (usually the feet and hands) come in contact with other objects. Clothing, although in contact with the skin, is not usually made of good conducting material. In some sports, however, special equipment and uniforms may be constructed of materials which are good conductors of heat, and then considerable heat exchange may occur via this avenue.

The transfer of thermal energy through a fluid (gas or liquid) moving over a surface is termed *convection*. Effective transfer of heat through convection requires movement (passive or forced) of the fluid involved. When there is no movement, the transfer of energy is by simple conduction. Convection is important in man for both internal (transfer of heat from the deep body tissues to the periphery) and external (transfer of energy from the surface of the body to the surrounding medium) heat exchange. The distribution of thermal energy within the body is accomplished primarily by movement of blood through the vascular system. During periods of peripheral vasodilation and vasoconstriction, transfer of heat to the surface is respectively facilitated and attenuated. Convective exchange from the surface is enhanced when air movement is increased. If there is little air movement a film of still air forms on the body surface and effectively insulates the body, since air is a poor conductor of heat. Interposition of clothing or other barriers between the body surface and the surrounding fluid also reduces convective heat exchange. Certain types of exercise such as running have the same effect as natural air movement on convective heat exchange.

The one physical avenue of heat exchange which does not require molecular contact for the transfer of energy is radiation. Radiation transfers heat between objects via electromagnetic waves. The passage of solar energy from the sun to the earth is an example of this phenomenon. However, interposition of materials between the source and the irradiated object effectively prevents transfer of energy via this route, as, for instance, when clouds pass between the sun and objects on the earth.

The rate of heat transfer by the above three routes depends primarily on the thermal gradient. When no thermal gradient exists between molecules, there can be no flow of energy. Heat transfer by conduction, convection, and radiation may be to or from the body, depending on whether the body surface is at a lower or higher temperature than its surroundings.

The last avenue of heat exchange is the evaporation of sweat. Exaporation is always a heat-dissipating mechanism. When sweat is evaporated at the surface of the body, it dissipates heat through the conversion of liquid to the gas phase (latent heat of vaporization); the rate of sweat evaporation depends on the vapor pressure gradient from the body to the surrounding air. When the vapor pressure of water in ambient air is greater than the vapor pressure at the surface of the body, sweat does not evaporate. Evaporation of sweat is the only avenue of heat loss in man when the environmental temperature is higher than body temperature (Fig. 19-1). The very great importance of this avenue of heat exchange will be further emphasized when the effect of barriers to the evaporation of sweat (for example, clothing and equipment, high ambient humidity) are discussed. Man also loses some heat by evaporation from the respiratory tract and from the surface of the body even if there is no overt sweat gland activity.

The ability of a man to exercise without imposing undue heat loads on himself or decreasing his performance capabilities is inversely related to the ambient temperature and the ambient water vapor pressure when these two factors exceed certain values (11, 15, 17, 18).

As the ambient temperature increases, the effectiveness of heat dissipation by convection and radiation decreases. When the ambient temperature is greater than the temperature at the surface of the body (33 C), the direction of heat transfer is reversed, and the superficial tissues gain heat from the environment. At this time, the only avenue of heat dissipation is through the evaporation of sweat. As the ambient water vapor pressure increases, the evaporation of sweat is impeded, and if the vapor pressure in air exceeds 40 mm Hg, evaporation of sweat approaches zero.

Heat, Exercise and Thermal Exchanges

The physiological responses to an imposed heat load are the same regardless of the source of the heat—metabolic (exercise) or environmental—and the desired end result, maintenance of deep body temperature, is also the same. During exercise the

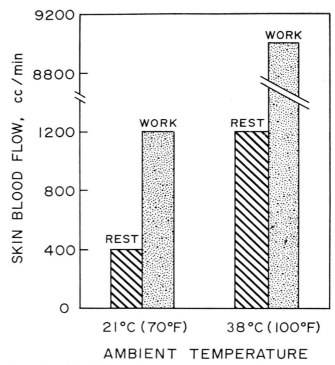

FIGURE 19-2. Skin blood flow of men at rest or working in a cool and a warm environment. (Data from Reference 9.)

initial rapid response to heat (vasodilation) is a means of increasing heat loss, while during exposure to environmental heat it is a means of decreasing heat gain (depending on ambient air temperature). This is perhaps a fine distinction, but it does emphasize the remarkable responsiveness of the cardiovascular system to quite different stimuli. During exercise in a cool environment the metabolic demands of the muscle require increased blood flow through the tissues. At the same time, the blood flow to the skin surface (Fig. 19-2) is increased markedly (9), and the extra heat produced in the muscle is carried by the blood to the skin surface. The skin temperature increases rapidly partly because of the increased blood flow to the skin, and partly because most muscle masses are close to the surface of the body;

heat loss is therefore facilitated. During acute exposure of a resting subject to high ambient temperatures, the flow of blood to the skin surface is increased rapidly (Fig. 19-2), thereby increasing skin temperature and decreasing the gradient between air temperature and body surface temperature. The net result of this response is that heat gain is decreased. Obviously, the greatest thermal demands are placed on an individual when he exercises in a hot environment. Here the threat is not only external (heat gain from the environment or at the least, a decreased ability to lose heat) but also internal (the increased metabolic heat production). The demands on the circulatory system are greatly increased, since the requirement for skin blood flow is very high (Fig. 19-2) (to facilitate heat loss) and there is also a requirement for muscle blood flow (to meet metabolic demands). The effect of this competition for available blood on man's ability to work on first exposure to hot environments will be discussed below.

It is clear that man's capability for moderate work in hot environments and even for work at high metabolic levels in cool environments would be severely handicapped if his avenues for heat dissipation were limited to radiation and convection. When the work level and/or the environmental temperature is high, the remarkable sweating capacity of man is required to augment or replace the other avenues of heat exchange. The initiation of sweating in exercising man is very rapid (5). Man may have the greatest sweating capacity of any animal and probably has the best surface (essentially devoid of hair) for evaporation of sweat (19), even though he may decrease the efficiency of evaporation by interposing barriers (clothing) between the skin and ambient air. Fortunately, most outdoor athletic events which may be conducted in hot environments use only minimal clothing (for instance, track shorts) or highly permeable clothing (for instance, baseball uniforms). Football uniforms probably present the most serious hindrance to evaporation of sweat and therefore pose the greatest thermal danger to the athlete (20). There is a problem associated with this type of exercise, since in both high school and college football there are deaths almost every year which are attributed to heat stroke (21, 22, 25). During the period 1963 to 1966, at least eleven football players died from heat stroke (25). These deaths occurred when both humidity and air temperature were high during the contest, but the primary factor was probably the hindrance to sweat evaporation contributed by the uniform. In addition, there is an increase in the death rate of the general population during periods of hot and humid weather (8).

It is of interest to note here what appears to be a difference in tolerance to a high core temperature, depending on whether the source of the heat load is internal or external. When high body temperatures (in excess of 39 C) are incurred by high work loads in a cool environment, the individual appears to tolerate them with remarkably little discomfort, and he loses little ability to work (23), whereas the same core temperature in a resting man exposed to heat alone is tolerated very poorly (14, 23). It is evident from laboratory observation that high body temperatures are also tolerated poorly when a man is working in the heat (15, 23). It should be kept in mind, however, that the caloric load of a man exposed to heat (at rest) is probably much higher than that of the same man exercising in a cool environment, since in the first instance the temperature throughout the total body mass more nearly approximates core temperature (14, 23). In exercising man the surface temperatures (and the temperatures of the underlying tissues) are much lower than the core temperature (23), so that for a given increase of rectal temperature, the calories stored by an exercising man are less than for a man resting in the heat. This may have some bearing on the difference in tolerance to high body temperatures.

Humidity and Tolerance

In warm environments physiological responses and tolerance vary with ambient humidity when this approximates or exceeds the vapor pressure at the surface of the body. At a given moderately high ambient temperature (36 C), the skin temperature, oral temperature, and sweat rate of a resting man have a critical ambient vapor pressure of 38 mm Hg. At vapor pressures above 38 mm Hg all three variables increase markedly (7). It follows

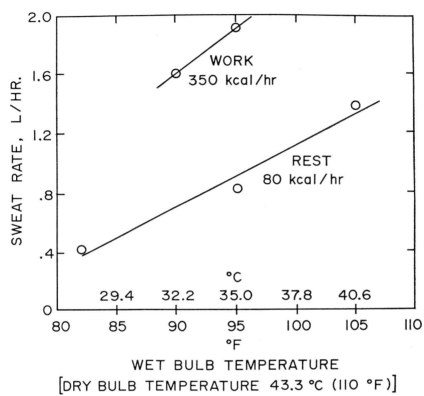

FIGURE 19-3. The effect of humidity (wet bulb temperature) on sweat rate of resting and working man in a hot environment. (Data from References 14, 15.)

that tolerance times measured by whatever criterion one chooses, (subjective or objective), also decrease as ambient vapor pressure increases (6, 14, 18). When the dry bulb temperature is high, the sweat rate of a resting man appears to increase in a linear fashion with wet bulb temperature (Fig. 19-3). This figure shows that the sweat rates of a working man may also increase linearly. This indicates that there is no critical vapor pressure for the initiation of sweating when the dry bulb temperature exceeds a certain level, which for resting man is higher than 36 C. The vapor pressure under clothing or uniforms has the same effect on evaporation of sweat and heat tolerance as ambient vapor pressure. Any barrier to free diffusion of water vapor from the surface of the body allows the air between the barrier and the skin to become saturated and thereby prevents the evaporation of sweat.

The net effect of restricting sweat evaporation is a loss of body water with no cooling. During exercise, disregard of either a natural high ambient vapor pressure or of a high vapor pressure imposed by clothing, uniform, or equipment will lead to incapacity in a short period of time.

Figure 19-3 indicates that body water losses are large when the humidity is high. Since the major portion of this water comes initially from the blood (1), the capacity to perform work will be seriously compromised unless strict water replacement protocols are initiated and adhered to. The phenomenon of voluntary dehydration has been well documented (1, 16), and therefore the individual must be disciplined to drink fluids. It has been amply demonstrated that electrolytes lost in sweat are adequately replaced at meal times if the diet is balanced and if the food is well-salted.

Work in the heat, as indicated earlier, places a large burden on the cardiovascular system and the available blood pool, since both the metabolic demands of muscle and the requirement for maintenance of thermal balance must be subserved. This requirement is met by repartitioning cardiac output so that a greater proportion of blood is diverted from the splanchnic organs and the kidneys to the muscles and skin (24). Depletion of the blood volume therefore impairs performance by decreasing the amount of blood that is available for the muscles and for the transport of heat to the surface of the body. The possibility of heat illness (heat stroke) is enhanced when this occurs.

Exercise and Acclimatization to Heat

It is common knowledge that the performance of work in the heat becomes less difficult, both physiologically and subjectively, with each successive day of work in the heat (3). Work which could not be brought to a successful conclusion on the first day of exposure is performed with relative ease after a week or ten days of exposure. The individual has become acclimatized. Acclimatization is manifested physiologically by a lower core temperature and heart rate and a higher sweat rate for a given bout of work (3, 23). An increased blood volume has also been postulated as a factor in the improved cardiovascular function with acclimatization (23, 28); however, other work has shown no increase of blood volume after acclimatization to heat (2), and an increase is probably not necessary to the acclimatization process. It is possible that increased venomotor tone (27) plays a role in the improvement of cardiovascular function during acclimatization.

Although early work indicated that acclimatization to heat would not occur unless a man worked in the heat (4), more recent studies (12) reveal that acclimatization can be conferred without work by the use of controlled hyperthermia for about one hour on each of fifteen days. This work leads to interesting speculation concerning such questions as the interrelationships of physical conditioning and acclimatization to heat (10, 13), exercise in the heat (13), acclimatization and heat tolerance at rest (14), and the degree of acclimatization conferred by physical conditioning alone (13, 26). Comprehensive comparitive studies should probably be conducted in all of these areas; studies are also needed to determine the relative benefits and deficiencies of the acclimatization produced by working in the heat as opposed to that induced by controlled hyperthermia. The results could have importance for the sports contestant as well as military personnel and the general population.

References

1. ADOLPH, E.F. and Associates: *Physiology of Man in the Desert.* New York, Wiley (Interscience), 1947.

2. BASS, D.E., BUSKIRK, E.R., IAMPIETRO, P.F., and MAGER, M.: Comparison of blood volume during physical conditioning, heat acclimatization and sedentary living. *J Appl Physiol, 12:*186-188, 1958.

3. BASS, D.E., KLEEMAN, C.R., QUINN, M., HENSCHEL, A., and HEGNAUER, A.H.: Mechanisms of acclimatization to heat in man. *Medicine, 34:*323-380, 1955.

4. BEAN, W.B., and EICHNA, L.W.: Performance in relation to environmental temperature: Reactions of normal young men to simulated desert environment. *Fed Proc, 2*:144-164, 1943.

5. BEAUMONT, W. VAN, and BULLARD, R.W.: Sweating: Its rapid response to muscular work. *Science, 141*:643-646, 1963.

6. BELL, C.R., HELLON, R.F., HIORNS, R.W., NICOL, P.B., and PROVINS, K.A.: Safe exposure of men to severe heat. *J Appl Physiol, 20*:288-292, 1965.

7. BREBNER, D.F., KERSLAKE, D.McK., and WADDELL, J.L.: The effect of atmospheric humidity on the skin temperatures and sweat rates of resting men at two ambient temperatures. *J Physiol (London), 144*:299-306, 1958.

8. BRIDGER, C.A., and HELFAND, L.A.: Mortality from heat during July 1966 in Illinois. *Int J Biometeor, 12*:51-70, 1968.

9. BROUHA, W.L., and RADFORD, E.P., JR.: In Johnson, W.R. (Ed.): *Science and Medicine of Exercise and Sports.* New York, Harper and Brothers, 1960, chap. 10.

10. BUSKIRK, E.R., IAMPIETRO, P.F., and BASS, D.E.: Work performance after dehydration: Effects of physical conditioning and heat acclimatization. *J Appl Physiol, 12*:189-194, 1958.

11. EICHNA, L.W., ASHE, W.F., JR., BEAN, W.B., and SHELLEY, W.B.: Upper limits of environmental heat and humidity tolerated by acclimatized men working in hot environments. *J Indust Hyg Toxicol, 27*:59-84, 1945.

12. FOX, R.H., GOLDSMITH, R., KIDD, D.J., and LEWIS, H.E.: Acclimatization to heat in man by controlled elevation of body temperature. *J Physiol (London), 166*:530-547, 1963.

13. GISOLFI, C., and ROBINSON, S.: Relations between physical training, acclimatization, and heat tolerance. *J Appl Physiol, 26*:530-534, 1969.

14. GOLDMAN, R.F., GREEN, E.B., and IAMPIETRO, P.F.: Tolerance of hot, wet environments by resting men. *J Appl Physiol, 20*:271-277, 1965.

15. IAMPIETRO, P.F., and GOLDMAN, R.F.: Tolerance of men working in hot, humid environments. *J Appl Physiol, 20*:73-76, 1965.

16. IAMPIETRO, P.F., VAUGHAN, J.A., MacLEOD, A.R., WELCH, B.E., MARCINEK, J.G., MANN, J.B., GROTHEER, M.P., and FRIEDEMANN, T.E.: Caloric intake and energy expenditure of eleven men in a desert environment. Tech. Rept. EP-40, QM R&D Center, U. S. Army, Natick, Mass., 1956.

17. Leithead, C.S.: Occupational heat stress and man's responses. *WHO Bull, 38*:649-657, 1968.
18. Lind, A.R.: A physiological criterion for setting thermal environmental limits for everyday work. *J Appl Physiol, 18*:51-64, 1963.
19. MacFarlane, W.V.: Human functions in hot regions. Studies on metabolism, hormones and habituations. *Triangle, 7*:55-65, 1965.
20. Mathews, D.K., Fox, E.L., and Tanzi, D.: Physiological responses during exercise and recovery in a football uniform. *J Appl Physiol, 26*:611-615, 1969.
21. Murphy, R.J.: The problems of environmental heat in athletics. *Ohio State Med J, 59*:799-804, 1963.
22. Murphy, R.J., and Ashe, W.F.: Prevention of heat illness in football players. *JAMA, 194*:180-184, 1965.
23. Robinson, S.: In Newburg, L.H. (Ed.): *Physiology of Heat Regulation and the Science of Clothing*. New York, Hafner, 1949, chap. 5.
24. Rowell, L.R., Brengelmann, G.L., Blackmon, J.R., Twiss, R.D., and Kusumi, F.: Splanchnic blood flow and metabolism in heat-stressed man. *J Appl Physiol, 24*:475-484, 1968.
25. Spickard, A.: Heat stroke in college football and suggestions for prevention. *Southern Med J, 61*:791-796, 1968.
26. Strydom, N.B., and Williams, C.G.: Effect of physical conditioning on state of heat acclimatization of Bantu laborers. *J Appl Physiol, 27*:262-265, 1969.
27. Wood, J.E., and Bass, D.E.: Responses of the veins and arterioles of the forearm to walking during acclimatization to heat in man. *J Clin Invest, 39*:825-833, 1960.
28. Wyndham, C.H., Benade, A.J.S., Williams, C.G., Strydom, M.B., Goldin, A., and Heyns, A.J.A.: Changes in central circulation and body fluid spaces during acclimatization to heat. *J Appl Physiol, 25*:586-593, 1968.

INDEX

fitness, 101-102
flexibility, 106
free fatty acid release, 120
frequency of, 100
glycogen, 121, 159
intensity, 100, 112
minerals, 121
muscle hypertrophy, 24-28
muscle strength, 98-111, 103-104
myoglobin, 122
oxidative metabolism, 118-119
oxygen uptake of muscle, 64
perceived exertion, 291
phosphocreatine, 121
sex, 98
speed, 106
stimulus to, 98-99
trainability, 101-102
trunk strength, 105
Transfer factor, *see* Pulmonary diffusing
capacity
Transformation, energy, 196-209
Transit time, pulmonary capillary, 138,
144, 146
Treadmill, 192-209, 240-265, 288, 320-
322, 371
Tubular (T) system, 8, 9, 10, 11
Turbulence, airway, 145

U

Urban children, 335

V

Valve area, 351
Vasodilatation, peripheral, 378, 380-381

Vasodilator stimulus, 68
Vasoregulatory asthenia, 182, 289
Velocity, contraction, 6-7, 12-13, 99
constant, phosphagen splitting, 164-
167
Veno-motor tone, 211, 235, 385
Venous oxygen tension, 135, 181-182
Ventilation/perfusion inequalities, 143-
144, 146
Ventilatory equivalent, 145
Ventricular fibrillation, 236
Vertical jump, 105
see also jumping
Visceral blood flow, 210-229
Viscosity, blood, 142, 366
muscle, 12-16, 192
Vital capacity, 266-267

W

Walking, 192-209
Warm-up, 240, 242, 245
Weakness, 352
Weight, body, 199-200, 238, 251, 257,
269, 326, 331-333
Wet bulb temperature, 383
White fibres, 362-363
Wind resistance, 204, 364
Women, Cooper's test, 259
industrial work, 79-80
isometric strength, 79-97
Work of breathing, 134, 144-146, 243
Wyndham extrapolation, 249, 321

Y

Yaw, 90, 92, 93, 94